INTRODUCTION TO
GEOGRAPHY:

Selected Readings

INTRODUCTION TO

GEOGRAPHY:

Selected Readings

edited by FRED E. DOHRS
Wayne State University

and LAWRENCE M. SOMMERS
Michigan State University

THOMAS Y. CROWELL COMPANY
New York
Established 1834

PREFACE

In compiling this volume of readings, we have sought materials from the rich literature available that would be especially suitable for introductory geography courses. We have endeavored to cover each of the main topics discussed in the majority of introductory texts, and although our organization is systematic, we have included articles pertaining to all of the major regions of the earth, thus making the collection suitable for courses of the regional type.

Introduction to Geography: Selected Readings focuses on three important aspects of the discipline: the evolution of geographic thought, the tools at the geographer's disposal, and the techniques available to the geographer in the practice of his craft. In making our selection, we have chosen not only classic articles but also those that reflect new developments in the field. The articles have been culled from a variety of sources, the largest number coming from the major American and foreign geographical periodicals. It has been our objective to choose articles that are not only readable, but that also represent divergent opinions and trends, both past and present.

To make this volume as useful as possible for teacher and student alike, several distinctive features have been included. Each section is preceded by a brief introduction that suggests the breadth and scope of the subject covered within the section, and its place within the field of geography as a whole. In addition, preceding each selection there are headnotes that place each article in relation to the topic being covered, as well as to the other articles in that section. We have also provided bibliographical notes on the opening page of each selection, which serve to identify the author and the source from which the selection was taken. Finally, to aid the instructor in making assignments, a table has been included that correlates chapters in selected introductory geography texts with the articles in this volume.

Footnotes, graphs, photographs, and tables that originally appeared in the articles, as a rule, have been omitted; only when we have deemed that they are vital to the meaning have they been retained.

Introduction to Geography: Selected Readings is the first of three volumes in the series. The two subsequent volumes, *Physical Geography: Selected Readings* and *Cultural Geography: Selected Readings*, will, when used with this collection, provide instructors of basic courses with an abundance of materials from which to choose, thus adding depth and interest to introductory geography. It is hoped that the inherent flexibility of the three volumes, as well as the coverage of the series as a whole, will allow the teacher to select articles consistent with his own emphasis and his own notions of how the course should be taught.

Deep appreciation is expressed to the authors and publishers of the articles included, and to colleagues and others who gave valuable suggestions and assistance.

F.E.D.

L.M.S.

CONTENTS

I. INTRODUCTION, 1

    1. The Circumference of Geography, 2
       Nevin M. Fenneman

    2. Geography in an Age of Revolution, 11
       Preston E. James

    3. The Regional Concept and the Regional Method, 19
       Derwent Whittlesey and Others

    4. Approaches to Regional Analysis: A Synthesis, 39
       Brian J. L. Berry

II. THE HISTORY OF GEOGRAPHICAL THOUGHT, 53

    5. The Concept of Location in Classical Geography, 54
       Fred Lukermann

    6. The Concept of Geography as a Science of Space, from Kant and Humboldt to Hettner, 74
       Richard Hartshorne

    7. The Morphology of Landscape, 90
       Carl O. Sauer

III. ENVIRONMENT AND DETERMINISM, 121

    8. Determinism in Geography, 122
       Robert S. Platt

    9. The Rise of Possibilism, 130
       George Tatham

IV. GEOGRAPHICAL DESCRIPTION, 139

    10. Mere Description, 140
       Lester E. Klimm

    11. The English Landscape, 141
       David Lowenthal and Hugh C. Prince

12. The American West, *156*
Walter Prescott Webb

13. Brazil: Complex Giant, *168*
H. O. Sternberg

V. GEOGRAPHICAL TOOLS AND TECHNIQUES, 183

14. The Role of Field Work, *183*
Robert S. Platt

15. Microgeographic Sampling, *187*
J. M. Blaut

16. The Potential Contribution of Cartography
in Liberal Education, *199*
Arthur H. Robinson

17. Generalization in Statistical Mapping, *212*
George F. Jenks

18. A Guide to the Interpretation and Analysis
of Aerial Photos, *231*
Kirk H. Stone

19. Measurement in Human Geography, *245*
J. T. Coppock and J. H. Johnson

20. On Perks and Pokes, *254*
Arthur H. Robinson

21. The Use of Computers in the Processing and Analysis
of Geographic Information, *258*
Richard C. Kao

VI. TRENDS IN THE SCIENCE OF GEOGRAPHY, 269

22. The Way Lies Open, *269*
J. Russell Whitaker

23. Geomorphology and General Systems Theory, *285*
Richard J. Chorley

24. The Changing Relationships of Economics
and Economic Geography, *302*
Robert B. McNee

25. Recent Developments of Central Place Theory, *315*
Brian J. L. Berry and William L. Garrison

26. Unified Field Theory, *327*
   Stephen B. Jones

27. Cultural Geography, *337*
   Edward Ackerman et al.

28. Theoretical Geography, *346*
   William Bunge

29. A Spatial Behavior Analysis of Decision Making in Middle Sweden's Farming, *359*
   Julian Wolpert

30. Where Is a Research Frontier?, *369*
   Edward A. Ackerman

   Correlations Table, *389*

I. INTRODUCTION

Geography, like most fields of knowledge, has undergone a process of evolution. It flourished as a well-developed descriptive science during the time of the Greeks and Romans, fell into neglect during the early centuries of the Christian era, and rose again during the Age of Discovery in the fifteenth and sixteenth centuries. Aided by the invention of the printing press, improvements in the science of navigation, and technological advancement of ocean-going vessels, knowledge of the world increased at a rate during the latter period that has never since been equaled.

From the Greeks to the Age of Discovery, factual knowledge about the earth increased, but little progress was made in formulating the theoretical nature of geography until the Germans applied themselves to the problem in the 1800s. Immanuel Kant, Alexander von Humboldt, and Frederick Ritter made significant contributions to geographical methodology. The work of Alfred Hettner, who defined geography as the science of areal differentiation, had a more forceful impact upon the development of the discipline in the United States than did English and French geographers.

Geography was late in emerging as a college and university discipline in the United States; the first course was taught by Arnold Guyot at Princeton in 1860. It was introduced at Harvard by William Morris Davis, a geologist. This association of geography with geology was typical until the 1920s and 1930s, and often still exists in smaller institutions. Present-day geography, however, so emphasizes the human factor that its cultural, economic, and political aspects dominate published research. Along with a change in the emphasis of phenomena studied, there has been an increase in the development of the conceptual and theoretical base of the discipline.

The readings in this first part take up some of the methodological problems encountered in the emergence of geography in the United States and fix the status of the field in the hierarchy of knowledge. The selections indicate that geography is both an art and a science and frequently bridges the gap between the two realms; that mathematics and statistics have become increasingly important tools in the attempt to sharpen the theoretical contributions of the discipline, and that regionalization as an approach to understanding the areal differentiation of space on the earth's surface remains a core concept.

1. The Circumference of Geography

Nevin M. Fenneman

Fenneman argues that regional geography is the heart of the science. He shows simply but effectively the relations, as he perceives them, between geography and the many other fields from which it draws much of its subject matter. As an integrator and relator of spatial knowledge, Fenneman recognizes some danger in "scientific trespass" by one discipline on another. Geography, he avers, should be identified, like other disciplines, not by its periphery but by its core, by what is unique to it—in this case, regional study.

But it is on the growing edges of a science, where contact is made with other fields, that some of the major break-throughs in knowledge are made. Fenneman's approach has been criticized on this ground, but in 1919 it was a much needed statement, and it still makes a. good introduction to a discussion of the place of geography in the hierarchy of knowledge.

It is a peculiarity of geography to be always discussing and debating its own content—as though a society were to be organized for the sole purpose of finding out what the organization was for. This is not said by way of criticism; indeed this very paper is a continuation of the same discussion. The situation is, however, unique and can scarcely fail to be remarked by on-lookers from other sciences, who have no such doubts as to what their subjects are about.

The basis of this constant concern is not greed but *fear*. Geography wages no aggressive wars and seems to covet no new territory. In certain quarters it bristles with defense; but it is mainly concerned with purging its own house rather than spreading its borders. To rule out "what is not geography" would seem from the discussions to be much more important than to find and claim geography where it has been passing under other names. The constant apprehension is that by admitting alien subjects we shall sooner or later be absorbed by a foreign power and lose our identity.

It is probably unnecessary to point out that this is purely an American attitude. Geography of the European brand has no such concern for its own purity or fear of being absorbed. Scholarly geographic treatises

SOURCE: *Annals of the Association of American Geographers*, IX (1919), 3-11. Reprinted by permission. The author, who taught at the University of Cincinnati, was one of the outstanding physiographers in American geography.

from Europe may contain long lists of botanical names, or geological descriptions, or chapters which might be transferred bodily to monographs on economics or history.

To many American geographers this would seem like betraying their cause and selling their birthright. There is an implied dread that if geography accepts the work and uses the language of other sciences, geography itself will be dismembered and its remains be divided among its competitors. It is worth while to consider this possibility, and a rough plan is here submitted for a partition of geography's domain.

Suppose geography were dead, what would be left?

Proposed Partition of Geography's Domain

Geology might easily take over topography, including its genetic treatment, which is physiography—in fact, has never given it up. So also

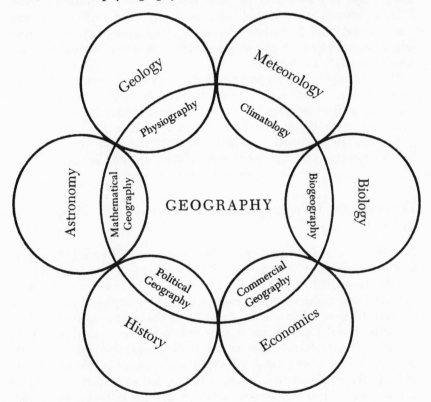

FIGURE 1: This diagram expresses the fundamental conception that sciences overlap and that each one of the specialized phases of geography belongs equally to some other science. Such a diagram will be helpful if not construed too strictly. In a loose way the central residual part of the circle may represent regional geography.

botany has never relinquished plant geography and ecology. Zoölogy does not forget the distribution of animals. Agriculture is now so specialized and so firmly entrenched that crops and their distribution, and their relation to all manner of factors, are studied without concern for geography. Meteorology has official standing in all civilized countries and could take care of climatology if geography were bankrupt. Moreover, meteorology is commercially employed and so has the satisfaction of being good for something beside being merely good "to teach." So it is not afflicted with heart searchings regarding its own content. Mining is abundantly treated by geology and economics. The geographer only borrows from these, smooths out their details, and relates their results to something else. So economics deals with all other industries and with commerce, sometimes availing itself of the aid of chemistry and other sciences and always paying its respects to engineering.

A good part of what is termed political geography is covered also by history, and history would be more rational if it included still more. Political science, ethnography, etc., cultivate other parts of the geographical field and do it more exhaustively than does geography. Mathematical geography is, of course, pure astronomy, except for cartography, which is straight mathematics.

Thus it seems that, with geography dead, all its tangible effects would be claimed by relatives and the estate could be settled up. To say the least, this is disconcerting. The case is not made better by the reflection that a large number of educated persons would see no reason for objecting to such a solution, provided only that geography were preserved for children up to the age when serious study should begin.

Dependence of Geography on Other Sciences for Its Material

At this point, while geography is confessing its limitations, it may as well be owned that, outside the field of exploration, the geographer is mainly dependent on others for his data. Aside from mere location, direction, and distance, almost every fact that he employs belongs quite as much to some other science. In so far as that fact represents a class, the entire class of facts is much more apt to be known exhaustively by the other science than by geography. If the geographer speaks of soils, the agriculturist knows more; if he speaks of mines, the geologist knows more; if the reference be to manufacturing, the economist's knowledge is more thorough, or at least more exhaustive; if the subject is the people, the ethnographer, sociologist, or economist has first-hand knowledge, and the geographer is generally a borrower; and so through the list.

With respect to all these data someone else is the original student, the "authority," and the geographer is merely "informed." How often is a geographer called in as an expert, and in what lines? This question is not intended to suggest a wholly negative answer, especially in view of the fact that three of our members are at present in Paris on the staff of the Peace Commission and nearly one-half of our members have been engaged in some expert capacity during the war. It does not follow, of course, that all these were engaged as geographers.

Concession has here been made freely because scholars outside of geography know these facts to be true, and there is nothing to be gained by claiming more than we can defend. If geography is not worth while despite these admissions, its business may as well be wound up.

Need of a Synthetic Areal Science

Reverting now to our former figure of speech, what has geography to say of its proposed demise, the division of its tangible effects and the settling of the estate? The obvious question arises: Would the decedent stay dead? If he were to come to life again, the situation would be embarrassing as between him and his relatives. Assuming that after his decease each of the branches named above as contributing to geography does its task well with respect to Russia, for instance, is there any likelihood that a craving would arise for a synthetic picture of the whole or a critical study of inter-relations? If so, who would satisfy this craving, and who could paint the picture, and what would be its value or standing among scholars?

To begin with, the first question answers itself. There is not one chance in a hundred that ten years would go by without a conscious craving, and an attempt to meet the craving, for a comprehensive view of the areal unit; and not one chance in a million that a century would elapse before such an interest would be the center of a new science. It matters no whit that all concrete data are already organized into other sciences, each more exhaustive and more critical with respect to its own data than the new science; it is absolutely certain that interest in the areal unit as such would clothe itself in appropriate form. It is the *areal relation*, after all, that makes geography.

To dwell on the kind of picture to be painted is not within our present purpose. In part it is a mere assembling of facts from diverse fields, facts joined together by the sole bond of a common locality. Whether we deride or apologize for this aggregation of facts, call it mere description, mere compilation, mere this or mere that (whatever it is, it is always "mere"), this humble task must still be performed before higher work is possible. Description bears the same relation to geography that narrative does to history. There can be no sound philosophy in either, based on faulty narrative or description.

But data thus assembled from diverse fields do not remain inert. They react on each other like chemicals to produce new compounds, that is, new truths. If the geographer knows less about soils and crops than the agriculturist, less of climate than the meteorologist, less of industry than the economist, less of society than the sociologist, he should still be supreme in this field of secondary compounds which cannot be formed by those who handle the data of one science only.

Value of "Scientific Trespass"

This point needs no elaboration here, but it is worth while recalling a passage from the presidential address of Dr. G. K. Gilbert before this association in this same city ten years ago. In explaining his choice of a subject, he announced himself as an advocate of the principle of "scientific trespass." "The specialist who forever stays at home and digs and delves within his private enclosure has all the advantages of intensive cultivation—except one; and the thing he misses is *cross-fertilization*. Trespass is one of the ways of securing cross-fertilization for his own crops, and of carrying cross-fertilization to the paddock he invades." Gilbert might have added that the geographer is, or should be, the great insect that carries pollen from field to field.

It is not intended here to concede that geography does not concern itself at all in the first-hand search for data. Geographers have, for example, done much for topography. Light on land forms has been by far the leading contribution of American geography (though it is a question whether anyone has contributed to this subject who was not first trained as a geologist).

Regional Geography the Core of the Science

Since geography *is to be*, it is quite right that physiography and climatology and the study of natural resources and even ecology should be of its family and bear its name, but the point here urged is that these are not the things which make geography *necessary* and *inevitable*. They may be necessary to it, but it is not necessary to them. All these might live with geography dead. All these and others belong to the regions of overlap, or ground common both to geography and to some other science, and having two parents, would not be totally orphaned if one died; but the study of areas as before described belongs solely to geography and is, moreover, an only child. If these figures are somewhat mixed, it may be well to add in plain English that the one thing that is first, last, and always geography and nothing else, is the study of areas in their compositeness or complexity, that is *regional geography.*

It is not to be implied for one brief moment that physiography and the other branches named are not geography. They all become so when directed toward a geographic purpose. But without the touchstone of areal studies, there is nothing to make physiography other than geology, ecology other than botany, the study of natural resources other than economics.

There is, then, in geography this central core which is pure geography and nothing else, but there is much beyond this core which is none the less geography, though it belongs also to overlapping sciences. Here belong physiography and climatology, mathematical and commercial geography. Still, *the seeds are in the core, and the core is regional geography,* and this is why the subject propagates itself and maintains a separate existence. Without regional geography there is no reason why geography should be treated as a separate branch.

This emphasis on areal relations instead of on the "elements" which enter into such relations is, of course, not new. It comes to much the same thing in practice as Ritter's "home of man" or Davis's "physical element and human element" or this and that man's "responses" or Keltie's "science of distributions" or Hettner's *"dingliche Erfüllung der Erdräume"* (material filling of the earth's surface). Nor is it necessary, for the purpose here in hand, to point out that every element (topography, vegetation, climate, etc.) can be treated with reference to its distribution as well as with reference to its types. Such a treatment belongs to regional geography. It should, however, be noted that the study of the distribution of any one element by itself falls somewhat short of that *distinctive* geographic flavor which comes only when the various elements are studied in their inter-relations.

Cultivation of the Central Theme of Geography as a Safeguard Against Absorption by Other Sciences

Let us now go back to the fear above alluded to, that our subject is going to be swallowed by something else. Why this constant dread? The situation at once suggests that we live too much on our borders and not enough in the center. If we dwell mainly in systematic physiography, why should not geology claim us as a vassal? If we live largely in commercial geography, we are in similar danger from economics; and why should it not be so? We can go round the circle with the same logic. A narrowly political geography of boundaries and capitals never had any reason for a separate existence apart from history.

If we are concerned for our independent existence no amount of fortifying our border will take the place of developing our domain. What we need is more and better studies of regions in their entirety, their compositeness, their complexity, their inter-relations of physical, economic, racial, historic, and other factors. No other science can swallow that and live.

Unnecessary Discrimination Against Geologic Terms

An illustration of warring on the border instead of farming our domain is found in our curious boycott of terms from other sciences even when needed to make the truth clear. It is not permissible to say that the Cumberland Plateau is co-extensive with the strong "Carboniferous" rock (even where that is true) or that the High Plains (of Nebraska and Wyoming) end at the north with certain late "Tertiary" formations. It is permissible to say that the Cumberland Plateau is as broad as certain "resistant" rocks, but a term which would enable us to locate those rocks on the geologic map is taboo. True, the plateau border can be made out on very large-scale and awkward-to-handle topographic maps, but such maps at best are empirical, while the geologic map is interpretative. Since when has geography become so reactionary? Why must we secrete the geologic map as medieval priests secreted the Bible?

In the debates concerning this point there has been the most curious oversight of common usage. "Carboniferous" and its like are dubbed "geologic time names." Such they are indeed, sometimes, just as "Carboniferous" might be the name of a man or a horse or a brand of shoe polish—all as irrelevant as geologic time—but the term also designates a body of material (in this case a system of strata) and, more important still, on the geologic map it stands for an *area*. "Triassic" indeed connotes geologic time, but the same word designates certain areas on the geologic map of the eastern United States. "Portage" is not only a Devonian epoch but a belt on the geologic map of western New York, a belt that must be spoken of and cannot be designated with equal clearness under any other name. In this manner, much use is properly made of geologic terms, not because they are names of epochs but because they are names of areas that force themselves on our notice by certain peculiarities, thus leading to rational explanations. For three-fourths of the United States the geologic map is beyond comparison the one most valuable map for interpreting topographic contrasts between adjacent areas.

Why must the words printed on it be classed as dangerous? The answer is: Geography is in danger of being swallowed, and self-preservation is nature's first law.

But "Cumberland Plateau" is a geographic term. How can the geologist say with impunity that the Carboniferous rocks are co-extensive with the Cumberland Plateau? Is not the danger mutual? Is his science not in danger of being swallowed by geography? The answer is: He is not afraid on that borderland where sciences overlap, because his own peculiar domain, which is not overlapped by geography or anything else, is too large and too well cultivated to admit of such fears. Our own safety lies in the same policy.

In our efforts toward self-preservation through purity, we have classed scientific terms as clean and unclean. The latter, such as Archean, Mesozoic, etc., cannot be touched without defilement. So we have built up a whole ceremonial by which we hope to be saved; but not so is salvation found. Its price to geography is no less than the diligent cultivating of its own peculiar field, the doing of something which the world needs and which no other science can do.

Animals have more than one way of evading the jaws of their competitors. The turtle is encased and puts up a good defense but is weak on the offensive. It is the same with the oyster. Others, like the squash bug, owe their safety to a peculiar flavor or odor. Still others specialize in modes of escape. But all such special provision belongs to the weak rather than to the strong. If geography will cultivate its own strength like the large mammals, it will not be necessary for it to encase itself like the oyster or cultivate the peculiar flavor of the squash bug to avoid being eaten.

In so far as there are frontiers between the sciences, let us have them ungarrisoned and let us have free trade. Let there be among sciences the same struggle for existence and law of survival that Darwin found among species. Then every field of study that answers to an intellectual need will have due recognition.

The Several Sciences Designated by Their Centers, Not by Their Circumferences

The subject announced for this brief address was "The Circumference of Geography." Presumably enough has been said to show that a science cannot be defined by its circumference. We may designate the center, and that should be enough. Everyone knows what botany is so long as we stay near the center, but where is its farthest limit? Far out in chemistry and medicine and geology, to say the least. And where is the limit of chemistry? Nowhere. Yet chemistry is not hard to define if it

be designated by its center instead of by trying to draw its circumference. So the center of geography is the study of *areas,* generally, of
course, in relation to man, for human habitation affords the most frequent utilitarian reason for such study and is also the center of the
greatest intellectual interest; but the comprehensive study of an uninhabitable region would still be geography.

It is not only the right but the duty of every science to develop all
parts of its domain, but it is none the less true of all, as of geography,
that their right to separate existence depends on their cultivation of that
part of their field which is not overlapped by others. Let there be no
misunderstanding; there is no intention of assigning more dignity to one
part of the field than to another or of asking any man to turn aside from
that which interests him to something else. There is no more inherent
worth in a center than in a border. But some of us have a philosophic
interest in viewing relationships, and in asking why the whole range of
knowledge has grouped itself around certain centers, and what it is that
keeps those centers, which have received names, somewhat permanent,
and what the advantage is in grouping knowledge around one center
rather than another.

Moreover, all of us have a very practical interest in seeing that our
own work should not suffer by isolation. We all want our own work to
have the advantage of connections, and it is greatly to our interest that
somebody should cultivate certain central fields even though most of us
work on the borders. The logic of events, if no other logic, has brought
together in this association a group of men of rather diverse interests.
We are disposed to think that this is not a mere chance but that something fundamental underlies our union. Much that interests the individual does not concern the whole; but we feel more or less intelligently
that there is profit in this intercourse and we want the relation to be
closer. If there is a class of studies that will make our separate fields
more important and more interesting to others and enable us to profit
more by our association, we want to know what that class is and to
encourage it.

Beside those who are, first and last, geographers, our association contains geologists, topographers, geodesists, meteorologists, ecologists,
zoölogists, geophysicists, historians, and economists. The list is not intended to be complete. We have joined ourselves together evidently
expecting to find a common interest. Where is the common ground on
which such diversity can meet? Interest in places, areas, regions is the
common bond.

This quasi-philosophical study of relationships is therefore important
to those whose privilege it is to direct research or to organize education.
If men in such position decide with eyes open that physiography and
commercial geography and anthropogeography and the rest should not

be merely geology, economics, ethnography, etc., they must act accordingly. The character of these subjects cannot be controlled by ceremonial law. The effective way is to set in the midst of them a great light, the light which comes alone from the comprehensive, rational, systematic study of regions.

2. Geography in an Age of Revolution

Preston E. James

James asks, "Has geography anything to offer to aid in the understanding of the changing world and its apparent chaos?" He emphasizes that the turmoil is part of a fundamental transformation developing from the spreading of the democratic and industrial revolutions throughout the world from the North Sea area. The changes in both man and landscape take place in the cores, or culture hearths, of eleven culture regions. James' attempt to place cultural geography in a tighter theoretical framework is indicative of a modern trend in the approach to this subject.

Democracy and autocracy are the words that stand for two incompatible systems of living. We are in the midst of a world-wide conflict between the supporters of these systems for the control of men's minds, and if a shooting war intervenes this will only postpone the ultimate decision between them. In the face of this situation if young people are to be prepared to perform the duties of responsible citizenship and to face the changing world without fear they must gain an understanding not only of the historical processes involved, but also of the differences from place to place and country to country on our contemporary earth. As never before they need the perspectives of both time and place. If geographers are to move forward with the opportunity now at hand, and if they are to meet the challenge of this age of revolution, then they must so structure the concepts and content of their field that its relevance to the modern world is immediately apparent.

. . . . . .

SOURCE: *The Journal of Geography,* LXII (1963), 97-103. The author is professor of geography at Syracuse University.

The Role of Theory

To arrive at an understanding of the structure of geography, it is necessary to consider the role of theory—both for the purposes of research
and for developing geographic perspective. A theory is a general or ideal
construction, a model, formulated for the purpose of explaining the
connections among observed facts. Explanation is supplied through the
description of a process of change. Explanations of observed facts are
provided by noting the previous conditions at some earlier period of
time and noting the processes of change that have brought previous
conditions to the conditions observed today. There is "mere description" which tells how much of what is where; and there is "explanatory
description" which adds the time dimension. Theory provides the ideal
description of a process from which confusing and often irrelevant
details have been removed. Theory builds the conceptual framework,
the structure, in relation to which specific facts become important.

The role of theory differs depending on its purpose. Theory as a
guide to the discovery of new theory through research study plays one
kind of role: theory as conceptual structure for the purpose of providing geographic insights, plays quite a different role. For the former,
theory is used to focus attention on a narrow range of observed facts
relevant to a specific question or problem. To find the answer to a
question a hypothesis is formulated. This is a kind of intuitive guess
as to what ideal construction might be useful. The hypothesis is confronted with new observations of fact. If the facts fit the ideal construction, and if no single fact refuses to fit, then a theory has been
identified. Used this way, theory has the effect of narrowing the range
of observed facts. The ultimate beauty of such theory is encompassed
in the mathematical formula—such as Einstein's $E = mc^2$.

But theory as a conceptual framework for providing geographic perspective tends to increase the range of observation. Theory tends to
make one sensitive to the ways in which a great variety of things fit
together in related and interconnected chains. Used in this way theory
attempts to embrace in one system a variety of otherwise confused
phenomena. Both uses of theory are needed: it is not a case of deciding
to seek one or the other kind, but rather of making it clear that both
kinds of formulation are needed.

Degrees of Generalization

Theory is a generalization regarding processes. But an important part
of the structure of geography has to do with the differences in the

degree of generalization. When the face of the earth is examined in detail by direct personal observation, generalizations can be made and verified by the use of directly observable facts. This is what one should call the topographic scale—the scale at which it is possible to observe and plot on a map the specific features of the human occupance. However, geographic study cannot be restricted to the immediately observable features of the earth, especially when the purpose is to provide world perspective for the education of non-geographers. Because of the stature of man and the curved surface of the earth on which he lives, the range of topographic observations is relatively small. At scales smaller than topographic it is necessary to deal with categories of things that spread beyond the horizon. For example, one can observe the character of a hill or valley directly; but the concept of a hilly upland is based on the summation and generalization of many topographic-scale views. The single 40-acre field of corn can be observed directly and its areal association with soil types and slopes plotted on a map; but the type of farming region must be generalized from many specific observations. Even statistical data that measure the characteristics of large areas are derived from someone's topographic-scale observations. Theory which is formulated to show the connections among directly observable features can also be verified by direct observation: but theory formulated to provide a conceptual framework to show the connections among phenomena generalized into broader categories can only be verified by the study of phenomena at the same degree of generalization.

The study of geography lost some of its vitality when so many of its students were denied the opportunity for direct observation in the field. The experience of making the initial transfer from the directly observed phenomenon to the word, map, or mathematical symbol on a piece of paper served to keep geographers in touch with reality, even when they were dealing with world regions. But whether or not students can be provided with field experience, and whether film strips and TV tape can bring the out-of-doors back into the classroom, if geographers are to provide a meaningful conceptual framework for the examination of world-wide features they must build theory appropriate to that degree of generalization.

An Age of Revolution

Has geography anything to offer to aid in the understanding of the changing world and its apparent chaos? Among young people one finds a widespread feeling of futility and insecurity and a mounting demand that ranks be closed in defense of institutions against the challenge of communism. Has the study of geography anything to offer that will help to illuminate the nature of the problems?

The archaeologists and historians can throw light on what is taking place. They will point out that this is not the first revolutionary age. Since the appearance of *homo sapiens* some 50,000 years ago there have been two other periods of fundamental culture change each creating a condition of collapse and chaos. The first revolution took place about 8000 B.C. when men in the southern part of Asia first learned how to cultivate plants and to domesticate animals. The second revolutionary period began when the early city civilizations appeared, when men learned the arts of public administration and the techniques of imperial conquest. The historians can go into some detail regarding the rise of Babylon, or Egypt, or of the Indus civilization or of the civilization of ancient China. Sometimes they neglect the other two early civilizations: that of Central America and that of the Andean countries.

The addition of the geographic perspective to these historical movements throws additional light on what happened. Each new way of making a living originated in a culture hearth; and from each culture hearth the new society pushed outward at the expense of its neighbors. Along the advancing fronts there was turmoil, conflict, chaos.

From the rise of these early civilizations which started about 4000 B.C. until the middle of the 18th century A.D. there was no fundamental change in the way man made a living from the land. Power was derived from human or animal muscles, from wind or falling water. If population increased and there was need for more food, this was produced by expanding the area of crops and by increasing the number of farmers. The size of cities was limited by the amount of food that could be transported to them.

Now suddenly man finds himself in the midst of the third great period of fundamental change in the relations of man to the land and of man to man. Geographers and others recognize the existence of two contemporary revolutions: the Industrial Revolution and the Democratic Revolution. And again the perspective of historical geography is needed. Sometimes the historians specializing in European history place end dates on these revolutions. But the geographers would emphasize that both revolutions started around the shores of the North Sea and are now in process of spreading from that culture hearth. It is possible to make maps decade by decade since 1760 to show the widening spread of the new society, the fronts where the new institutions are in direct conflict with the old.

The Industrial Revolution is more than just the developing of industry. Essentially, it results from the use of controlled inanimate power. Man ceases to be a lifter and mover and becomes a skilled maker and repairer of complex machines. But as a result of all this there is a vast increase in the capacity to produce and a corresponding increase in the volume and variety of raw materials taken from the earth. With the new sources of power, transportation facilities can now move a huge volume of goods from place to place. For the first time in history cities of more than a million inhabitants can be supplied with food. The proportion of urban people rises steeply. The proportion of people employed in farming decreases. Advances in medicine, hygiene and education result in decreasing the death rates with the resulting population explosion. Research and development are given highest priority in order to keep man's technology of production ahead of the increasing numbers of people. All these and other changes are a part of the Industrial Revolution.

The Democratic Revolution started at about the same time and in about the same area. This consists of a demand for equality before the law, for the right to select one's own form of government, for an end to colonialism and subservience, for freedom of access to knowledge. These are all aspects of the Democratic Revolution.

Both revolutions have been spreading from the area of origin around the North Sea and both have spread somewhat differently. Furthermore, both revolutions have continued to develop new and even more fundamental changes as they spread. But the areas into which spread has taken place are not all alike: there are varied habitats, varied pre-industrial and pre-democratic societies; and each has reacted in a somewhat different manner to the impact of the new technology or the new ideas of human dignity. Our one world, which has been brought more closely together than ever before by the new technology of transport and communications, has never been more sharply divided as a result of the impact of the revolutionary changes on pre-existing ways of living. There is a greater difference than ever before between rich and poor nations, between democratic and autocratic governments.

With every change in the technology, and in the attitudes and objectives of people, the meaning of the physical and biotic features of the earth must be reevaluated. What was a natural resource to one society may cease to be a resource to another; what was a barrier to movement, ceases to be a barrier with change in the technology of transport and even what was once good farm land may cease to be rated as good land. The story of the transformation of the North American grasslands from poor range land to first-class farm land as a result of the invention of barbed wire serves to underline one of the basic concepts of modern geography—that the significance to man of the physical and biotic features of his habitat is a function of the attitudes, objectives and technical skills of man himself. With each step in the spread of the two contemporary revolutions from the area of origin, the significance of the land base had to be reconsidered.

A Sequence of Ideas

The following is a summation of ideas listed in sequential form:

1. The earth is differentiated by the physical and biotic character of the habitats, and by the resource base of states.

2. It is differentiated also in terms of population, economic conditions and political institutions.

3. For some two centuries two great processes of fundamental change associated with the Industrial and Democratic Revolutions have been going on and new ways of living have been spreading over the earth from the area of origin around the North Sea.

4. As the two revolutions spread they have also continued to change so that the impact they make along their advancing fronts is not exactly the same as the impact they made a century ago.

5. Distinctive, social, economic and political reactions have been produced by the impact of these revolutions on pre-existing societies.

6. The signficance to man of the features of his habitat changes with changes in man's attitudes, objectives and technical skills, requiring new evaluation of the resource base.

7. Such evaluation is aided by grouping the resulting cultures into culture regions, in each of which there is a distinctive reaction to the impact of the two revolutions.

8. The distinctive regional character is most clearly observable in the cores of regions and around their margins there are wide zones of transition where the characteristics of neighboring regions are mingled.

9. Eleven major regions can be defined tentatively, subject to revision with more precise study of their characteristics, or with a continuation of the revolutionary process.

10. These distinctive regions in their geographic arrangement on the earth have a meaning not found in the separate consideration of the elements that make them up.

The Culture Regions

The eleven culture regions are:

EUROPEAN / The core of this region includes the North Sea culture hearth where the two revolutions originated and the bordering area of Western and Central Europe where strong pre-industrial and pre-democratic institutions created strong resistance to both revolutions. It includes also two marginal areas: Norden where both revolutions are far advanced; and Mediterranean Europe where they are retarded.

SOVIET / The Soviet Union and Eastern Europe where the Industrial Revolution is being rapidly advanced by a "command economy," but where the reaction to the Democratic Revolution is to deny all aspects of it.

ANGLO-AMERICAN / Where both revolutions have been developed beyond the ideas and technologies brought from Europe.

LATIN-AMERICA / Which is today feeling the full impact on the advancing fronts of both revolutions, with a resulting complex pattern of rich and poor, democratic and autocratic.

NORTH AFRICA-SOUTHWEST ASIA / The "crossroads" region, the dry belt that separates Europe from southern Asia and from Africa south of the Sahara, which has long been the scene of efforts to find and control routes of passage and which is now enormously complicated by the discovery of oil.

SOUTH ASIA / The center of Indian culture where nearly 500,000,000 people struggle toward economic development within the framework of free institutions.

SOUTHEAST ASIA / The "shatter belt" between India and China where these two giants have been at least indirectly in conflict for thousands of years.

EAST ASIA / The center of Chinese culture where a vast number of people struggle toward economic development within the framework of a communist society, and which also includes Japan where the two revolutions have gone forward rapidly since World War II.

AFRICA SOUTH OF THE SAHARA / Where African peoples, still largely organized in tribal units, are attempting to form modern states and where the legacy of European colonialism produces great differences in the reactions to the two revolutions.

AUSTRALIA-NEW ZEALAND / At the end of the earth, remote in the midst of the "Water Hemisphere" where both revolutions have been developed without hindrance from pre-existing societies.

PACIFIC / The islands of the South Pacific where long isolated native peoples were overwhelmed by World War II.

These regions are the contemporary result of processes of economic, social and political change defined as the Industrial and Democratic Revolutions. The elements of the equation are: (1) the habitats or resource bases that must be constantly re-interpreted; (2) the pre-existing societies; (3) the two revolutions which have continued to develop as they spread from Western Europe and (4) the resulting culture region, 'each with certain homogeneous characteristics in its core resulting from reaction to the impact of revolutionary change.

Here is a theoretical model, a conceptual framework, designed in accordance with the structure of the field of geography for the purpose of giving geographic perspective to a world of seeming chaos. Actually the chaos is a part of a process of fundamental transformation to a new

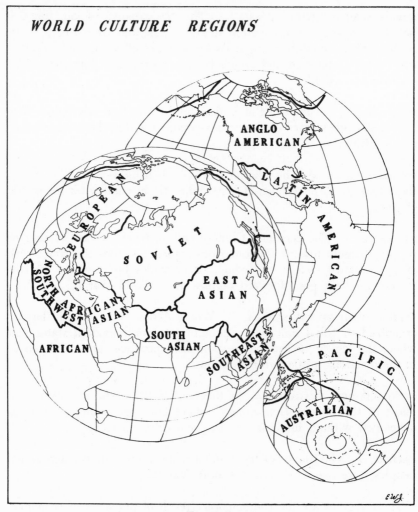

FIGURE 1.

order which has not yet emerged. In the process of transformation a pattern of change has appeared and conflict and confusion have developed along the advancing front where the old order crumbles before the new. But the ultimate order is not yet clear, for the process of change itself changes. Complex, yes: but not a picture that permits one to shrink away in fear or to seek refuge from futility.

What kind of a program does this suggest for young Americans? It is clear that in this struggle of ideas it is not enough to be against communism. No battle and no contest was ever won by defense alone. A program for Americans calls for the positive and enlightened support for the continued spread of the Democratic Revolution of which the peoples of Europe, Anglo-America and Australia-New Zealand are the custodians; it calls for the continued effort to enlarge and perfect democratic ideas and practices at home and it calls for a study of the concepts written in the Constitution and the acceptance by every individual of the responsibility for patterning a way of life based on these concepts. It is necessary to accept the fact that in this revolutionary period there can be no policy that leads to security: there are only choices among risks.

3. The Regional Concept and the Regional Method
Derwent Whittlesey and Others

The region has been fundamental as a generalizing concept for much geographical research and study. Because the laboratory of the geographer is "out-of-doors," it is necessary to find ways of expressing meaningful physical and cultural associations or patterns within given areas. These areas may be as small as an individual field or city block, or as large as the world or such parts of it as the Amazon Basin and the earth's water areas. Generalizations concerning large areas have been highly useful in teaching and research. The goal of geography is to determine the degree of spatial similarity or differentiation from place to place, and one of the most convenient tools of summarizing such expression has been the region. Considerable thought has gone into making regions more precise and the concept more rigorous. There has been continuing, serious discussion among

*geographers about which approach, the regional or the
systematic (looking at a single topic or phenomenon), is more
appropriate for meaningful geographic study. Although the
systematic now predominates in research, the results almost
always indicate regional variations of the phenomena under
study. Thus, the regional concept and method remain
important to the introductory student, layman, teacher, and
researcher.*

Geographers are in general agreement that regional study is an essential
part of their craft. However, they do not claim for their discipline
exclusive rights to the regional concept. The recognition of regional
distinctions figures in all disciplines that deal with features which vary
from place to place on the earth. History, while concerned primarily
with tracing human events through time, finds those events occurring
in particular areas. Each of the disciplines that treats of one kind of
process or group of processes gives consideration to the resulting phenomena as they are associated in particular places. This aspect of each
such discipline is generally known as ecology.

In geography, the subject of investigation and presentation is the
areal differentiation of the face of the earth. Geography focuses on the
similarities and differences among areas, on the interconnections and
movements between areas, and on the order found in the space at or
near the earth's surface. It utilizes the ecological contributions of other
disciplines in so far as they aid in interpreting spatial distributions.
Likewise geography reaches back through time for pertinent space-
order of the past, and sometimes it finds in the historical perspective a
background for forecasting trends of change in space-order.

This chapter examines the regional concept and the method of
regional study from the geographic point of view. The word "region"
has been traditionally used, and remains widely current, as meaning an
uninterrupted area possessing some kind of homogeneity in its core,
but lacking clearly defined limits. Its unifying traits may or may not be
explicitly stated. More often than not the term refers to an area
smaller than a subcontinent, but too large and varied to be readily
identified as uniform throughout.

For many years geographers have been trying to shape and sharpen
the technical meaning of the term "region" into an instrument more
powerful than the non-technical usage provides. No other word exists
to convey the idea embodied in the procedure of regional study, and a

SOURCE: Preston E. James and Clarence F. Jones, eds., *American Geography: Inventory and Prospect* (Syracuse, N.Y.: Syracuse University Press, 1954), pp. 21-68.
The chapter from which this selection has been excerpted was largely the work of
the late Derwent Whittlesey of Harvard University.

word to express the regional concept is found in all the principal languages. In this volume the word is employed to mean an area of any size throughout which accordant areal relationship between phenomena exists. The area is singled out by applying specific criteria to earth-space, and it is homogeneous in terms of the criteria by which it is defined. But a region, as the word is employed here, is more than homogeneous; it possesses also a quality of cohesion that is derived from the accordant relationship of associated features. The observation and measurement of the phenomena brought to the fore, by specific criteria, from the diversified background, and the search for accordant areal relationships among these phenomena, constitute the regional method or the procedure for discovering order in earth-space. The order is expressed in the form of regional patterns made up of specifically defined characteristics and distributed within clearly outlined borders.

The term "area" is almost universally used to mean a geometric portion of earth-space, with no implication of homogeneity or cohesion.

. . . . .

The Region: Theory and Procedure

. . . Any segment or portion of the earth surface is a region if it is homogeneous in terms of such an areal grouping. Its homogeneity is determined by criteria formulated for the purpose of sorting from the whole range of earth phenomena the items required to express or illuminate a particular grouping, areally cohesive. So defined, a region is not an object, either self-determined or nature-given. It is an intellectual concept, an entity for the purposes of thought, created by the selection of certain features that are relevant to an areal interest or problem and by the disregard of all features that are considered to be irrelevant.

A Monistic Goal for Regional Study

The regional method conceived in these terms is a method common to all phases of geographic study. Yet in the entire body of publications on the region that were examined by the committee no comprehensive analysis of the elements and characteristics of the region was discovered. The prime objective in regional study in North America has been the presentation of the characteristics of particular regions, a natural tendency in a world and continent where thousands of presumptive areal homogeneities challenge inquiry and interpretation. The studies produced have treated different categories and ranks of regions with little or no thought of their relations to each other and with no attempt to formulate a systematic method of handling them.

Search for a frame to support a comprehensive analysis led to the view that geography may properly be considered a monistic discipline studied by two approaches, rather than a dualistic study falling into two discrete parts. The study of a topical field in geography involves the identification of areas of homogeneity, which is the regional approach; the study of regions that are homogeneous in terms of specific criteria makes use of the topical approach, because the defining criteria are topical.

A key to a workable monistic frame of reference for regional study was discovered in identifying the characteristics whereby areas are differentiated and regions recognized. These are listed on pages 28–29. The prime factors pertaining to regional study marshalled themselves in this check-list. Regions, when tested by these indices, were seen to range in one comprehensive series from those defined in terms of single features to those representing highly complex associations of features.

The Procedure of Regional Study

How shall areas be differentiated and regions recognized? It seems that among the numerous geographers who have contributed to this report there is a considerable difference of opinion regarding the procedure of regional study. The underlying purpose in all cases is the same: to reach a fuller comprehension of the order of earth-space. Some feel that this purpose has been served when regions are identified, their internal arrangement has been brought out, and their external relations to other regions have been measured. In short, that these things constitute the order of earth-space. Others emphasize the need for seeking the significance of observed order in terms of causes and consequences. The first group finds its challenge in the areal homogeneities that are apparent on the face of the earth and is concerned to examine these areas more closely with regard to the quality of homogeneity, the internal connections, and the external relations. The second group finds its challenge in unsolved questions of the relations between processes and phenomena, of the modifications of process in particular places, and of the areal relations of phenomena. Of the two approaches to regional study, the regional and the topical, the first group of geographers emphasizes the regional approach, the second group the topical approach.

The committee was not disposed to judge between these two approaches to regional study, because it recognized that differences of emphasis are essential for the full development of the subject. Every homogeneous area can be analyzed into its topical elements, a procedure likely to sharpen the investigator's perception of its make-up. Conversely, attention to the regional setting of a topic broadens the student's understanding of its connections. Indeed, the regional and topical points of view are not really separable. The experienced student of regions will make use of both approaches, yet the degree to which he emphasizes one or the other may turn out quite different products.

The regional approach to regional study starts with the homogeneous area, which is accepted as a hypothesis. The area is then examined with a view of discovering its components and connections. The region is analyzed with respect to the various elements which in association give it character, and is interpreted sagely against the investigator's background and grasp of topical geography. The region, seen as a complex association of features, guides the procedure.

The topical approach to regional study starts with a problem. There is a question of cause-and-effect to be answered or a question of policy to be clarified. The topics or features relevant to the problem are defined and their regional patterns brought out separately and compared. Accordant areal relations are identified by cartographic analysis. The complex association of features seems less important than do the component regional systems that make it up.

For both of these approaches the regional concept is fundamental, and for both of them some parts of the regional method are employed. Yet the results can be strikingly different. The one seeks the greatest possible synthesis, the other the most complete analysis. The one has an appeal for scholars with a certain turn of mind, the other has an appeal for scholars of a somewhat different turn of mind. The largest measure of progress in regional study seems likely to be achieved by the successful merging of the two approaches.

Essential Considerations in Regional Study

Various attributes of regions have been mentioned or implied in some of the technical discussions already cited. No over-all statement regarding these attributes has been found, nor any systematic analysis of how these attributes might be used in regional study. There is no generally accepted terminology. In an attempt to fill the gaps, certain essential considerations regarding the attributes of regions will be discussed under six headings: 1) criteria; 2) categories; 3) characteristics; 4) cores and boundaries; 5) compages; and 6) regional consciousness.

Criteria

The region, in the technical sense proposed in this chapter, is an area in which accordant areal relations produce some form of cohesion. It is defined by specific criteria and is homogeneous only in terms of these criteria. The face of the earth with its complex associations of phenomena could theoretically yield an infinite variety of regional patterns, each brought forth by the application of different criteria.

Obviously not all patterns of homogeneous areas can have equal significance. Simply drawing lines on maps based on random criteria may be good fun and might even be justified by the hope that hitherto unknown patterns and relationships might be discovered. But an investigation which is successful in identifying and presenting regions must seek meaningful patterns, and should contain the demonstration that the patterns presented are, in fact, significant.

What are meaningful patterns? In geographic study a homogeneous area has meaning when it can be shown to correspond or coincide in its position on the earth with other homogeneous areas. But the identification of an accordant relationship, as stated in the introduction to this volume, does not prove a causal relationship. The regional pattern has both meaning and significance when it can be interpreted in terms of systematically related processes, operating through time.

These general principles can best be clarified by an example. For the sake of simplicity the treatment of a single feature, slope, will be considered. Slope is a continuity, and isograms of various kinds can be applied to it as criteria for the purpose of bringing out the variations of degree. Contour lines (20 feet, 40 feet, 60 feet and so on) indicate the direction of greatest degree of slope, which is at right angles to the lines. But the area between the 20-foot contour and the 40-foot contour, although it is homogeneous with respect to the criteria defining it, is not a region unless it can be shown to have accordant relations with other phenomena. In parts of the United States where detailed studies of land quality and land use have been made, it was found that slopes ranging from 0° to 3° could be plowed and cultivated without serious loss from accelerated erosion. The same observations elicited the criterion of 8° as the maximum slope suitable for tillage by machinery. The slope region 3°-8° suffers soil erosion when so handled, but not enough to offset the advantage of using machines. The areas homogeneous in terms of these criteria are meaningful areas because of the accordant relationship between slope and erosion; they are slope regions. They are shown to be further signicant in that the process of accelerated erosion is causally related to the degree of slope.

Effective regional study is founded on the selection of meaningful criteria. The purpose of the study having been stated, criteria intended to bring out relevant distinctions can sometimes be formulated in advance of actual field observation. Such formulations are hypothetical and subject to considerable revision in the field. Even when the criteria for identifying regions have been adjusted to the area under study, they need to be continuously scrutinized and evaluated as the field work progresses. An experienced field observer notes certain apparently re-curring associations, such as relatively level land and land used for crops without serious soil erosion. He attempts to identify and state the criteria that will bring forth regional patterns having the closest degree of accordance.

Criteria previously used in other areas or pertinent to other problems should be introduced only after testing. The slope regions mentioned above exemplify this warning. The slope class defined as $0°-3°$, appropri-ate in the area where it was devised, may prove to be too inclusive in some areas. Testing in Puerto Rico led to reducing the criterion to slopes of $0°-2°$. The slope class defined as $3°-8°$ is found to be inapplicable to regions of the humid tropics where the hoe is the common agricultural implement and machinery is not used.

The criteria by which regions are identified not only determine the outlines of homogeneous areas; they also determine the amount of varia-tion or range in character permissible within a region. If this variation is so great that it obscures instead of illuminates areal relations with other phenomena a new set of criteria must be formulated.

Categories

The regional method fits a frame of study widely used in non-laboratory subjects, namely, the sorting and grouping of data according to specified criteria. It is a method of examining areal differentiation on the face of the earth, of finding similarities between areas, and of revealing the patterns of interconnection between areas. Ideally the regional pattern that results would be the product of mechanical sorting of the data with a minimum of value judgments. Actually, the study of geography un-avoidably and frequently entails the making of value judgments of several kinds. Among them, generalization takes first place because geographers always seek to reduce earth-patterns to a scale, less than outdoor size, that permits analysis and comparison.

This inherent quality of geographic study can be stated as a ratio: neither the earth nor any part of it can be reproduced on a scale as large as 1/1; at any scale smaller than 1/1 some generalization of the phe-nomena that occupy area is inevitable. One test of a competent geo-graphic product is the skill evinced in making the value judgments on which illuminating generalizations are built. Such is the essential nature of the regional method, and of geography.

There are many different categories of regions. The committee once listed more than fifty pertaining to nearly every aspect of the physical, biotic, and societal environments, defined in terms relevant to a great variety of purposes. Regions range from relatively simple delineations of single features, such as slope categories, to highly complex areas embracing the entire content of the human occupance of earth-space. Regions also differ according to the nature of their internal cohesion and structure.

SINGLE, MULTIPLE, AND "TOTAL" REGIONS / In considering the classes of regions it is useful to think of them as ranged in three basic types: 1) those defined in terms of single features; 2) those defined in terms of multiple features; and 3) those defined in terms which approach the totality of the human occupance of area. These types may be outlined as follows:

1. Single-feature regions, such as the slope categories in the example previously given, in each case delineate an individual phenomenon that is examined in relation to other phenomena in the search for accordant relationships. The geographers who prefer the topical emphasis in their approach to regional study favor the construction of regions of this type and the identification of recurrent associations of phenomena through the technique of matching maps of two or more single-feature systems. Such regions must not be thought of as "unit areas" in the sense that they are not further divisible; for within the limits set by the criteria they include a certain amount of variation or range of character, as within the limits of 3° of slope, or even within the area of a single field of grain.

2. Multiple-feature regions are differentiated on the basis of combinations or associations of features. Sometimes they may be constructed through matching single-feature regions; or else they may be sufficiently distinctive and cohesive to be observed and mapped directly in the field. Such regions fall into three subtypes:

a. Associations of intimately connected features which are highly cohesive because they have been produced by one kind of process. Examples are climates (defined as an interplay of temperature and moisture), soil types (defined in terms of slope, soil, and drainage), or types of agricultural land use (defined by the mode of handling a particular association of crops and livestock). Terms designating many different varieties of regions of this subtype may be found in the dictionary.

b. Associations of features less intimately connected than those of the preceding subtype because they have been produced by different kinds of processes, as, for example, an economic region (defined in terms of a resource base together with its associated use). Regions of this subtype lack dictionary names, but are widely employed in geographic study.

c. Associations of features only very loosely connected. One of these is the traditional natural region (theoretically defined in terms of climate, terrain, soil, vegetation, animal life, water and minerals). Its counterpart, the total cultural region (presumably compounded of economic, social, and political distributions), has not been effectively defined.

3. The third major type of region is differentiated in terms of the entire content of human occupance of area. Such a region is an association of inter-related natural and societal features chosen from a still more complex totality because they are believed to be relevant to geographic study.

A good many geographers studying regions of type 3 have assumed that they imply an obligation to sort regionally the entire content of earth-space. All who have commented on this point during the preparation of this report have agreed that so comprehensive an undertaking lies beyond the competence of geography, because in every such region items are found that have no meaning when referred to the features, processes, and sequences being investigated. This intermixture of relevant and irrelevant is demonstrated in the field where the student is confronted with the whole mass of phenomena, and the impropriety of including everything in his interpretation becomes glaringly apparent. When the reach of such regional studies is restricted to the human occupance of area, the concept promises to be useful.

Some are critical of this kind of regional study, even when thus limited, because they believe that it generalizes so many diverse elements that it may be untruthful. In this view, type 3 appears as a special sort of multiple-feature region, and would be listed in the foregoing classification as type 2d. Others are convinced of the necessity for making a distinction between types 2 and 3. They hold that a separate frame is needed for encompassing that part of the entire content of earth-space which they believe to lie within the field of geography and also within the grasp of geographers.

To find a term without burden of other connotations, and to avoid misunderstanding arising from words now in use, it is here proposed to adopt for the type of region differentiated as to human occupance of area the term *compage*.[1]

UNIFORM AND NODAL REGIONS / No matter what criteria are invoked in defining them, geographic regions of all kinds may also be grouped under two heads according to whether they are uniform or nodal.

Uniform regions are so throughout. The uniformity is not complete,

[1] Compage (kŏm-pāj (e)'), singular noun. Used 1550-1694; now obsolete. An adaptation from the Latin *compages,* a joining together, structure; from *com-*, together plus *pag-*, root of *pangere,* to fasten or fix.

Compages (kŏm-pā-jiz, or kom-pa-jez), both singular and plural. Used since 1638. A system or structure of many parts united (Webster). A whole formed by the compaction or juncture of parts; a framework or system of conjoined parts; a complex structure; a solid or firm structure (Oxford).

(It is recommended that compage be used in the singular, and compages in the plural only.)

for there is always a certain range of characteristics permitted by the criteria, and there are irrelevant differences which are disregarded. But within the limits set by the criteria, regions of this kind are uniform. A climatic region is an example. If it is a multiple-feature region its uniformity is defined in terms of the association of features.

Nodal regions are homogeneous with respect to internal structure or organization. This structure includes a focus, or foci, and a surrounding area tied to the focus by lines of circulation. For example, an area of newspaper circulation is a single-feature nodal region, the trade area of a town a multiple-feature nodal region. Nodal regions of like character may lie adjacent to each other, or one such region may be surrounded by nodal regions of different character. A nodal region may coincide with other nodal regions of different character, selected by the application of different criteria. Internally nodal regions are marked by a diversity of function that goes far beyond the range of minor variation permitted in uniform regions. Circulation, including the movement of people and goods, communications, and other aspects of movement, is a primary attribute. Hence the nodal region is bounded by the disappearance or the differential weakening of the tie to its own focus in favor of some other focus. Its boundary lines tend to run at right angles to the lines that tie it together.

Characteristics

Once criteria have been set up for defining regions of any category, the regional pattern is disclosed by applying the criteria to facts concerning the area, facts obtained by observation and inquiry. The task is to discover existing features, processes, and sequences, and to generalize the connections between them in order to illuminate the regional qualities and eliminate distracting details.

To test the soundness of the criteria chosen, it is useful to check the areas thereby differentiated against certain norms that are generally accepted as regional traits or characteristics. Some of them are almost too obvious and basic to require statement; others are not widely utilized, perhaps because they have not been clearly recognized. A check-list of characteristics that serve the regional geographer is given here.

Several characteristics pertain to both uniform and nodal regions. Hence *every kind of region* differentiated may properly be checked against these items.

A1. The region is unique, in that it differs in location from all other regions of the same category.

A2. The region enfolds a three-dimensional segment of earth-space. Viewed broadly regions are intimately associated with the thin water-envelope that limits human life. This hydrosphere, including water-vapor and ice, lies between the atmosphere and the lithosphere and penetrates both. Regions may extend indefinitely above and below the hydrosphere. In practice, however, most regional patterns are shown as possessing length and breadth on the earth's surface, and only occasionally, as in a block diagram, is the third dimension above or below the surface shown.

A3. The region incorporates an association of coherent features. This characteristic exists in all kinds of regions. Areas homogeneous in terms of single features are to be considered as regions only when they are shown to possess areal qualities accordant with one or more other regional systems.

A4. The present character of the region is partly derived from conditions that existed and events that occurred in past times—historical, archeological, and geological. Changes in physical, biotic, and societal features rarely occur without leaving traces significant for the study of succeeding regions. Thus, Roman roads and Roman law are imprinted on the landscape of contemporary Western Europe. The pace and velocity of change may also need to be taken into account, as well as the mere persistence of the evidence of change. The present is merely the latest moment available for observation. These matters are discussed in chapter three.

A5. The region is defined by criteria inherent in the category to which it belongs, not by traits that pertain to other categories of regions. For example, a climatic region is not defined by vegetation. By means of separate analyses, different kinds of regions are kept distinct from each other, even where they occupy the same, or nearly the same area, as do Mediterranean climate and Mediterranean vegetation. A degree of correspondence in area between regions belonging to different categories may occur; sometimes it amounts to coincidence. This correspondence may be accidental, or it may betoken some degree of cause and effect, often in association with still other features. To attribute the traits of any one category of region to any other often leads to confusion, if not also to false conclusions. Nevertheless, where data covering inherent traits are lacking or insufficient, tentative regional divisions can sometimes be deduced from related known aspects of the geography of the area under study. For instance, a polar climate might be areally mapped as coincidental with tundra, a vegetational distribution. Such regions should be presented as hypothetical only, accompanied by a warning to the reader.

A6. The region occupies a fixed position in a hierarchy of regions of the same category, in which those of each successively higher rank consist of aggregations of regions of the next lower rank (for example, minor civil divisions, counties, States, the United States). Conversely a given region may be one subdivision of a region of higher rank. Regions that form subdivisions of another region are, of course, smaller than the latter, but otherwise the ranks have no connotation of size. No region can belong to more than one rank.

Hereafter, in order to keep in view these two equally useful approaches to the construction of regions, this concept of hierarchies will be designated by the term "aggregation-subdivision." Every category of regions, from those of the single-feature group to compages, has its own ranks of aggregation-subdivision, designated by terms appropriate to the regional character.

A *uniform region* needs to be checked for two distinctive characteristics in addition to those applicable to uniform and nodal regions alike.

B1. The uniform region is homogeneous because all parts of its area contain the feature or features by which it is defined. No region is uniform in the absolute sense, for all regions are generalizations based on selected items. It follows that the single-feature uniform region drawn at a very large scale (that is, in the lowest rank of the hierarchy of regions) contains the fewest irrelevant features and so approaches most closely to uniformity. The compage drawn on a very small scale includes the greatest number of irrelevant features, and so is the least strictly uniform. (It should be noted that in a compage either uniform or nodal characteristics may dominate.)

B2. The uniform region includes among the features by which it is defined a certain range of intensity or character permitted by the criteria. The range is least at the bottom of the hierarchy and greatest at the top. Because of these permitted variations within the region, it is not without textural variety or grain; for example, the crests and troughs of a region of ridges and valleys, or the checkering of crop and fallow in a region of extensive wheat growing.

While the uniform region has two characteristic attributes of its own, the *nodal region* has no less than four, in addition to those applicable to all regions.

C1. The nodal region is homogeneous because the whole of its area coincides with an integrated design of internal circulation. This unity of organization, and not the spread of specific features throughout its whole area, differentiates it from other regions.

C2. The nodal region contains a focus (occasionally more than one) that serves as a node of organization. The focus is likely to be a center of communication and is most often urban. It may lie outside the region in exceptional cases, but it must be closely connected with the region by one or more lines of communication; for example, the port of Oporto is connected with the upriver Port Wine District. The same place may serve as the focus of two or more nodal regions. These may be in different ranks of a single category, as where a city is a county seat and a State capital, both functions being administrative. Or they may belong to different categories, whether in the same or different ranks; for example, Salt Lake City, which is a State capital, the headquarters of the Mormon Church, and the transport center of the Great Basin.

C3. The nodal region is enmeshed by a pattern of circulation. This circulation may be an expression of mobility or communication only, such as exchange of people, goods, ideas, or telephone calls. It may involve force, as in government exercised from a focal political center. Lines of force in this sense should be clearly distinguished from mere movement or lines of flow. The circulation need not be equipollent in every direction; indeed, it rarely is. Its reach may vary, as when a focus lies at one side of its region. Its intensity may vary, as in the volume of trade between a commercial center and a thinly peopled rural area on one side, and on the other a more densely populated and urbanized area.

C4. The focus of a nodal region is linked to the remainder of the region by ties of different intensity and different character. Commonly the focus lies within the core area, beyond which spreads the marginal area of the region. Distance itself tends to weaken the ties to the focus, as the perimeter of the region is approached. Nearly always other conditions of the area (it may be the terrain, a language boundary, or a pattern of trade restrictions) so modify and contort the simple effect of distance that an ideal concentric design is not developed. Aside from varying intensities of connection with the focus, ties differ in character. In a succession of areas tributary to a city the following distinct patterns may appear: a close net of roads and rails, affording commuter travel; prolongation of main routes with regular but less frequent traffic; areas with no rails and few poor roads. All these areas lie within the same nodal region because their relations to other nodes are unimportant in comparison.

Cores and Boundaries

By definition, regions are differentiated segments of earth-space. When portrayed on a map the several segments must be separated, either by lines or zones. Where regions are sorted out of a continuity (see chapter one, p. 10), the boundaries are given precise definition. They are troublesome mainly because of the difficulty of deciding upon the appropriate isograms, although making the physical measurements may be taxing. Regions of this kind have no cores, since the transition from one limit to the other is continuous (as 0° to 3° of slope). Where regions are defined by discontinuities, or occupy an area of discontinuous distribution, regional peripheries are likely to be acutely troublesome because they are transitional, or zonal, and at the same time critical.

The attention of geographers has perennially been drawn to boundaries, because of the need for regional demarcation in a discipline that centers on the variation or variety of associated phenomena in earth-space. Preoccupation with peripheries has diverted emphasis from areas where the criteria are met more closely. This is most serious in the case of regions defined by differences of kind and differences of enumeration.

Cores of Regions

A region marked off by differences of kind in a discontinuity includes an area where the characteristics of the region find their most intense expression and their clearest manifestation. This may conveniently be called the core of the region. Although the whole region is homogeneous in terms of the criteria by which it is defined, the peripheral parts of it are distinguished from the core by an increased intermingling of extraneous characteristics. Hence the selection and presentation of the regional character is best accomplished by exposition of the core area.

In uniform regions the core comes closest to the ideal expression of the criteria whereby the region is selected. In a single-feature language region, for example, the core includes that part of the whole area where a single mother tongue is found. The peripheral areas show an increasing proportion of other languages until the limits of the region, as defined by the criteria, are reached. In a multiple-feature region such as the Corn Belt, a certain range of characteristics is tolerated by the criteria of its definition; within the core of the Corn Belt, however, are found all the chracteristics commonly used to describe the whole region. The core of a uniform region possesses two qualities which may be blurred in the peripheral zone: it exists as a recognizable and coherent segment of earth-space, defined by the criteria of its selection, and it differs notably from neighboring core areas.

In nodal regions, the core is the most representative portion of the entire area and the part most closely tied to the focus. For example, in a region of newspaper circulation, the core is the area approaching complete coverage. It should be noted that the core and the focus are not synonymous, even though the focus ordinarily lies within the core. The focus is one of the salient features of the nodal region's structure; the core is the epitome of the region's character, whether uniform or nodal. The cores of adjacent nodal regions may closely resemble one another, because the distinguishing feature is nodality and not uniformity.

Within any category, an occasional region may have so little internal variety that the core embraces the whole of it, but more commonly the periphery is transitional, partaking of the character of two or more cores. It follows that comparison of different cores produces a sharper areal distinction between regions than can be found in the fuzzy interpenetration of peripheral areas. Hence rough delimitation of cores is commonly the easiest and surest way of undertaking areal differentiation and comparison.

Boundaries of Regions

Boundary lines used to separate regions are of three sorts, depending on whether they are drawn in discontinuities, continuities, or areas of discontinuous distribution.

Boundary lines in a discontinuity separate regions which differ in kind. Sometimes such boundaries are sharp and easily observed in the field. For example, the edge of an ore body where it is cut off by a fault is clear even when examined in minute detail. There are places where climatic boundaries between humid and arid conditions are abrupt, as along the crest of the Sierra Nevada. Boundaries separating regions created by the activities of man are usually sharper than the naturally marked boundaries they replace, as where open grassland and deep forest stand side by side as a result of repeated fires, or where the line between desert and oasis is drawn along an irrigation ditch. Discontinuities contrived by man may be essentially linear: only the width of a street often separates blighted and redeveloped areas in a city. Sharpest of all, since they are geometric lines with length but no breadth, are the boundaries that men survey, such as political boundaries or the limits of land property.

But most boundary lines in discontinuities are not abrupt. The peripheral zones are marked by a varied intermixture or interfingering of component features. Vegetation boundaries, especially if they have not been modified by human occupance, are often notably transitional, as where the boreal forest borders the tundra through a wide zone of mixed tundra and stunted trees. In parts of the low latitudes the zone of mixture between forest and savanna is so wide that further study may bring out an additional category of forest-grassland mixture. The humid-semiarid boundary in North America is commonly shown as a single line based on an average of many years, yet its zonal character is revealed by plotting the position of the boundary year by year. Examined in detail the boundaries between soil types often exhibit such a mixture of characteristics on their margins that the beginner is bewildered in his attempt to map them. Man-made boundaries are also transitional in many places, as where the commercial core of a city is being enlarged at the expense of a bordering blighted area, or where the city is expanding into the rural countryside through what has come to be known as a rurban zone. A geometric boundary usually evolves into a zone, minor as where a hedge marks a property line, or major along national boundaries, especially in densely settled areas. Along some national boundaries workers pass without interruption back and forth, as between Canada and the United States at Detroit, or between Belgium and France; along other boundaries there are elaborate fortifications, customs barriers, and other structures scattered over a wide zone on either side of the line.

The demarcation of boundaries in discontinuities may give trouble in actual practice, although the rules of procedure are simple in abstract statement. In uniform regions the boundary is drawn where the distinctive characteristics of adjacent core areas are least discernable or fade into each other. In nodal regions the boundary is drawn where attraction to adjacent foci is equal. If there is no overlap, the boundary is drawn where the attraction is zero.

In some cases the boundary of a multiple-feature region in a discontinuity can be most effectively located by matching the maps of several component single-feature regions. These boundaries may all fall within a boundary-girdle where they correspond or perhaps even coincide. The meaning of the boundary-girdle depends on the meaning of the several regional categories superimposed to make it. Mere piling of lines does not prove the existence of an important regional division unless the significance of the associated regions is determined; but such a piling of lines points to the probability that a significant boundary can be derived.

Quite apart from the quality of the boundary as a sharp line or a wide zone of transition, and independent of its demarcation, is the geometry of its depiction on a map. If the map-scale is very small, the width of a pen line may spread a sharp linear boundary over more than its fair share of space, or may occupy the whole breadth of a zonal boundary. A zonal boundary around a single-feature region comes closest to exact map representation when it is drawn at a scale which permits the pen line to coincide with the zone of transition. A boundary representing correspondence of more than one feature is precise only where the separate lines coincide.

Boundary lines drawn in a continuity are of very different character. They do not represent divisions between differences of kind, for the same kind of feature exists on both sides of the line. The differences are those of degree or intensity. The lines reveal the pattern of the phenomenon in question: the direction of greatest variation in intensity is always at right angles to the bounding line. In this book, the kind of isogram that connects points of equal value is called an isarithm; the kind that passes through areas of equal ratio is called an isopleth. In either case, isograms are, at least theoretically, precise.

Because of this quality of isograms drawn athwart a continuity, they are useful in determining the position of boundaries in pertinent discontinuities. The boundaries of agricultural regions, for example, may be given strong support through the conversion of discontinuities into continuities and the plotting of isopleths, as when areas of crops or pasture are converted to ratios of cropland or pastureland to total area. The quantitative character of isograms as computed lines on a map does not confer special validity on them as boundaries of discontinuities, because the criteria for determining them are based on value judgments in the first place. Yet isograms do provide for a uniform application of the selected criteria, and therefore may serve as guides to the demarcation of the boundary of a discontinuity.

The boundaries used to outline areas of discontinuous distribution, such as those within which population is enumerated, present special problems of interpretation and procedure.

Whatever the kind of boundary, on a map the line depicting it always strikes the eye. It therefore tends to appear more real than the zone it symbolizes, and to divert the attention from the cores it separates.

. . . . .

Regional Consciousness

Regional consciousness is a form of group consciousness that derives from a sense of homogeneity of area. It usually applies to uninterrupted space, whether a continuous extent of land or the opposite coasts of a unifying body of water. Regionalism, although a word much used, is inadmissable in geographic study because it is overlaid with special meanings and generally serves non-geographic interests. A recent critique of regionalism points out that the word represents not only a state of mind (regional consciousness), but also a frame for collecting information about areas, a hypothesis to account for the interrelation between areas, a tool of administration and planning, and a cult. These four connotations do not include the dictionary definition, sectionalism. Those who feel that the term regional consciousness is clumsy, may prefer to substitute the single word, regionality, which lacks dictionary definition, and is therefore available as a synonym.

The most obvious occurrence of regional consciousness is in political regions. When identified with sovereign states it is rampant under the name of nationality or patriotism. It may appear in particular areas within a state, strongly if the state is composed of sharply differentiated regions, as in the Soviet Union, weakly or limited to certain phases of life when contacts with other regions are intimate, as in northern interior United States. Internal barriers may heighten and perhaps occasion regional awareness, as in Canada. Where a sovereignty is divided along lines that mark sub-nationalities, regional consciousness may quietly persist without rancor, as in cantons of Switzerland; or it may be invoked as an aid in a struggle for autonomy, as in Scotland, or for independence, as in Poland. A feeling of insecurity or inferiority may promote regional consciousness, whereas the portions of sovereign states seated firmly in the political saddle, such as the Humid Pampa of Argentina, are unlikely to feel the need of it. Constituent members of a sovereign state may join forces to gain regional advantages, as the states of Northeast Brazil have done. Conversely, regional consciousness may provide foundation stones for a superstructure jointly raised, as Benelux.

Regional awareness appears in conurbations, not because they may have a legal status different from the surrounding countryside, but because they contrast with it in appearance, comprise social units with distinct economic functions and common problems of servicing, and possess both focus and nodal pattern.

In regions of the higher ranks, self-awareness may be furthered by the leadership of a focal city, as in the case of Spokane in the Inland Empire. In rare and disputed instances, two or more foci may simultaneously be centers of a single regional outlook, as San Francisco and Los Angeles in California. Landscape in the sense of scenery, whether beautiful or not, is often a factor in creating regional awareness.

It seems to be true that the only areas, other than political regions, in which a sense of regional consciousness appears, are compages. If names belonging to regions of other categories have a connotation of regional consciousness they are being used in a dual sense. The following samples of the dual usage are taken at random from several categories. Locational regions: East End (London), an urban neighborhood or locality. Climatic regions: Thermal Belt of North Carolina, a resort district. Landform regions: Southern Appalachians, a province of distinctive occupance. Soil regions: Black Belt of Alabama, a district having an economic and social character of its own. Vegetation regions: Landes, a French *pays* of district rank. Crop regions: Bordeaux Wine area, a district set apart by the appearance and mode of rural life. Mining regions: the Iron Range northwest of Lake Superior, a collection of isolated localities. Language or religious regions: French Canada, a province sharply differentiated by its way of social life.

From the foregoing it will be observed that compages of all ranks may have overtones of regional consciousness. Self-awareness appears reliably in the locality. Where people are in close touch with each other, only a hermit can avoid a sense of community with his neighbors. Its existence in the district stems from a common way of life, as in the *pays* of France. On analysis, this seems to grow out of contacts between small groups of people, repeated and varied, and continued long enough to establish a sense of shared existence. It may be accentuated where there is also isolation, either natural or societal. Central Alaskan settlements in the pioneering stage exhibit vigorous regional consciousness, as does likewise the relict Wendish (Slavic) settlement in the Spree near Berlin. Provinces have often been differentiated in part by the criterion of regional consciousness. Brazil's South may be cited in point. Some realms have only vague suggestions of regional consciousness, but in others it clearly appears, perhaps only where there is a firm connective element, as sea-trade in Atlantic Europe, or Arab culture in the Near East.

Compages of any rank may lack regional consciousness. In such cases, their reality as regions may exist only in the minds of their authors, and not in the hearts of their residents. Thus, West Africa and the Pocahontas Coal Region have utility as geographic tools, but they appear to lack regional consciousness.

Where it does exist, regional consciousness appears to deepen human solidarity within a region, thus contributing to its stability. A region clearly aware of itself is likely to appear to its inhabitants and to outsiders, to have an independent existence. This psychology is an element of the regional complex. It helps to stamp the area with tangible features, such as a distinctive architecture and a tempo of human movement. It is an expression of innate loyalties that reinforce the external evidences of its regional individuality.

The intensity of attachment to a region varies with individual inhabitants, with the character of the region, and with the impact of history. Switzerland and Nebraska may serve as contrasting illustrations of extremes. Likewise, any one person may feel attachment to more than one region, say to neighborhood, city, province, and nation.

Section is a term with a connotation of regional consciousness. It is widely used in the United States by historians and sociologists, and therefore needs to be understood by geographers who may wish to equate it with their concept of the region. It has been defined as the historical doublet for the geographers' region. It has been utilized as an areal fulcrum for political leverage, with the object of achieving autonomy and independence. In both senses it has a political character and is dynamic. As currently used in geographic writings, it appears to add nothing but confusion to the geographer's study of areal differentiation.

The Outlook for Regional Consciousness

Regional consciousness appears in a good many areas. Where it is coextensive with political units, its boundaries are clear. To assess its weight in the balance with the other features that make up a region is baffling, because it is intangible and therefore not readily measured by instruments familiar to geographers. Yet it cannot be ruled out in the qualitative sense, even though no means have been devised to measure its quantitative value for recognizing and interpreting regional character. Regional consciousness occurs more often than not in compages. This has led some to think of them as analogous to biological creatures, a dangerous habit of mind because it leads to untenable conclusions.

That regional awareness will continue indefinitely to hold its place among regional phenomena is doubted by some, presumed by others.

It is possible to demonstrate current waxing or waning in one or another particular place. Where the regions of several categories tend to coincide, regional awareness is usually present. A notable case is California; there climate, terrain, water supply, agriculture, and cultural heritage have for a century contributed to a regional differentiation which has evolved out of the socio-political unity of the United States. Conversely, when isolation in a generally uniform area gives way to economic and social intercourse, regional feeling is likely to weaken. Several instances can be found in Africa, where enemy tribes have expanded across the no-man's-land that formerly separated them, and now associate peaceably.

Certain trends in contemporary life tend to undermine regional consciousness, particularly in its more bigoted expression, usually called provincialism. With technological advance, increased ease of communication and movement smooths away differences rooted only in tradition, and blurs and widens the peripheral zones between regions. The current tendency to substitute the mobile individual for the earthbound social group as the unit of society, loosens or breaks the hold of group-solidarity and weakens regional cohesion. North Americans need to remember that this shift is farther advanced in the United States and Canada than it is in any other part of the world.

In spite of fraying in many places, regional consciousness, once firmly established, maintains a tenacious hold. This is notably true so long as natural and societal environment together provide a distinguishing set of conditions for regional individuality. The distinctive quality of Tehuantepec within Mexico illustrates this tendency. It may be equally true even though one or more contributing aspects of the natural environment is obliterated. Thus drainage of marsh barriers and increase in waterborne traffic between Netherlands and Germany leave the two nationalities still confronting each other along their historical delta-margin boundary. A recognizable pattern of regional consciousness may persist in the face of altered conditions in the societal environment. Today, in the Solid South, two parties contest local elections, each deriving its strength from the same districts as did their ante-bellum forebears. In France the map of party locale has changed little through four republics, two monarchies, and two empires.

On the whole, regional awareness seems to be a concomitant of areal diversity, and promises to persist as an element in regional differentiation. It appears least subject to change where the natural environment is harsh and isolating to an extreme degree, and the societal environment is sharply or traditionally distinctive. Where conditions of nature or culture are markedly changing, the pattern of regional consciousness may be altered without destroying its essence. New ways of using space, and faster communication may result in changes in shape or size of regions, or in their disappearance, without obliterating regional consciousness. It may persist as an element in the new pattern of regions, as does the sense of nationality in conquered states. Or it may be transferred from one set of phenomena to another. This seems to have occurred in New England, where factory cities have largely replaced rocky farms as the focus of regional awareness. Some have assumed that a single political frame for the entire earth would obliterate regional consciousness. This seems unlikely, because, as political loyalties come to cover larger areas, governmental policy will have to take account of the diversity of pattern in regions of other categories.

4. Approaches to Regional Analysis: A Synthesis

Brian J. L. Berry

Recent attention has been given to the application of new concepts and techniques to regional analysis. New terms, such as "systems analysis" and "geographic matrix" are also being applied. Berry suggests that these newer concepts and techniques might make regional analysis more useful. He is a major spokesman for the more rigorous quantitative-theoretical approach to geography and indicates a possible trend in regional research. Most of the studies of the past that dealt with parts or regions of the world have been descriptive and empirical.

In my dictionary I find a synthesis defined as "a complex whole made up of a number of parts united." The suggestions of complexity and unity are bothersome, however, because the synthesis of approaches to regional analysis presented in this paper is simplistic at best, and we have all found that the parts hardly seem united at times. There is perhaps only one advantage to be gained from the simplification—that poorly developed or new approaches to studying the geography of an area may be identified more readily.

The paper begins with certain assertions concerning geography's role among the sciences. A synthesis of apparently dichotomous approaches to geographic understanding is then proposed, and the concluding re-

SOURCE: *Annals of the Association of American Geographers,* L (March, 1964), 2-12. The author is associate professor of geography at the University of Chicago.

marks are directed to the question of new approaches. The route towards such new approaches begins with analysis of the inadequacies of the proposed synthesis, and continues with discussion of possible solutions to the inadequacies via generalizations produced in General Systems Theory.

Geography among the Sciences

James Conant describes science as an interconnected series of concepts and conceptual schemes that have developed as a result of experimentation and observation and are fruitful of further experimentation and observation as man explores his universe. He characterizes the methods of exploration—scientific method—as comprising speculative general ideas, deductive reasoning, and experimentation. Like all brief statements on any subject, these are ambiguous and incomplete outside of the expanded context given them by the author. They do provide a useful setting for the first thesis of this paper, however, that: *Geographers are, like any other scientists, identified not so much by the phenomena they study, as by the integrating concepts and processes that they stress.*[1] James Blaut expresses the point nicely, saying that the objects dealt with by science are not natural entities, ultimate objects, but are rather sets of interlocking propositions about systems.

Systems may be viewed in a variety of ways, and hence the variety of propositions that may be developed concerning them. The particular set of propositions stressed by any science depends upon its point of view, the perspective in looking at systems that it instills into its members as they progress from novices to accepted membership in that select professional core that serves as guardian and proponent of the viewpoint. As Kenneth Boulding has said, subjects "carve out for themselves certain elements of the experience of man and develop theories and patterns of research activity which yield satisfaction in understanding, and which are appropriate to their special segments." Within this context, our second and third theses are thus that: *The geographic point of view is spatial* and that *the integrating concepts and processes of the geographer relate to spatial arrangements and distributions, to spatial integration, to spatial interactions and organization, and to spatial processes.*

[1] This contrasts with Hartshorne's view that geography is a chorological science similar to the chronological sciences but contrasting with the sciences classified by categories of phenomena. See *The Nature of Geography*, Chapters 4, 5, and 9, and *Perspective on the Nature of Geography*, Chapters 2, 3, and 11. We are not alone in questioning Hartshorne's views, for a similar debate has been raging for some time in history. Anyone interested in this debate should refer to the journal *History and Theory*.

But the experience of man encompasses many systems, and the geographer does not apply his spatial perspective to all. The second and third theses define the way of viewing, but not that which is viewed. Which system is examined by geographers? Hartshorne properly describes it as comprising "the earth as the home of man." A geographer is so trained and inclined that he assumes a spatial perspective in his analysis. But this perspective is not his sole perquisite, for other scientists take such a viewpoint. His contribution is that it is he who provides the spatial perspective so important to any understanding of the system comprising the earth as the home of man. This definition logically excludes from geography studies of other systems from a spatial viewpoint. We are well aware, for example, that when certain physical systems covering the earth are studied apart from their relevance to man, even from a spatial point of view, the job is done by people in other disciplines—geologists, meteorologists, and oceanographers, among others. Similarly, bubble chamber work proceeds from a spatial viewpoint at the microlevel, and is undertaken by physicists.

What is this system comprising the earth as the home of man? It can be described as the complex worldwide man–earth ecosystem. An ecosystem logically comprises populations of living organisms and a complex of environmental factors, in which the organisms interact among themselves in many ways, and in which there are reciprocal effects between the environments and the populations. Biologists, botanists, and ecologists study such ecosystems from a spatial point of view, of course, but the geographer is the person who concentrates upon the spatial analysis of that worldwide ecosystem of which man is a part. The earth as the home of man is a gigantic ecosystem in which man, with culture, has become the ecological dominant. His earthly environments are thus not simply—and less and less—the physical and biological, but also the cultural of his own creating. The fourth thesis thus becomes: *Geography's integrating concepts and processes concern the worldwide ecosystem of which man is the dominant part.*

There is a further problem which emerges at this point. Definition of the system which geography studies from a spatial point of view is perfectly adequate to differentiate geography's role from that of the physical and biological sciences. Many social sciences study the man-made environments, however: political, economic, social, cultural, psychological, and the like, studied by political scientists, economists, sociologists, anthropologists, and psychologists. We resort to our second thesis. None of these sciences examines the man-made environments from a spatial point of view, whether it be to examine spatial distributions or associations of elements, the organization of phenomena over space, or the integration of diverse phenomena in place. Other distributional and organizational themes are stronger and more central to the other social sciences. Thus, whereas it is the system which is studied which differentiates geography from the physical and biological sciences, in studies of man and his works it is the spatial perspective that differentiates. Within the worldwide ecosystem of which man is the dominant part, man creates for himself many environments. These environments are not studied in their totality by geographers, only in their spatial facets.

Dichotomies within Geography

Debate about approaches to geographic understanding has traditionally run to dichotomies: natural as opposed to human; topical or systematic versus regional; historical or developmental as contrasted with functional and organizational; qualitative versus quantitative; perks versus pokes. Richard Hartshorne has gone to great lengths to show that many of these dichotomies are either meaningless or useless, but the fact that dichotomies have emerged at all suggests that *the spatial viewpoint has several facets.* In his seminal paper "Geography as Spatial Interaction" Edward Ullman has gone so far as to argue that the essential intellectual contributions of human geography can be summarized in terms of a dichotomy, the dual concepts of *site* and *situation.* Site is vertical, referring to local man–land relations, to form and morphology. Situation is horizontal and functional, referring to regional interdependencies and the connections between places, or to what Ullman calls spatial interaction.

Existence of several facets poses problems, even if we agree that, as dichotomies, they are of little utility. Boulding argues that the most significant "crisis in science today arises because of the increasing difficulty of profitable talk among scientists as a whole." Very descriptively, he says that "Specialization has outrun Trade, communication . . . becomes increasingly difficult, and the Republic of Learning is breaking up into isolated subcultures with only tenuous lines of communication between them. . . . One wonders sometimes if science will not grind to a stop in an assemblage of walled-in hermits, each mumbling to himself in a private language that only he can understand. . . ." Is this to be our fate within geography, with analytically minded economic urbanists off building their fragile models, anthropologically oriented cultural ecologists sequestered in some primitive backwoods contemplating their navels, and the like? As Boulding continues, "the spread of specialized deafness means that someone who ought to know something that someone else knows isn't able to find it out for lack of generalized ears." His solution is "General Systems Theory to develop those generalized ears . . . to enable one specialist to catch relevant communications from others."

A system is an entity consisting of specialized interdependent parts. Most systems can be subdivided into subsystems by searching for modules with high degrees of internal connectivity, and lower degrees of intermodule interaction. If larger modules can be partitioned into smaller modules, it is possible to talk of a hierarchy of systems and subsystems.

What we will try to do here is to construct a simple system that depicts the variety of approaches to regional analysis. The traditional dichotomies will be included either as parts of the frame of reference which specifies how the system is separated from the rest of science (the balance of science can be termed the "environment" of the system) or as modules of the system. It is this system that constitutes the synthesis of approaches to regional analysis. The fact that a system has been created emphasizes the unity of the spatial viewpoint. The many facets are not dichotomous or polychotomous, but interdependent; each feeds into and draws upon the others. Moreover, by treating the system so created as one would any other system within the framework of General Systems Theory, poorly developed or new approaches to the geography of large areas may be identified and elaborated. In this way the gift of the "generalized ears" can be used to catch communications from scientists who have forged ahead of us in the development of their particular sets of propositions about the systems they see and study.

A Geographic Matrix

Reflect for a moment on the nature of a single observation recorded from the spatial point of view. Such an observation refers to a single characteristic at a single place or location, and may be termed a "geographic fact." This geographic fact usually will be one of a set of observations, either of the same characteristic at a series of places, or of a series of characteristics at the same place. The two series need to be examined more closely. If the characteristic recorded at the series of places varies from place to place, it is common to refer to its spatial variations. These variations may be mapped, for just as the statistician's series are arranged in frequency distributions, geographers like to arrange theirs in spatial distributions. Study of the resulting spatial patterns displayed in the map is one of the essentials of geography. As for the series of characteristics recorded at the same place, they are the stuff of locational inventories and the geography of particular places.

With such inventories it is the geographer's common practice to study the integration of phenomena in place.

Now assume a whole series of characteristics has been recorded for a whole series of places. Perhaps we can imagine that complete "geographic data files" are available (whether such a dream may really be a nightmare is another topic). An efficient way to arrange the resulting body of data is in a rectangular array, or matrix. What does this "geographic matrix" look like? Each characteristic accounts for a row, and each place for a column, as in Figure 1. The intersection of any row and column defines a cell, and each cell is filled by a geographic fact, the characteristic identified in the row, and the place in the column.

At this juncture one might object and say that there is surely an infinity of characteristics and therefore an infinity of possible rows, and at the limit also an infinity of infinitesimal locations on the earth's surface providing an infinite number of possible columns. This is true; all converges to infinity in the long run. However, to quote Keynes' well-

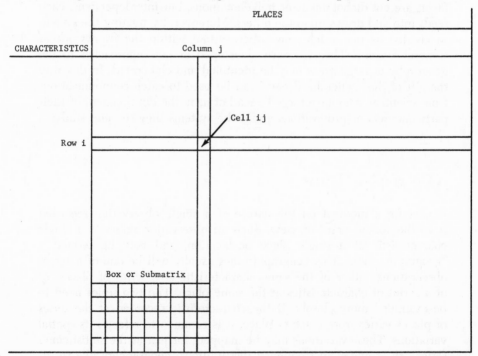

FIGURE 1: *The Geographic Matrix.* A row of this matrix presents the place-to-place variation of some characteristic, or a spatial pattern of the variable which can thus be mapped. Each column contains the locational inventory of the many characteristics of some place. Every cell therefore contains a "geographic fact": the value assumed by some characteristic at some place. Comparison of complete columns is the study of areal differentiation in its holistic sense, and leads to regional geography. Comparison of rows implies the study of spatial covariations and associations, and leads to topical or systematic geography.

worn maxim, in the long run we shall all be dead. In practice, for any particular problem in any particular context there is some specification of rows (characteristics) and columns (places) that is meaningful and useful. The present discussion is phrased so as to be applicable whenever there is such a problem, whatever the problem and consequent specification of the rows and columns may be, just so long as the viewpoint is spatial.

Given a geographic matrix as described above, how many approaches to regional analysis are possible? One can examine:

(a) the arrangement of cells within a row or part of a row;

or (b) the arrangement of cells within a column or part of a column. The former leads to study of spatial distributions and maps, the latter to the study of localized associations of variables in place, and to locational inventories. Surely we would agree that the two approaches are the bases of all geography.

Next steps might be:

(c) comparison of pairs or of whole series of rows;

and (d) comparison of pairs of columns or of whole series of columns. The former involves studies of spatial covariations, or spatial association. If the columns are complete, running across all characteristics outlined in Figure 1, the latter implies the study of areal differentiation in its holistic sense.

A fifth possibility is:

(e) the study of a "box" or submatrix (see Fig. 1).

It is evident that this kind of study could involve some or all of steps (a)–(d) above, but with something additional—the ability to use findings, say, from studies of spatial association to enrich an understanding of areal differentiation in the partitive sense of the box, or of areal differentiation to explain cases which deviate from some generally expected pattern of spatial association between variables. Each approach could indeed feed into and enrich the other.

A Third Dimension

The definition of a geographic fact presented to this point is deficient in one respect, since a single characteristic observed at a single location must necessarily also be observed *at a particular point in time*. At any other time it would be different; variation is temporal as well as spatial. Time, too, may be subdivided infinitely, but it is useful to think of the geographic matrix with a third dimension arranged as in Figure 2 in a series of cross sections or "slices" taken through time in the same manner as rows were drawn through the infinity of characteristics and columns through the infinity of places. Each slice thus summarizes or captures the variations of characteristics from place to place at a certain period of time. Our historical geographers follow this pragmatic procedure. Andrew Clark, for example, noted that "the cross sections which geography cuts through the dimension of time . . . must have a certain thickness or duration, to provide a representative picture of existing situations."

It will be obvious that for any time period, each of the five possible approaches to geographic analysis previously outlined may be taken. "Geographies of the past" can be studied in this way. Yet there are additional possibilities introduced by the temporal dimension:

(f) comparison of a row or part of a row through time, the study of changing spatial distributions;

(g) comparison of a column or part of a column through time, the study of the changing character of some particular area through a series of stages, otherwise termed the study of sequent occupance;

(h) study of changing spatial associations;

(i) study of changing areal differentiation;

(j) comparison of a submatrix through time, a process that could involve all of the preceding approaches individually, but more properly undertaken requires their interplay.

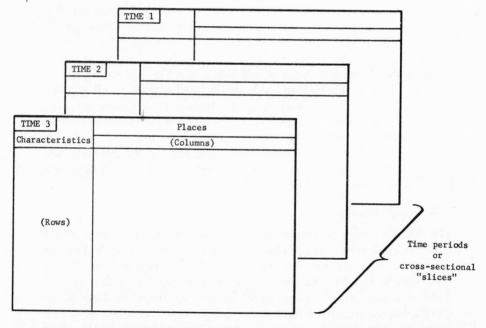

FIGURE 2: *A Third Dimension.* The third dimension, time, may be introduced by arraying a whole series of geographic matrices such as were presented in Figure 1 in their correct temporal sequence. Each time period thus forms a "slice" of the three-dimensional cake, and every slice has all the features described in Figure 1. It will be obvious that such an arrangement makes possible examination of rows through time, of columns through time, and of boxes through time.

The Ten Approaches

It is thus possible to conceive of ten modes of geographical analysis which may be applied to further an understanding of geographic data files such as are depicted in Figure 2. These ten modes fall into three series. The first [(a), (c), (f), and (h)] includes studies of the nature of single spatial distributions, of the covariance of different distribu-

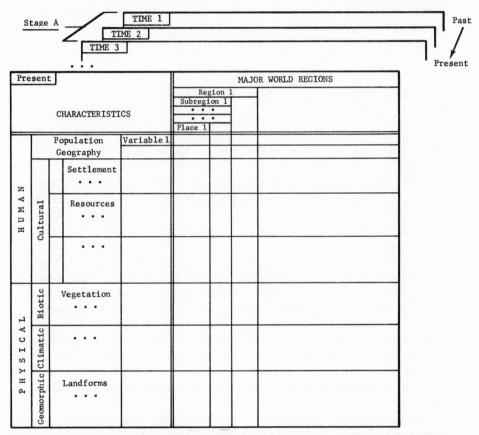

FIGURE 3: *Traditional Grouping of Dimensions*. Geographers have traditionally grouped variables into an ascending hierarchy of rows, the topical subfields. The broadest distinction is between human and physical geography. Within the former it is possible to isolate that part concerned with culture in its holistic sense, and within culture, the social, economic, and political. Economic is further subdivided into resources, industrial, etc. Industrial itself has been further subdivided, and so forth. Hartshorne also speaks of the study of areal differentiation as leading towards the identification of a hierarchy of world regions, formed by successive grouping of places and smaller regions into larger more general regions. This is to be seen in the arrangement of the columns. Finally, arrangement of the successive slices into "stages" is the work of the historian. Given this reference framework, it is possible to locate such things as "Changing industrial structure of the English Midlands and the Ruhr during the industrial revolution" with ease, and to ascertain their immediate relevance to other undertakings in geography.

tions at the same period of time or of the distribution of the same phenomenon at different periods of time, and of the covariance of different distributions through time. A similar series of three levels characterizes the second series [(b), (d), (g), and (i)], which spans locational inventories, studies of areal differentiation and of sequent occupance, and investigations of changing areal differentiation. The third series [(e) and (j)] involves, at its simplest, the cross-sectional interplay of studies of spatial distributions and associations, locational inventories and areal differentiation, and at its more elaborate level the interplay of all nine of the earlier analytic modes.

Traditional Groupings of Rows and Columns

Figure 3 shows the ways in which geographers have traditionally grouped rows and columns of the matrix, and also the conventional ways of grouping the cross-sectional slices, for which we are indebted to historians.

The most common categorization of variables is into one of geography's classic dichotomies, human and physical. Within the human it is conventional to differentiate between variables dealing with collections of people and their numerical and biological characteristics, and those dealing with culture, here used in the holistic sense of the set of man-made variables intervening between man and the earth's surface. These intervening variables may be classified into urban, settlement, transportation, political, economic, and the like. Each of these can be, and has at times been, further subdivided to create further systematic "fields." Economic, for example, is often subdivided into: resources, agricultural, manufacturing, and commercial. These in turn involve further subdivisions, until very limited groups of associated characteristics may be said to define "topical fields." Such is always the pressure of increasing specialization, and, at the extreme, overspecialization.

Clearly, row-wise groupings of variables of interest correspond with with the topical or systematic branches of geography. The essence of this kind of geography is thus the first of the three series of modes of geographical analysis. By the same token, groups of columns form regions (most conventionally, such groupings have been based upon countries and continents, or upon physiographic or climatic criteria). Analysis of such groups of columns is regional geography, with its basis the second series of modes of geographical analysis, emphasizing locational inventories and areal differentiation. *If the object of systematic geography is to find those fundamental patterns and associations characterizing a limited range of functionally interrelated variables over a wide range of places, the object of regional geography is to find the essential characteristics of a particular region—its "regional character" based upon the localized associations of variables in place—by examining a wide range of variables over a limited number of places.*

Yet neither a topical specialty nor study of a particular region can be sufficient unto itself. More profound understanding of spatial associations can only come from "comparative systematics" cutting across several topical fields, from an understanding of local variabilities, and from appreciation of the development of patterns through time. Indeed, geography's first, unlamented, theories about man's distribution on the surface of the earth, those of environmental determinism and their wishy-washy derivatives possibilism and probabilism, postulated particular patterns whereby arrangements of characteristics from place to place in the "human rows" of Figure 3 were determined by arrangements of physical characteristics in the physical rows with, in many respects, the former, as a reflected image of the latter. The whole idea of study of man-land relationships is the idea of comparative systematics.

Similarly, "regional character" can only be evaluated in its integrative sense by proper comparative study of regions, the study of areal differentiation. But here we must pause. What is the basis of regional character? Is it the repetitive appearance of a common theme or themes throughout the entire set of variables recorded for the places within the region, which theme or themes differs from those of other regions? If it is, and there is every reason to believe so, then the understanding of regional character presumes an analysis of spatial associations, simplified because it is undertaken for a relatively small number of places, but complicated because it must be defined for many variables. Only by such study can underlying and repetitive themes be identified. Much the same point can be made, for topical studies as well. They are regional because they involve the study of a certain number of variables within the confines of a certain set of places. Whether we call a study topical or regional, then, is basically a function of the relative *length* and *breadth* of the portion of the geographic matrix which is studied. Likewise, whether we classify a study as historical geography or not depends upon the *depth* of the portion of the matrix studied relative to its length or breadth, or else the distance of the slice studied from the present.

To extend the argument further, selection of the columns to be studied is not entirely independent of the rows under investigation in American geography today. If a person is studying things in the economic, urban, and transportation rows, it is likely that his studies will also be confined to those columns encompassing "modern" urban-industrial societies. Similarly, if the rows under study involve culture in its partitive sense of cultures, settlement forms, language, religion, ecology, and man–land relations, then it is quite probable that the columns embracing the study will be restricted to preliterate and/or "nonwestern" or "preindustrial" societies. Although there are different modes of analysis, on no account, therefore, can it be said that the several series are undertaken independently of one another, nor should they be.

Perspectives on the Economic Geography of the United States

Let us now use this matrix, and later a critique of its inadequacies, to see how well or how thoroughly we have studied the economic geography of the United States.[2] We should first define a submatrix in which the rows embrace those variables of interest to economic geography and the columns encompass all places in the U.S. By projecting the box backwards, we get historical depth.

Studies of this box *per se* have been done very well. The spatial distribution and associations of many variables have been mapped and analyzed. The character of the economic enterprises of most places is well known, as is the historical development of most of the major industries. Attempts of varying degrees of quality have been made to define the relatively homogeneous economic regions of the country both in the partitive sense of agricultural regions, manufacturing regions and the like, and in the holistic sense of real multivariate uniform economic regions. Spatial aspects of the economic growth of the country have been the subject of many investigations.

Yet serious limitations to a general understanding of the economic geography of the country should also be noted. We have already argued that an understanding of the spatial association of any single set of variables requires an evaluation of their actual covariance and theoretical relationship to many other sets of variables, since we are dealing with a system of which interdependence is the essence. Explicit and implicit hypotheses relating to such broader associations are restricted to something which varies between hard-nosed and softheaded environmentalism. Similarly, more profound understanding of areal differentiation hinges upon comparative regional investigations. This literature is also limited. A third problem is that the model we have developed embraces most of the approaches conceived and undertaken by geog-

[2] The evidence supporting these remarks will be found in Brian J. L. Berry and Thomas D. Hankins, *A Bibliographic Guide to the Economic Regions of the United States,* a study prepared for the Commission on Methods of Economic Regionalization of the International Geographical Union, and published as Research Paper No. 87, Department of Geography Research Series, University of Chicago, 1963.

raphers, but not all; the model itself is limited. There are important geographic questions which the matrix we have developed does not show.

The discussion was initially phrased in terms of General Systems Theory. This theory tells us what some of these unanswered questions are. Any system, including the "worldwide ecosystem of which man is the dominant part" can be viewed at a variety of levels, the first three of which are those of *static structure, connectivity of parts (functional organization)*, and *dynamic processes*. Figure 3 shows the ways in which the system of interest to geography may be viewed at the first of these levels, that of static structure—of frameworks and patterns in space and time. It says nothing at all about the second level of interconnections across areas, connectivity of places, flows and interactions, let alone of the third, that of dynamic, interrelated processes. Studies of the economic geography of the United States at the second level are fewer in number and more limited in scope compared with those at the static level, in spite of the early efforts of Platt and the later investigations of Harris and Ullman. The growing central place literature is undoubtedly the best example of the level at which the spatial organization of the U.S. economy is understood. This literature refers to a single sector, the distributive, and is generally confined to the local level of very small urban places. There is no understanding of the spatial organization of the U.S. economy that compares with our understanding of the static patterns, no functional regionalization to match the uniform.

There is no longer any real reason why this gap should exist, in spite of the complexity of the system which has to be clarified. What needs to be grasped is roughly as follows:

1. We live in a specialized society in which there is a progressively greater division of labor and scale of enterprise, accompanied by increasing degrees of regional specialization.

2. But in spite of the increasing diversity of people as producers, as consumers they are becoming more and more alike from one part of the country to another, consuming much the same "basket of goods" wherever they may live, as well as increasingly large baskets because of rising real incomes.

3. The physical problem in the economic system is therefore one of articulation—ensuring that the specialized products of each segment of the country are shipped to final consumers; seeing that consumers in every part of the country receive the basket of goods and services they demand and are able to purchase; bringing demands and supplies into equality over a period of time.

4. Articulation requires flows of messages, of goods and services, and of funds. The flows appear to be highly structured and channeled, with

major metropolitan centers serving as critical articulation points, as follows: products move from their specialized production areas to transshipment or shipping points in the locally dominant metropolitan centers; a complete matrix of intermetropolitan product transfers takes place on a national basis, with each metropolitan center shipping out the specialized products of its hinterland, and collecting the entire range of specialized products from other metropolitan centers spread throughout the country to satisfy the demands of the consumers residing in the area it dominates; distribution then takes place from the metropolis to its hinterland through the medium of wholesale and retail contacts organized in the familiar central place hierarchy. In the reverse direction move both requests for goods and services, and funds to pay for goods and services received, so that the flows are not unidirectional.

The foregoing seems simple enough *but it is mostly unsupported by substantive studies of the spatial organization of the economy of the United States.* Here is a pressing need for careful analysis and synthesis. The amount we do not know at only the second level of viewing the system of interest to geographers is immense, without raising such third-level questions as the ways in which the complex spatial organization of the country is changing through time, and why. The challenge is great, and if these considerations constitute poorly developed or new approaches to the economic geography of the United States, it is towards their solution that we should be moving.

II. THE HISTORY OF GEOGRAPHICAL THOUGHT

Man has always been concerned with the nature of his homeland and the known world, but it was not until the Golden Age of Greece that the science of geography or the description of the earth as a recorded discipline was firmly established. Some developments had taken place previously—the construction of the first known map by the Egyptians, for example—but because there are no written records, a great deal of the thought of the earliest periods is lost to us.

The Greeks possessed a remarkable understanding of geography, such men as Ptolemy, Aristotle, Strabo, and others making major contributions to the science. Modern geography concerns itself to a great extent with the nature and evolution of the discipline, but the continuing emphasis on location, place, distance, and patterns of distribution makes today's unifying concepts the same as those used by the Greeks. We apply different and sometimes more powerful tools than the Greeks, but their objective of understanding "earth spaces" remains as the organizing framework for scholarly research.

Greek literature is rich in observations about areas known directly to the geographers of the classical era. They were curious also about other things, such as the shape of the earth, how to portray the earth on a flat plane, and the practical value of geographical observations to military commanders.

The articles in this part consider the contributions of these men and their philosophic concern with the concept of location and set forth some twentieth-century ideas on the evolution of geography.

5. The Concept of Location in Classical Geography

Fred Lukermann

In our preoccupation with the idea that all significant advances are modern, we sometimes overlook the contributions of the ancients, particularly the Greeks. The foundations of geography rest on their achievements. As Lukermann points out, the concept of location—a modern concern—was the central concern of the Greeks. Long before the current emphasis on the scientific method, new tools and methods of observation, and a sharpened focus upon research design, the Greeks developed the science of geographical description. Lukermann's selections indicate how remarkable their achievement was.

This paper is a study of the one central theme in geography—location. Although primarily concerned with the origin and early development of that concept in ancient geography, it is also concerned with the significance of the concept today. In the twentieth century geographers have been almost continuously concerned with the relevance of location in the methodological constructs of environmentalism, and landscape or regional geography; yet it remains one of the least well-defined terms in the vocabulary of geographical studies—largely a negative theme and a tool for criticism, rather than an analytic, descriptive concept.

It is from this perspective that classical geography will be examined. If today location is the measure of all things geographic, ". . . the unquestionable possession of our science, our very own, that can be called 'geographic' with a higher right than any other elements . . ." then it must be the central theme of the earliest geography as well. In addition, the use of location as an analytic, descriptive concept rather than as a tool of criticism can be made clearer in the context of a more primitive usage.

In classical geography, location was used to describe relation, quantity, and process. It was the philosophical "where." The studies in which the concept had greatest application were geography, chorography, and topography as developed under Ionian logography and Hellenistic

SOURCE: *Annals of the Association of American Geographers*, L (June, 1961), 194-210. The author is associate professor of geography at the University of Minnesota.

science. Unfortunately these Greek studies in which the concept was once integral have lost their specific and original meanings, and the successive translation of the original terminology of location into other languages has diffused and transposed their reference.

"Geography" was defined as the demarcation of the earth's surface by processes of world-wide pervasiveness. "Geographical location" was referent solely to natural process. "Chorography" was defined as the description of "given" areas. "Chorographical location" was referent solely to the total relational content within the given area. "Topography" was defined as the order of discrete units one to the other. "Topographical location" was referent solely to the contiguity of places.

Since modern geography has inherited a "confusion of tongues," geography, chorography, and topography have ceased to be methods of description. The vocabulary of location—place, space, region, area—once the sharpest tool of description, has become a methodological orphan. At present the concept of location is sorely in need of rehabilitation, preferably within the context of its ancient home.

Turning to classical geography we may take as our first text the most complete definition of geography and its allied disciplines now extant—the *Geographical Guide* of Claudius Ptolemy.

The Classical Context

It is written in the *Geographike Uphegesis* of Claudius Ptolemy that

Geography is the representation, by a map, of the portion of the earth known to us, together with its general features. Geography differs from *chorography* in that chorography concerns itself exclusively with particular regions and describes each separately, representing practically everything of the lands in question, even the smallest details. . . .

It is the task of *geography* on the other hand, to present the known world as one and continuous, to describe its nature and position, and to include only those things that would be contained in more comprehensive and general descriptions. . . .

Again, *chorography* deals, for the most part, with the nature rather than with the size of the lands. It has regard everywhere for securing a likeness but not, to the same extent, for determining relative positions. *Geography*, on the other hand, is concerned with quantitative rather than with qualitative matters, since it has regard in every case for the correct proportion of distances, but only in the case of the more general features does it concern itself with securing a likeness, and then only with respect to configuration.

Therefore, chorography has need of *topography*, and no one can be a chorographer unless he is also skilled in drawing. But geography has no such absolute need of topography for by using mere lines and annotations it shows positions and general outlines. . . .

The above paragraphs written in the middle of the second century A.D. are generally held to be the source of the modern definitions of geography, chorography, and topography. Those definitions, in what was to be their simplest and most reduced form, were established at the very beginning of the modern period in the work of Varenius and Kant. Since that time they have been much extended in polemic but little altered in essence. Kant, as recorded in his lectures of the late eighteenth century, had reduced the concepts to simply:

Geography is the description of the whole earth.

Chorography is the description of a more limited area.

Topography is the description of a single place.

Under what conditions and circumstances this cursory categorization by Kant of the Ptolemaic tradition came about is not of direct concern, but it is important to note that it did take place just at the dawn of the most recent methodological awakening. The point of significance is that the elaborate substantive and procedural meaning given in Ptolemy, which is representative of the classical discipline, had been exchanged for a simple classification by form and scale at the beginning of the modern period. Thus any understanding of the classical meaning of the terms from a modern connotation is precluded and specific reference of the classical terms stands completely separated from modern denotation.

An understanding of geography, chorography, and topography in the classical period must be undertaken from internal perspectives. Meaning and reference must come exclusively from the contemporary source material and must be expressed in the classical process of doing geography, chorography, and topography.

In trying to reconstruct the classical discipline it is understood that Ptolemy is neither the epitome nor culmination of classical geographical studies. Rather, he is one of the sources, a source of change and creation as well as a carrier of a continuing tradition and theme. Ptolemy is our last classical source, but in reality he is also a mediate point in a line of intellectual genesis. This is true of all sources. They all have antecedents. They all are antecedents. It is in this context of change and creation that the search is made for a more lucid, operational, and specific meaning of geography, chorography, and topography than we have inherited.

As there is no observed beginning or end of men's thoughts on our subject we may start the analysis with Ptolemy. According to his interpretation, geography is a map (*diagraphos*) of the known world. It is a representation of general features, of an earth which is one and continuous, of things which would be contained only in a comprehensive description. Geography describes the nature, proportion, position, and configuration of these general features and is, therefore, quantitative in its concern.

Ptolemy has told us what is done in geography. How it is done is not so explicitly stated, but it can be revealed from his own work and other sources. In that revelation it will be made clear that the "general features" to be described are of a comprehensive character because they are consequences of natural processes which are comprehensive in effect. The demarcation of the known earth by natural process, when located and mapped, is geography. Geography is the "writing" on the earth by nature. Geographical location is the relation of places through natural process. Chorography is the separate description of particular areas. It attempts to describe everything in true likeness. Chorography is not concerned either with the delineation of areas or their comparison.

Ptolemy does not tell us explicitly how chorography is done, but classical studies labeled as chorography reveal the method. Chorography starts with the area as given. All features within the area are described in detail as they actually occur. Any feature or thing described chorographically is, thus, "located" in relation to every other feature within the given region.

Topography is defined by Ptolemy within a chorographic context. The reason for this is clear. Chorography, by describing a feature in terms of its contacting or environing features, is describing the feature by giving it place. To describe the place of a thing is to mark it off by identifying the things that bound it. Topographical description is simply the distribution of anything, or to put it more simply, the location of a thing, i.e., its place.

If what has been said so far is acceptable as a possible digest of Ptolemy's views, and if Ptolemy is in any sense representative of classical research, it should be possible to analyze other sources in a similar way. This is not to presuppose that classical scholars were any more in agreement than modern scholars, but some general consensus must be postulated before we can talk about a discipline at all.. That is why we have talked rather loosely about being able to *reveal* the process of doing geography from the source material, even though we have not found in the Ptolemaic source an explicit statement on how to do geography, chorography, and topography.

What follows is an attempt to substantiate, as acceptable general statements for the classical period, the methods and processes of doing geography, chorography, and topography. The essence of all the methods is *location*—the placement of things.

GEOGRAPHY: the place of natural process acting everywhere upon the known earth.

CHOROGRAPHY: the integral place of all parts of a given whole.

TOPOGRAPHY: the place of a discrete unit, series or group of units.

Having established an arbitrary end to the classical period with Ptolemy we turn now to its beginning. We will seek to establish in Homer the recognizable roots of geo-description, choro-description, and topo-description.

The Geographical Idiom

Strabo and Eratosthenes, in recounting the origins of their discipline, looked back to Homer as their earliest source; not because they found "geography," "chorography," and "topography" in the poet, for they did not, but rather because they found a way of thinking, an epithetical pattern of speech relating man to place, which they themselves used. These nuclear elements of earth description found in the poets are the earliest methodological source materials of any extent which reveal the process of thinking geographically. In Homer, in the Homeric Cycle, in Hesiod, in Aeschylus, and the dramatists, the inter-relating of man and his surroundings, i.e., the knowledge of place, first becomes a recognizable pattern of expression in literature. How to describe "where something is" becomes idiomatic in Western culture.

This birth of a discipline is recognized by the earliest classical geographers, but is perhaps best summarized by Strabo.

Generally speaking, it is wrong to place the poetry of Homer on the same level with that of other poets, and to decline to rank him above them in any respect, and particularly in the subject that now occupies our attention, namely, geography. For if you did no more than go over the *Triptolemus* of Sophocles or the prologue to the *Bacchae* of Euripides, and then compare Homer's care with respect to geographical matters, it would be easy for you to perceive this difference, which lies on the surface. Indeed, wherever there is need of an orderly sequence in the place he mentions, Homer is careful to preserve that order, not only in regard to places in Greece, but equally in regard to those beyond the limits of Greece.

The use of the epithet to identify places is characteristically and familiarly Homeric, as are the itineraries, whether of Gods or men.

. . . They that held the *hollow land* of Lacaedaemon with its many ravines. . . .

. . . and *vine-clad* Epidarus. . . .

. . . Lyctus and Miletus and Lycastus, *white with chalk,* and Phaestus and Phytium, *well-peopled* cities; and all they beside that dwelt in Crete *of the hundred cities.*

. . . them that dwelt in *deep-soiled* Larisa. . . .

and

. . . captains from *afar*, from Alybe, where is the *birthplace of silver.**

. . . Hera darted down and left the peak of Olympus; on Pieria she stepped and lovely Emathia, and sped over the snowy mountains of the Thracian horsemen, even over their topmost peaks, nor grazed she the ground with her feet; and from Athos she stepped upon the billowy sea, and so came to Lemnos, the city of godlike Thoas. There she met Sleep the brother of Death and she clasped him by the hand. . . .

Beyond these snippets of areal description and allegorical topographies Strabo further declares Homer to busy himself

. . . about the geography both of the individual countries and of the inhabited world at large, both land and sea; for otherwise he would not have gone to the uttermost bounds of the inhabited world, encompassing the whole of it in his description.

Particularly cited is Homer's world view: that the *oikoumene* is surrounded by "Oceanus that floweth ever back upon himself." This reference to tidal action and further references to temperature regions and the position of the earth under the heavens are taken as the first evidence of man's analysis of earth features as demarcated by nature's universal process.

More sophisticated to modern ears are the geographical idioms of the Cycle and Hesiod.

There was a time when the countless tribes of men, though wide-dispersed, oppressed the surface of the deep-bosomed earth, and Zeus saw it and had pity and in his wise heart resolved to relieve the all-nurturing earth of men by causing the great struggle of the Ilian war, that the load of death might empty the world. And so the heroes were slain in Troy, and the plan of Zeus came to pass.

When the Pleiades, daughters of Atlas, are rising, begin your harvest, and your ploughing when they are going to set. Forty nights and days they are hidden and appear again as the year moves round, when first you sharpen your sickle. This is the law of the plains, and of those who live near the sea, and who inhabit rich country, the glens and dingles far from the tossing sea,— strip to sow and strip to plough and strip to reap, if you wish to get in all Demeter's fruits in due season, and that each kind may grow in its season.

Thus at the birth of alphabetic writing in Greece, before the sixth century B.C. and probably as part of an oral tradition going back to Achaean/Mycenaean times of the second millenium, there is a literature, geographic in content if not in name, identifying a method of description and observation undeniably analytic and empirical.

In the next three centuries what had been a geographical idiom became a literature. Descriptions exclusively devoted to the distribution

---

* The italics are Lukermann's. Eds.

or place-relation of earth features and human events were published by the Ionian logographers. Along with the sciences and history, geographical study became a more structured inquiry and consequently became a more narrow and specific field of observation and analysis. Although there was as yet no rubric such as "geography," "chorography," and "topography," to designate these studies, the root words *ge, choros,* and *topos* were becoming generic in their application to certain conditions and types of description—descriptions which we have already identified in the poetic literature.

Hecataeus of Miletus is generally credited with the first specific work of geographical significance among Ionian prose writers. It exists only in *fragmenta* and *testimonia,* but it is fairly certain that the title was either *Ges Periodos* ("Circuit of the Earth") or *Periegesis* ("About or Around the Earth"), and that it was divided into two books, *Europe* and *Asie.* It was a description of the known world not unlike the itineraries of Homer and Aeschylus and those associated with the telling of the voyage of the Argonauts, but was ordered as to direction and sequence of peoples and places away from the Aegean and along the coasts of the inner seas and outer Ocean. Interior places and peoples were appended when known with their closest approaching coasts. Hecataeus is only one of many writers of such descriptions variously titled *Ges Periodos, Periegesis,* and *Periplous* ("About or Around the Coasts"), all essentially structured as topographies and only incidentally as descriptions of environmental differences or descriptions of peoples.

. . . (Hecataeus of Miletus) says in his *Circuit of the Earth*: "Near the city Alazia is the River Odrysses, which flows out of Lake Dascylitis from the west through the plain of Mygdonia and empties into the Rhyndacus." But he goes on to say that Alazia is now deserted and that many villages of the Alazones, through whose country the Odrysses flows, are inhabited, and that in these villages Apollo is accorded exceptional honour, and particularly on the confines of the Cyziceni. Menecrates in his work entitled *The Circuit of the Hellespont* says that above the region of Myrleia there is an adjacent mountainous tract which is occupied by the tribe of the Halizones.

The logographers in general contributed much geographical material although their major interest may have lain elsewhere. A fragment of Thales of Miletus on the Delta is an example of one type. The map attributed to Anaximander of Miletus is another. Hippocrates of Cos in his comparison of Greece and Asia Minor is a third.

Now that we have discussed the sources and course of the Nile we shall endeavour to set forth the causes of its swelling. Thales, who is called one of the seven wise men, says that when the etesian winds blow against the mouths of the river they hinder the flow of the water into the sea, and that this is the reason why it rises and overflows Egypt, which is low and a level plain. But this explanation, plausible as it appears may easily be shown to be false. For if what he said were true, all the rivers whose mouths face the etesian winds would rise in a similar way; but since this is the case nowhere in the inhabited world the true cause of the swelling must be sought elsewhere.

. . . It was in the reign of Cleomenes that Aristagoras the despot of Miletus came to Sparta . . . he brought with him a bronze tablet on which the map of all the earth was engraved, and all the sea and all the rivers.

. . . and the lands wherein they dwell lie next to each other, as I shall show you:—here are the Ionians, and here the Lydians, who inhabit a good land and have great store of silver (showing as he spoke the map of the earth which he had brought engraved on the tablet) "and next to the Lydians" (said Aristagoras in his speech) "you see the Phrygians, to the east, men that of all known to me are the richest in flocks and in the earth's produce. Close by them are the Cappadocians, whom we call Syrians; and their neighbours are the Cilicians, whose land reaches to the sea yonder; wherein you see the island of Cyprus lying. . . .

. . . I hold that Asia differs very widely from Europe in the nature of all its inhabitants and of all its vegetation. For everything in Asia grows to far greater beauty and size; the one region is less wild than the other, the character of the inhabitants is milder and more gentle. The cause of this is the temperate climate, because it lies towards the east midway between the risings of the sun, and farther away than is Europe from the cold. Growth and freedom from wildness are most fostered when nothing is forcibly predominant, but equality in every respect prevails. Asia, however, is not everywhere uniform; the region, however, situated midway between the heat and the cold is very fruitful, very wooded and very mild; it has splendid water, whether from rain or from springs. While it is not burnt up with the heat nor dried up by drought and want of water, it is not oppressed with cold, nor yet damp and wet with excessive rains and snow. Here the harvests are likely to be plentiful, both those from seed and those which the earth bestows of her own accord, the fruit of which men use, turning wild to cultivated and transplanting them to a suitable soil.

It is in Herodotus, however, that there is preserved the greater part of the Ionian geographical contribution. Within his *Histories* are long passages solely devoted to the description of *topos* and *choros*—place and country. In the descriptions of Egypt, Libya, and Scythia, in Books II and IV, the argument is classically geographical. Where is this place? What is the nature of this place and its occupants? What is the form and size of this place?

Now if we agree with the opinion of the Ionians, namely that nothing but the Delta is Egypt, whereof the seaboard reaches, according to them, from what is called the watchtower of Perseus, forty schoeni to the salting factories of Pelusium, while inland it stretches as far as the city of Cercasorus, where the Nile divides and flows thence to Pelusium and Canobus (all the rest of

Egypt being, they say, partly Libya and partly Arabia); if we follow this account, we can show that there was once no country for the Egyptians; for we have seen that (as the Egyptians themselves say, and as I myself judge) the Delta is alluvial land and but lately (so to say) come into being.

The country of Cyrene, which is the highest part of that Libya which the nomads inhabit, has the marvellous boon of three harvest seasons. First on the sea-coast the fruits of the earth are ripe for reaping and plucking; when these are gathered, the middle region above the coast, that which they call the Hills is ripe for gathering: and no sooner is this yield of the middle country gathered than the highest-lying crops are mellow and ripe, so that the latest fruits of the earth are coming in when the earliest are already spent by way of food and drink. Thus the Cyrenaeans have a harvest lasting eight months.

. . . The Scythian race has in that matter which of all human affairs is of greatest import made the cleverest discovery that we know: I praise not the Scythians in all respect, but in this greatest matter they have so devised that none who attacks them can escape, and none can catch them if they desire not to be found. For when men have no established cities or fortresses, but all are house-bearers and mounted archers, living not by tilling the soil but by cattle-rearing and carrying their dwellings on waggons, how should these not be invincible and unapproachable?

This invention they have made in a land which suits their purpose and has rivers which are their allies; for their country is level and grassy and well watered and rivers run through it not greatly fewer than the canals of Egypt.

Finally in Xenophon and Aristotle a certain synthesis is reached. Principles and generalizations which had slowly been gathered together after centuries of experience with the Aegean environment and culture were put to practical purpose. Xenophon in the essay on *Ways and Means* showed his fellow Athenians that prosperity and power lay in their "geography" if they would but recognize it.

Now as I thought over my ideas, one thing seems clear at once, that the country is by its nature capable of furnishing an ample revenue. To drive home the truth of this statement I will first describe the natural properties of Attica.

The extreme mildness of the seasons here is shown by the actual products. At any rate, plants that will not even grow in many countries bear fruit here. Not less productive than the land is the sea around the coasts. Notice too that the good things which the gods send in their season all come in earlier here and go out later than elsewhere. And the preeminence of the land is not only in the things that bloom and wither annually: she has other good things that last forever. Nature has put in her abundance of stone, from which are fashioned lovely temples and lovely altars, and goodly statues for the gods. Many Greeks and barbarians alike have need of it. Again, there is land that yields no fruit if sown, and yet, when quarried, feeds many times the number it could support if it grew corn. And recollect, there is silver in the soil, the gift, beyond doubt, of divine providence: at any rate, many as are the states near to her by land and sea, into none of them does even a thin vein of silver ore extend.

One might reasonably suppose that the city lies at the center of Greece, nay of the whole inhabited world. For the further we go from her, the more intense is the heat or cold we meet with; and every traveller who would cross from one to the other end of Greece passes Athens as the centre of a circle, whether he goes by water or by road. Then too, though she is not wholly sea-girt, all the winds of heaven bring to her the goods she needs and bear away her exports, as if she were an island; for she lies between two seas: and she has a vast land trade as well; for she is of the mainland. Further, on the borders of most states dwell barbarians who trouble them: but the neighbouring states of Athens are themselves remote from the barbarians.

All these advantages, as I have said, are, I believe, due to the country itself. . . .

Aristotle, tutor of Alexander the founder of a hundred cities, wrote the prolegomena of "planning" as a study in location theory.

. . . The proper configuration of the country it is not difficult to state . . . : on the one hand it should be difficult for enemies to invade and easy for the people themselves to march out from, and in addition, on the other hand, the same thing holds good of the territory that we said about the size of the population—it must be well able to be taken in at one view, and that means being a country easy for military defence. As to the site of the city, if it is to be ideally placed, it is proper for it to be well situated with regard both to the sea and to the country. One defining principle is that mentioned above—the city must be in communication with all parts of the territory for the purpose of sending out military assistance; and the remaining principle is that it must be easily accessible for the conveyance to it of the agricultural produce, and also of timber-wood and any other such material that the country happens to possess.

The Methodology of Description

Xenophon (a pupil of Socrates) and Aristotle (a pupil of Plato) represent a new approach to inquiry just becoming coherent in the Athens of the fourth century B.C. A synthesis was being made of all knowledge, drawing together threads from many sources, Oriental as well as Greek. One aspect of this synthesis, particularly pertinent in the genesis of the geographical discipline, was the attempt of Plato, Aristotle, and Theophrastus to provide a logical structure to the study of cosmography: that is, the position of the earth in the Universe directly conditions any analysis of the effect of universal processes on the earth's surface. To describe the *general* features of the known world predicates *general* principles of explanation, and explanation involves first of all a definition of terms.

The words *ge, choros,* and *topos* are the terms of interest. The meaning and reference of *ge* is no problem. For the geographer and in geographical description it has always referred to the known earth, that is, the *oikoumene.* As to classical knowledge, there was no part of the known world of any great extent that was uninhabited.

The words *choros* and *topos* are a problem particularly in their translation into other languages. This confusion in the Latin and English/French/German analogues of the Greek fortunately does not apply to the Greek connotation of the words themselves. In classical Greek usage and in Aristotle's explication of the terms there is little variation or range in meaning. We may take as standard the following definition of the words for classical literature.

Choros should never be translated as space (*spatium*) if the connotation of that word is "empty" or "absolute" space, i.e., implies extension or duration without the presence of a body or thing. The Greek word for absolute or empty space was *kenos* (void) or *chaos. Choros* literally means "room" and may safely be translated in context as area, region (*regio*), country (*pays*) or space/place—if in the sense of the boundary of an area. *Choros* technically means the boundary of the extension of some thing or things. It is the container or receptacle of a body.

One of the earliest philosophical examinations of *choros* is in the *Timaeus* of Plato which probably borrows heavily from Pythagorean doctrine as viewed by Parmenides. *Choros* in the cosmographical context of the place of Being is usually translated as space, but space here obviously means the place where something is.

The most extensive analysis of *choros/topos* in classical literature is in Aristotle. In his discussion of *topos* he uses the term *choros* exclusively in the sense of area—an extended place. In both the *Organon* and in the *Physics, choros* is always identified with a body and distinguished from the concept of void; but it is in the *Physics* that the intimate link between *choros* and *topos* is made explicit. There more than in any other place in classical literature, the dependence of chorography upon topography is clarified. *Choros* and *topos* are the relationship of things. There is no space or place without things. On the other hand, we cannot mean by the place of something, or the space of something, the thing itself. We must mean by *choros* and *topos,* space and place as the relative position of things one to another.

Aristotle sums up the meaning of *topos* by saying that place is continuous and quantitative; it is the common boundary of parts and, therefore, has position and is limited.

. . . a "place" may be assigned to an object either primarily because it is its special and exclusive place, or mediately because it is "common" to it and other things, or is the universal place that includes the proper place of *all* things.

I mean, for instance, that you, at this moment, are in the universe; and in the air because on the earth; and in like manner on the earth because on the special place which "contains and circumscribes you, and nothing but you."

and so:

. . . whatever fixed environing surface we take our reckoning from will be the place.

and finally:

. . . "the place" means the boundary of that which encloses it.

Aristotle has, then, no absolute concept of either space or place. From all perspectives his concept is relative. Place or space description is simply an analysis of relative location. For topography this can only mean location relative to contiguous parts, and for chorography only location relative to the common areal boundary, i.e., the given whole.

The pupil of Aristotle, Theophrastus, is generally cited for bringing the discussion of space/place to its penultimate logical conclusion: that it is the order and place of bodies in relation to each other. It seems wise, considering these arguments, to limit the translation of *topos* in context to place, location (*locus*) or space—if in the strict sense of spatial relationship.

The Science of Geography

Studies in topography and chorography continued with virtually no methodological change between the fourth century B.C. and the time of Ptolemy. The change that did occur was largely a greater specialization of description and the multiplication of *Periploi* and *Periodoi*, either as independent treatises or books of multiple volume histories. As might be expected, a more sophisticated treatment and a more variegated content characterized the later works as the Hellenistic age endured and spread.

Ephorus, the historian, is an example of this sophistication in combining chorographic/topographic description, as are Polybius and Arrian.

Ephorus declares that Boeotia is superior to the countries of the bordering tribes, not only in fertility of soil, but also because it alone has three seas and has a greater number of good harbours; in the Crisaean and Corinthian Gulfs it receives the products of Italy and Sicily and Libya, while in the part which faces Euboea, since its seaboard branches off on either side of the Euripus, on one side towards Aulis and the territory of Tanagra and on the other towards Salganeus and Anthedon, the sea stretches unbroken in the one direction towards Egypt and Cyprus and the island, and in the other direction towards Macedonia and the regions of the Propontis and the Hellespont. And he adds that Euboea has, in a way, been made a part of Boeotia by the Euripus, since the Euripus is so narrow and is spanned by a bridge only two plethra long.

Now he praises the country on account of these things; and he says that it is naturally well suited to hegemony, . . .

Of topography proper, Pliny's description of the Taurus is exemplary and undoubtedly borrows much from his predecessors.

. . . It is itself an immense range, and holds the balance between a countless number of tribes; its right-hand side, where it first rises out of the Indian Ocean, faces north, and its left-hand side faces south; it also stretches westward, and would divide Asia in two at the middle, were it not that in dominating the land it encounters the opposition of seas. It therefore recoils in a northerly direction, and forming a curve starts on an immense route, nature as it were designedly throwing seas in its way at intervals, here the Phoenician Sea, here the Pontus, there the Caspian and the Hyrcanian, and opposite to them Lake Maeotis. Consequently owing to their impact the mountain twists about between these obstacles, and nevertheless sinuously emerging victorious reaches the kindred ranges of the Ripaean Mountains.

A more specific type of chorographic description is scattered throughout Strabo and is most often attributed to the "Chorographer"; but the description has a conventional formula used throughout the classical period. The technique was to find a natural and geometric figure in which to frame the regional description. As might be expected, there was difficulty in getting consensus over what was a natural boundary and whether it formed a recognizable geometric figure. Apollodorus especially aroused Strabo's ire in describing Asia Minor, Strabo's native area.

. . . But the greatest absurdity is this, that, after calling the peninsula triangular in shape, he represents the "exterior sides" as three in number; for when he speaks of the "exterior sides" he seems privily to exclude the side along the narrows, as though this too were a side, but not "exterior" or on the sea. If, then, these narrows were so shortened that the exterior side ending at Issus and that ending at Sinope lacked but little of joining one another, one might concede that the peninsula should be called triangular; but, as it is, since the narrows mentioned by him leave a distance of three thousand stadia between Issus and Sinope, it is ignorance and not knowledge of chorography to call such a four-sided figure triangular. Yet he published in the metre of comedy a work on chorography entitled A Description of the Earth (Ges Periodon).

The difficulty in finding a figure such as a leaf or triangle on which to hang one's chorography led to a pseudo-comparative method of describing a place or area in terms of another place or area. Polybius employed this method to advantage in describing the Hellespont by using the Pillars of Hercules as an analogue more familiar to his Roman readers. Sicily and the Peloponnesus are similarly compared. Self-confessed geographers and chorographers like Strabo and Eratosthenes, however, continued to search for natural and geometrical analogues because "the representation of non-geometrical figures is not easy to describe."

A truly comparative chorography, more precisely a topographic chorography, was never fully developed in classical literature. Incipient examples, again, are found largely in the historians rather than among the chorographers. Herodotus is the best early example developing an areal comparison of cultures explained by a topographical description, in this instance by cultural diffusion.

For it is plain to see that the Colchians are Egyptians; and this that I say I myself noted before I heard it from others. When I began to think on this matter, I inquired of both peoples; and the Colchians remembered the Egyptians better than the Egyptians remembered the Colchians; the Egyptians said that they held the Colchians to be part of Sesostris' army. I myself guessed it to be so, partly because they are dark-skinned and woolly-haired; though that indeed goes for nothing, seeing that other peoples, too, are such; but my better proof was that the Colchians and Egyptians and Ethiopians are the only nations that have from the first practised circumcision. The Phoenicians and the Syrians of Palestine acknowledged of themselves that they learnt the custom from the Egyptians, and the Syrians of the valleys of the Thermodon and the Parthenius, as well as their neighbours the Macrones, say that they learnt it lately from the Colchians. These are the only nations that circumcise, and it is seen that they do even as the Egyptians. But as to the Egyptians and Ethiopians themselves, I cannot say which nation learnt it from the other; for it is manifestly a very ancient custom. That the others learnt it from intercourse with Egypt I hold to be clearly proved by this—that Phoenicians who hold intercourse with Hellas cease to imitate the Egyptians in this matter and do not circumcise their children.

Later examples are found in fragments and epitomes collected in Diodorus Siculus and Arrian for their descriptions of India, Arabia, and Ethiopia. Most notable is the regionalization of lands bordering the Erythraean Sea on the basis of the dietary habits of the inhabitants as recorded by Artimodorus and Agatharchides. Arrian, based on Megasthenes and Onesicritus as well as on Artimodorus and Agatharchides, compared the peoples, cultures, fauna, climate, and landforms of India and Ethiopia in his *Indica*. There, however, because of the "natural" explanation offered for similar cultures, *et al.*, it would be more exact to classify the method of comparison as a geographic chorography. Natural process is the "locating" factor rather than cultural diffusion as in the case from Herodotus.

It is with the geographic rather than the chorographic/topographic context that the last four centuries of the classical period are usually identified in the genesis of the discipline. The "science" of geography had begun with the construction of the Ionian world map, and ever since the most compelling theme had been its reform. It was in this reform that Aristotle had made his greatest substantive contribution to the field, and it is in this type of study that the greatest advances in later knowledge were to be made. The reform started much earlier than with Herodotus but his objections are the earliest recorded at any length.

. . . And I laugh to see how many have ere now drawn maps (*periodos*) of the world, not one of them showing the matter reasonably; for they draw the world as round as if fashioned by compasses, encircled by the river of Ocean, and Asia and Europe of a like bigness. For myself, I will in a few words show the extent of the two, and how each should be drawn.

The objections of Herodotus were directed against the worlds of Homer, Anaximander, and Hecataeus which presumed a world-encircling ocean and a circular landmass. The objection was based, not on the fact that this was wrong in theory, but on the fact that it had never been observed. The conceptions were myth, and myth was alien to *istoria* (inquiry). Herodotus described only the known earth—the *oikoumene;* beyond the known world nothing was presumed but the unknown. Geography as distinct from cosmography retained this tradition. Knowledge of the shape of the earth and its position relative to heaven was necessary but incidental; geography henceforth was to be limited to the empirical study of the features of the *oikoumene*.

Aristotle, as cosmographer and geographer, made the same objections; but more explicitly and in character with the newer Hellenistic science.

The way in which present maps (*periodos*) of the world are drawn is therefore absurd. For they represent the inhabited earth as circular, which is impossible both on factual and theoretical grounds . . . the facts known to us from journeys by sea and land . . . confirm the conclusion that its length is much greater than its breadth. For if one reckons up these voyages and journeys, so far as they are capable of yielding any accurate information, the distance from the Pillars of Heracles to India exceeds that from Aethiopia to Lake Maeotis and the farthest parts of Scythia by a ratio greater than that of 5 to 3. Yet we know the whole breadth of the habitable world up to the unhabitable regions which bound it, where habitation ceases on the one side because of the cold, on the other because of the heat; while beyond India and the Pillars of Heracles it is the ocean which severs the habitable land and prevents it forming a continuous belt round the globe.

The concept of hot and cold uninhabited areas of the earth was a cosmographical not a geographical notion of describing features of the known world; but as Strabo later points out, cosmographical notions are antecedent and necessary to proper geographical description.

Now let us see what Poseidonius has to say in his treatise on *Oceanus*. For in it he seems to deal mainly with geography treating it partly from the point of view of geography properly so called, and partly from a more mathematical point of view. . . . Now it is one of the things proper to geography to take as an hypothesis that the earth as a whole is spheroidal—just as we do in the case of the universe—and accept all the conclusions that follow this hypothesis, one of which is that the earth has five zones.

Poseidonius, writing in the second century B.C., attributed the concept of the earth's five zones to Parmenides of the fifth century, and there is no reason to doubt that theories of a spherical earth under a spherical heaven, or heavens, were common philosophical conjectures of the sixth and fifth centuries B.C. Aristotle in the fourth century was a systematizer of such knowledge, depending primarily on his own observations and the synthesis advanced by Eudoxus in the early part of the century. For Parmenides, for Eudoxus, and for Aristotle, the zones were celestial; that is, the grid of the celestial sphere(s) was "projected" on to the earth sphere thus identifying the arctic and tropic circles which bounded the frigid, temperate, and torrid zones. The arctic, tropic, and equatorial circles throughout classical study remained part of the celestial grid. A fragment of Polybius illustrates this geo-graphical methodology of location relative to extraterrestrial but natural process.

Polybius the historian has composed a book with the title *On the part of the globe under the Celestial Equator,* that is to say in the middle of the torrid zone. He says that the region is inhabited, and has a more temperate climate than that of those who inhabit the extremities of the torrid zone. On the one hand he cites the accounts given by those who have actually visited the region, and can testify to the fact, and on the other he argues from the nature of the sun's movements. For at the solstices the sun remains a long time near the tropic circles both in approaching them and receding from them, so that we actually see it stay in their neighbourhood for about forty days; for which reason the length of the day remains almost the same for about forty days. So owing to the length of its stay over the climates lying under the tropic circles, that region is burnt up and is uninhabitable owing to the excessive heat. But from the equinoctial circle or equator the sun recedes rapidly, so that the length of day rapidly increases or decreases after the equinoxes. It is reasonable then to suppose that the climates situated under the equator are more temperate, as the sun does not prolong his stay near the extreme point but rapidly recedes from it.

Geo-graphical location by terrestrial natural processes have already been noted in the idiomatic literature by citations from Hesiod, Thales, Herodotus, and Hippocrates. Aristotle in the *Meteorologica* systematically discusses such earth processes as vulcanism, alluvial deposition, and temperature, wind, and water systems as differentiating areas. His students, Theophrastus and Dicaearchus, carried on the tradition in the analysis of floral and faunal distributions and mountain landforms.

. . . the distinctions between the fruitless and fruit-bearing, flowering and flowerless, seem to be due to position and the climate of the district. And so too with the distinction between deciduous and evergreen. Thus they say that in the districts of Elephantine neither vines nor figs lose their leaves.

. . . And in fact there seems to be some natural difference from the first in the case of wild and cultivated, seeing that some plants cannot live under the conditions of those grown in cultivated ground, and do not submit to cultivation at all, but deteriorate under it; . . .

. . . If anyone were to plant our palm at Babylon, it is reasonable to expect that it would become fruitful and like the palms of that country. And so would it be with any other country which has fruits that are congenial to that particular locality; for the locality is more important than cultivation and tendance. A proof of this is the fact that things transplanted thence become unfruitful, and in some cases refuse to grow altogether.

Dicaearchus is generally credited with extending the old Ionian, world line of orientation: Pillars of Hercules–Rhodes–Taurus Mountains–eastward along the mountain chain to the *Imaus* (Himalayas). This natural boundary became the main parallel for Eratosthenes' reformation of the world map (*pinaka*). Eratosthenes' selection of natural features and settlements for determining the lines of parallel and the lines of meridian served also as the basic orientation for regionalizing the *oikoumene* into natural areas and conventional forms (*sphragides*). These natural sections became the *given* areas for chorographical description along with islands, peninsulas, ethnic areas, vegetation zones, etc.

. . . And the account given by Eratosthenes is as follows: India is bounded on the north from Ariana to the eastern sea, by the extremities of the Taurus, which by the natives are severally called "Paropamisus," and "Emodus" and "Imaus" and other names, but by the Macedonians "Caucasus"; on the west by the Indus river; but the southern and eastern sides, which are much greater than the other two, extend out into the Atlantic sea, and thus the shape of the country (*choras*) becomes rhomboidal, each of the greater sides exceeding the opposite side by as much as three thousand stadia which is the same number of stadia by which the cape common to the eastern and southern coast extends equally farther out in either direction than the rest of the shore.

While Eratosthenes is more justly famous for his almost perfect calculation of the circumference of the earth than for geographical description, that calculation, by definition, was a cosmographical rather than a geographical triumph. The most important mark of the classical discipline as a *science* was the writing of Eratosthenes' *Geographika* in the third century before Christ. It was the first recorded use of the word "geography" and set the direction of study for the next twenty centuries. Eratosthenes' geography was, nonetheless, substantively primitive and crude. The new reformed map of the world still lacked an ordered grid of proportionately spaced parallels and meridians, and the concept of *klimata* was still ill-defined and non-comprehensive. The principle of "fixing" places relative to the inclination (*klima*) of the sun by gnomon was known to the Ionians and is claimed to have been systematized by Eudoxus; but such *klima* did not as yet define the parallels. The *klimata* of Eratosthenes were actually narrow bands immediately spanning his irregularly placed, terrestrially determined parallels. They were therefore non-contiguous and were located by the parallels rather than by the gnomon.

It was left to Hipparchus and Poseidonius in the next century to construct the earth grid and the climatic zones as Strabo, Pliny, Ptolemy, and modern geographers know them. Hipparchus laid out the present earth grid of latitude and longitude and Poseidonius is credited with making the *klimata* contiguous belts bounded by the new earth grid. The possibility of determining parallels of latitude from the observation of similar climatic conditions was recognized and *vice versa*. The importance of this analytic method is that it made possible the integration of past chorographic and topographic description into the new world map. Qualitative environmental descriptions could now be quantified, i.e., given latitude, and gnomonic site calculations could be qualitatively described by analogy. The full fruition of this procedure comes in Ptolemy's *Geographike Uphegesis*. Very few site readings by gnomon were available even by the time of Ptolemy and it is fairly certain that practically all the latitude and longitude readings of the *Uphegesis* are readings from a map which was constructed from a collation of chorographic and topographic descriptions dating back from Marinus to Homer.

The Synthesis of Strabo

The developments from Eratosthenes to the time of Augustus are best summarized in the fragments and testimonies preserved in Strabo. The seventeen books of his *Geographia* contain the major classical synthesis of geography, chorography, and topography. We can logically reconstruct geographical studies of the pre-Christian era from other sources, but our knowledge of how it was done is derived largely from Strabo. In this querulous, garrulous Pontic Cappadocian we have half the library of classical geography, and his view of its nature, purpose, and practice remains the most authoritative statement ever written.

That view is quite easily summarized because it is essentially philosophic. Geography, chorography, and topography are a disciplinary whole. There is no doubt that they are differing methods of description, limited as to perspective, but asking essentially the same root question—"where?" Inasmuch as they ask the question for differing reasons they are specialized studies and are so distinguished in classical literature; yet they remain a single discipline because they describe but the one thing—place.

Strabo was a Stoic and so was not interested in the "causes" of things as was Aristotle. He was a describer of things, not an analyst, and sometimes seems to lack intellectual purpose and direction. Despite these convictions his subject overwhelmed him—Strabo could not escape the logic of what he was doing. In describing the "where of things" he was bound to answer by searching for order and thereby creating a relational framework. The recognition of a relational framework can involve merely description. (The necessary existence of an underlying causal nexus can remain a moot question, unexpressed.) So it was for Strabo who admits no search for cause.

. . . in Poseidonius there is much inquiry into causes and much imitating of Aristotle—precisely what our school avoids, on account of the obscurity of the causes.

Acceptance of the description of relation, not the search for cause, is sufficient for understanding Strabo and classical geography. Denying design and embracing contingency does not subvert the necessary description of place. Place is not determined, but is a condition of existence—it can not be written off as of no account.

. . . a distribution of animals, plants, and climates as exists is not the result of design—just as the differences of race, or of language, are not either—but rather of accident and chance. And again, as regards the various arts and faculties and institutions of mankind, most of them, when once men have made a beginning, flourish in any latitude whatsoever and in certain instances even in spite of the latitude; so that some local characteristics of a people come by nature, others by training and habit.

Strabo, thus, comes to the point. What is to be described and how does one *do* a description? His limitations are those of all classical geographers, "who would fix positions for the whole of the inhabited world."

. . . my first and most important concern, both for the purposes of science and for the needs of the state, is this—to try to give, in the simplest possible way, the shape and size of that part of the earth which falls within our map, indicating at the same time what the nature of that part is and what portion it is of the whole earth; for this is the task proper of the geographer. But to give an accurate account of the whole earth and of the whole "spinning-whorl" of the zone of which I was speaking is the function of another science.

Strabo would write for the needs of the state but he would caution against recording "the diversified political divisions which are made by the rulers," for they are transitory. Rather, the geographer should tell of "the physical and ethnic distributions which have been made" and "not only of the facts of the present, but also sometimes of the facts of the past." In reality the needs of the state are similar to those of the philosopher.

. . . the geographer does not write for the native of any particular place, nor yet does he write for the man of affairs of the kind who has paid no attention to the mathematical sciences properly so-called; nor, to be sure, does he write for the harvest-hand or the ditch-digger, but for the man who can be persuaded that the earth as a whole is such as the mathematicians represent it to be, and also all that relates to such an hypothesis. And the geographer urges upon his students that they first master those principles and then consider the subsequent problems; for he declares, he will speak only of the results which follow from these principles; and hence his students will the more unerringly make the application of his teachings if they listen as mathematicians; but he refuses to teach geography to persons not thus qualified.

The synthesis in geography of the chorographic and topographic specialties and their dependency in turn upon geography is never questioned. For Strabo the inter-relation verges on a law of nature: "in the study of geography we inquire not merely into the shapes and dimensions of countries, but also, as I have said, into their positions with reference to each other." The parts of the oikonmene to be described are like parts of the body, that is, they are natural units defined by natural boundaries. Recognition of what is given in nature is the first prerequisite of geography.

. . . in the case of geography, we must indeed make sections of the parts when we go over them in detail, but we must imitate the limb-by-limb amputations rather than the haphazard amputations. For only thus it is possible to take off the member that is significant and well-defined, the only kind of member that the geographer has any use for. Now a country is well-defined when it is possible to define it by rivers or mountains or sea; and also by a tribe or tribes, by a size of such and such proportions, and by shape where this is possible. But in every case, in lieu of a geometrical definition, a simple and roughly outlined definition is sufficient.

It must be emphasized that what is given in nature is only the first prerequisite. That is where one begins. There is, beside the chance of nature, the attributes of place resulting from human design.

. . . since different places exhibit different good and bad attributes, as also the advantages and inconveniences that result therefrom, some due to nature and others resulting from human design, the geographer should mention those that are due to nature; for they are permanent, whereas the adventitious attributes undergo changes. And also for the latter attributes he should indicate such as can persist for a long time, or else such as can not persist for long and yet somehow possess a certain distinction and fame, which, by enduring to late times, make a work of man, even when it no longer exists, a kind of natural attribute of a place; . . .

Herein lies the essence of Strabo—the search for "a kind of natural attribute of a place." He admits to no philosophic determinism, whether of physical or cultural process. Strabo rather is searching for the persistent effect. In seeking out the most stable configuration of human behavior he allies it with the more stable patterns of nature. Culture, thus, becomes part of the *oikoumenic* natural process and undifferentiated from the other general features to be comprehensively described in geography.

The work of Strabo is in many ways the logical culmination of classical geography. Unlike the later studies of Pliny and Ptolemy, which are selective specializations, Strabo's *Geographia* is a full corpus of all that came before. The integration of geography, chorography, and topography in one literary whole is, as far as we know, unique in the classical period. What seemed in the past to be either divergent or self-contained trends are brought into comprehension around the central thesis of location. Strabo's signal contribution is in the philosophical awareness of the importance of the concept of place as an integrating theme in all three studies. That is not to say that he viewed the three types of description as equal, for he did not, but neither did he dissolve the three perspectives into one undifferentiated whole.

For Strabo and for classical geography geographical description was primarily the observation, analysis, and explanation of "where." There were natural locations, natural boundaries, and natural regions. "Why" was a legitimate question although not often answered. Chorography was the description of a region. Topography was the description of a distribution. Geography, chorography, and topography were the "sciences" of relationship. The analysis of process, cultural and natural, was the objective of description, and genesis was its mode of classification.

6. The Concept of Geography as a Science of Space, from Kant and Humboldt to Hettner

Richard Hartshorne

In the seventeenth century, the philosophical and methodological foundations of geography came under serious discussion in Germany. The philosopher Immanuel

*Kant provided a rationale of the position of geography
in the hierarchy of knowledge, emphasizing the understanding of space—chorography. As Hartshorne, one of the
leading American methodologists, indicates,
Humboldt, Ritter, and Hettner built only indirectly on
Kant, but basically all agreed on the organizing structure
of geography. Hartshorne's interpretation of Hettner's ideas
has been of signal importance in American methodological
thinking. In the following article, Hartshorne examines
the relation between current and past theoretical frameworks and the resulting intellectual problems.*

The Problem

Numerous geographers writing in recent years concerning the nature
and scope of their subject have described the relation of their field to
other fields of science in terms of a concept said to stem from Immanuel
Kant and from Alexander von Humboldt. Whatever may be the original
source of the concept, its importance in currrent geographic thought
stems from the writings of Alfred Hettner, the German master of the
methodology of geography. We are not concerned here with the validity
of the concept, which is of course in no way dependent on who originated or supported it. As a study in the history of geographic thought,
this paper is concerned with the possible origin, or origins, of the concept and its significance to geography during the past century and a half.

Hettner's first brief statement of the concept appears in his earliest
methodological paper, with which he inaugurated in 1895 the *Geo-
graphische Zeitschrift*, the journal which he edited for forty years. Noting that the materials of study in geography included a vast diversity
of facts, so that many had doubted whether they could be united in a
single science, he wrote:

If we compare the different sciences we will find that while in many of them
the unity lies in the materials of study, in others it lies in the method of study.
Geography belongs in the latter group; its unity is in its method. As history
and historical geology consider the development of the human race or of the
earth in terms of time, so geography proceeds from the viewpoint of spatial
variations.

Hettner published a full explanation of his concept a decade later,
most completely in a paper analyzing the system of the sciences in the
Preussische Jahrbücher, somewhat less extended, as part of what was
to become the most famous of his methodological papers, "Das Wesen

SOURCE: *Annals of the Association of American Geographers*, XL (June, 1958),
97-108. The author is professor of geography at the University of Wisconsin.

und die Methoden der Geographie," in his own journal. In contrast to the "systematic sciences" which study each a particular category of phenomena, whether of nature or of man, the historical or chronological sciences study the association of diverse phenomena in particular periods of time or in development through time, and the spatial, or chorological sciences study the associations of diverse phenomena in sections of space, or areas. In this sense, the historical sciences include historical geology, pre-history, and history proper (the history of literate peoples). The spatial sciences include astronomy and geography and, we may now add, geophysics. No sharp or absolute lines can be drawn between the three groups, for in many cases studies overlap, but the viewpoint is basically different in each case.

Immediately following the publication of the two articles in 1905, another German geographer, Schlüter, challenged the concept, but Hettner was able to show that within the same paper Schlüter had expressed essentially the same conclusion. In the following decades Hettner's concept became well known and widely accepted among German geographers. In his inaugural address at Edinburgh in 1908, Chisholm based his statement of geography on Hettner's concept. In 1921 Michotte in Belgium based his orientation on Hettner's statement which he described as *"la classification habituelle."* But in neither case does the concept appear to have been taken up by others in these countries. Even after the appearance in 1927 of Hettner's volume on the methodology of geography, which was widely acclaimed in other countries, little attention was paid to his re-statement of this basic concept. The only student of the philosophy of science to give serious consideration to it, to the best of my knowledge, was Victor Kraft, in Vienna, who in 1929 disscussed it and evidently found it in general acceptable.

The concept has become widely known to English-speaking geographers as a result of its presentation, in 1939, in *The Nature of Geography*, essentially in Hettner's terms. Numerous American and English geographers have used it as the basis for their consideration of the place of geography in the system of sciences.

Hettner evidently did not presume the concept was original with him. In his longer paper of 1905 he expressed surprise that the principal of the chorological sciences had escaped the attention of students who studied the classification of the sciences "even though a number of methodologists of geography have long declared it as the authoritative principle of geography. He also noted that Kant had suggested this principle in his lectures on geography, but, according to a footnote to his other paper, this fact was brought to his attention only as he was completing his own writing—i.e., long after he had formulated his own concept. In the re-publication in his volume of 1927 he introduced a quotation from Kant to demonstrate the similarity of ideas, but with no implication of any connection. At no time does he appear to have recognized any connection between his concept and the views of Humboldt. The similarity between the two was first demonstrated by Döring in 1931, and in 1939 I pointed out the similarity of ideas of all three students—Kant, Humboldt, and Hettner.

Subsequent writers, using the materials presented in *The Nature of Geography,* have generally assumed that this demonstration of similarity established a direct connection. But Hettner himself recognized no such connection and none has yet been established.

The purpose of the present paper therefore is to trace the history of the concept from its earliest origins to its exposition by Hettner in 1895 and 1905. Our concern is not merely with the bibliographical question but also with the more general problem of what conditions in the general climate of scientific thought may have caused students at certain periods to overlook this concept whereas later students were to find it important to their thinking.

Before 1750

Prior to the eighteenth century few students of geography felt any need to determine the status of their subject in the general field of knowledge; its importance was sufficiently assured by popular interest and general utility. In that century, however, an increasing number of students became concerned to establish geography as an integral field of knowledge, rather than merely a utility servant of commerce and government, or the handmaid of history. Geography, they were wont to assert, was similar and comparable to history—not a part of history, but coordinate with it.

This similarity has been recognized by so many students of many different countries that we may assume it to be readily observable as an empirical fact in the geographic literature. To seek its earliest origin we would no doubt need to go back to the period of ancient Greece, to men like Herodotus who wrote both history and geography.

The earliest definite statement of the comparison of geography and history that I have found is that of J. M. Franz in 1747. At the same time, moreover, Franz and other students of that period recognized a close relationship between geography and astronomy, both of which they included under a common term—cosmography. Indeed, the first geographical society in Germany, which Franz founded was called *die Cosmographische Gesellschaft.*

Kant and Humboldt—1756-1859

The earliest statement in which history and geography are not merely compared with each other but contrasted with the viewpoint of the systematic sciences, each defined in terms of categories of phenomena, is found in the introductory lecture of an elementary course in geography which Immanuel Kant gave at Königsberg during most of the second half of the eighteenth century. Kant himself never published these lectures, but numerous handwritten copies were circulated among students and at least one had been sent by Kant to a government official in Berlin. More than a century later, Adickes found a score of such manuscript editions of Kant's course. Certain of these formed the basis for the publication by Rink, in 1802, of Kant's lectures. By painstaking comparison of these many versions, Adickes has demonstrated that while the larger part of Rink's publication, the latter part, is based on materials used by Kant in the early years of the course and later discarded, the first part, including his statement of the relation of geography to other sciences, represents essentially the form in which Kant presented it in 1775 and subsequent years.

Nearly a decade before the publication of Kant's lectures, the same basic concept of the nature of geography as a field of study was stated by Alexander von Humboldt in his first major publication, written in 1793 when he was 24 years old. Although Humboldt had been trained primarily in courses in economics and government finance in preparation for administrative work in government, his personal interest focussed on nature studies, particularly in botany and geology, and he had been introduced to geography in the field by George Forster, one of the first of the scientific explorers. He evidently felt the need to establish a logical basis for a distinction between geography and other sciences. He outlined this distinction in a long footnote to his 1793 article and indicated subsequently that it continued to represent his concept of geography by re-publishing the same footnote in another article a decade later and again in the *Kosmos,* fifty years after its first publication.

Since this statement of Humboldt's of 1793 is the earliest known publication of the concept under discussion, and because it is available only in the Latin form in which Humboldt published his first major work, it is translated here in full (from a photostat copy of the original, in the Library of Congress). The more readily available re-publication in the *Kosmos* differs slightly in wording.

Geognosy (*Erdkunde*) studies animate and inanimate nature . . . both organic and inorganic bodies. It is divided into three parts: solid rock geography, which Werner has industriously studied; zoological geography, whose foundations have been laid by Zimmerman; and the geography of plants, which our colleagues have left untouched. Observations of individual parts of trees or grass is by no means to be considered plant geography; rather plant geography traces the connections and relations by which all plants are bound together among themselves, designates in what lands they are found, in what atmospheric conditions they live, and tells of the destruction of rocks and stones by what primitive forms of the most powerful algae by what roots of trees, and describes the surface of the earth in which humus is prepared. This is what distinguishes geography from nature study, falsely called nature history; zoology (*zoognosia*), botany (*phytognosia*) and geology (*oryctognosia*) all form parts of the study of nature, but they study only the forms, anatomy, processes, etc., of individual animals, plants, metallic things or fossils. Earth history, more closely affiliated with geography than with nature study, but as yet not attempted by any, studies the kinds of plants and animals that inhabited the primeval earth, their migrations and disappearance of most of them, the genesis of mountains, valleys, rock formations and ore veins . . . the earth surface gradually covered with humus and plants, denuded again by violent stream floods, and once more dried and covered by grass. Thus zoological history, the history of plants, and the history of rocks, which tell only the past state of the earth, are to be clearly distinguished from geography.

Both in substance and in terminology, this statement reflects the thinking of Abraham Gottlob Werner, under whom Humboldt was studying at the time, at the mining academy at Freiberg, Saxony. During the previous decades and more of teaching, Werner had separated materials formerly taught together in a single course into separate courses on minerals, which he called "*oryctognosie*," and on the study of rock formations and forms of mountains, which he called "*geognosie*" or "*Erdkunde*"—in either case, literally, "the knowledge of the earth." Humboldt extended this distinction in respect to botany and zoology and also, apparently, added the comparison with the historical aspect of natural science.

There is no similarity in phrasing or in structure between this statement of Humboldt's and that of Kant. Nevertheless they are consistent in recognizing the same three divergent points of view in science. Was the statement which Humboldt published in 1793 inspired or influenced by the statement which Kant presented annually in his lectures since at least as early as 1775?

It is almost certain that there was no personal connection between the young Humboldt and the venerable Kant. During the period when they might have met, Kant never left Königsberg, and there is no mention of a visit by Humboldt to Königsberg in the voluminous correspondence which records his travels as a young man in Germany.

There were, however, many other ways in which Humboldt might have learned of Kant's concept. Before his college days, he and his older brother Wilhelm heard much of Kant's philosophy and work in physics in the intellectual circle in which they lived in Berlin. His studies at the University of Frankfurt made him familiar with Kant's philosophy. Wilhelm, with whom he was very close, was a great admirer of Kant, "has read all his works and lives and moves in his system." But Alexander himself appears to have had far less interest in the philosopher, even a negative reaction against him.

It is, of course, possible that Humboldt could have seen one of the manuscript copies of Kant's lectures in geography, either at Frankfurt or at Göttingen, or in Berlin. But it seems unlikely that he would have been greatly interested in handwritten copies of elementary lectures—prepared and sold to enable students to pass a course—in comparison with the great amount of printed works that Kant had published.

In any case, there is no evidence that Kant's ideas about geography came to Humboldt's attention before 1793, or that he even was aware of Kant's interest in geography. In later years, however, Humboldt did almost certainly make use of the statement which Rink published for Kant in 1802.

Thus, in his lectures of 1827–28, if we can rely on the edition published a century later, he stated that his title *"physische Weltbeschreibung"* was taken from Kant. But in explaining this title in his own publication, in the *Kosmos*, he merely says that it was an extension from the earth to the universe of *"die alte ausdrucksvolle Bennennung physische Erdbeschreibung"* and names no specific source. This, however, is the term used in Rink's edition of Kant's lectures, whereas, as Adickes has shown, Kant probably said *"physische Geographie"* which Rink had changed to the Germanic form. Likewise in defining his term *"physische Weltbeschreibung,"* Humboldt wrote that it considers *"die Welt als Gegenstand des äusseren Sinnes,"* placing that phrase in quotation marks but without reference; the phrase is to be found in Kant's introductory lecture. Further, as shown in the following passages, Humboldt contrasted his view of geography, or cosmology, with the "system of nature" of other sciences just as Kant had done, and with considerable similarity of phrasing—but again without reference to source.

Humboldt: "Die systematisch geordneten Verzeichnisse aller organischen Gestaltungen, die wir ehemals mit dem allzu prunkvollen Namen von Natur-Systemen bezeichneten" . . . "Die Einzelheiten . . . können logisch in Classen und Gattungen geordnet werden."

Kant: "Sage ich z.B. die Rindeart wird unter das Geschlecht . . . oder unter die Gattung . . . gezählt, so ist das eine Eintheilung, die ich in meinem Kopfe mache, also eine logische Eintheilung. Die *Systema naturae* ist gleichsam eine Registrar des Ganzen, wo ich alle Dinge, ein jedes in seine ihm eigenthümlich zukommende Classe setze."

Humboldt: "Solche Anordnungen führen . . . als ein naturbeschreibender

Theil, den anmassenden Titel von Natur-Systemen . . . als Verzeichnisse gewähren sie nur ein formelles Band; sie bringen mehr Einheit in die Darstellung als in die Erkenntnis selbst."

Kant: "Indessen dürfte man die Systeme der Natur . . . richtiger wol Aggregate der Natur nennen, denn ein System setzt schon die Idee des Ganzen voraus, aus der die Mannigfaltigkeit der Dinge abgeleitet wird. Eigentlich haben wir noch gar kein *Systema naturae.* In den vorhandenen sogenannten Systemen der Art, sind die Dinge bloss Zusammengestellt, und an einander geordnet."

We conclude, therefore, that (1) in later years Humboldt studied Kant's statement as published in 1802 and made important use of it; (2) when he wrote his own basic statement in 1793 he almost certainly did not have before him any of the numerous manuscript copies of Kant's lectures that were circulating in Germany; (3) it is entirely possible that he may at some earlier date have seen such a copy or may have heard of Kant's concept from any of many possible sources, but we have no scrap of evidence that he did. It is entirely possible, if not probable, that the two men arrived at similar conclusions entirely independently.

Other Geographers in the First Half of the Nineteenth Century

It is difficult to demonstrate that either Kant's or Humboldt's statement had any significant influence on the thinking of other students of the time. The appearance of two conflicting editions of Kant's course at a time when he was too senile to judge either as authentic raised immediate doubts as to the reliability of either. The elementary form of the lectures was no doubt unimpressive and the greater part of their substantive material was clearly antiquated; not until a century later was it discovered, by Adickes' research, that for the latter part of the volume, the editor had used a manuscript of Kant's that was already over forty years old.

Humboldt's original statement, though published three times in all, appeared each time only as a footnote, and in Latin. The statements in his lectures of 1827–28 were not published for over a century, and his most detailed discussion is hidden in the midst of his long introduction to the *Kosmos,* where it is confused with several other questions he was endeavoring to clarify.

In any case, most of the students of the time may have found the simple comparison with history adequate to assure status to geography. The term "science" had not yet become a fetish bestowing magical authority on those who acquired title to its use. Kant and Humboldt had both been attracted to geography from studies of nature rather than history. Each of them also had a universalist view of the field of knowledge and hence a concern to clarify the position of the subject he was presenting in relation to the total field. Few geographers then, or perhaps now, felt that need.

Karl Ritter evidently did not feel the need; so far as I can find he made no attempt to state the position of geography in relation to the whole field of knowledge. He did, however, express frequently the comparison of geography and history, and in one case at least in terms that seem to echo those of Kant.

Ritter: "Das Nebeneinander der Ortlichkeiten . . . das Nacheinander der Begebenheiten oder der Aufeinanderfolge und Entwicklung der Dinge."
Kant: "Begebenheiten, die aufeinander folgen . . . Begebenheiten, die neben Einander im Raum vor sich gehen."

Likewise in explaining the interest of geography in phenomena which are also the subject of study in the systematic sciences, Ritter's method of expressing the concern of the latter fields is similar to Humboldt's statement:

Ritter: "nach den Stoffen, Formen und inwohnenden Kräfte des materials an sich."
Humboldt: "formas, anatomen, vires scutantur."

Ritter also, it should be noted, recognized the logical similarity of astronomy and geography.

In the methodological literature of the time of Humboldt and Ritter, and for half a century later, I have found but one publication that shows clear indication of familiarity with the statements which both Kant and Humboldt had made concerning the position of geography among the sciences. In a little-known essay published in 1834, Julius Fröbel stated the concept in terms that to me are clearer than those of Humboldt and in more complete form than those of Kant, for he recognizes geography as one of a group of "spatial sciences," the "cosmographic sciences." Although the statement itself is presented without reference to sources, elsewhere in the same essay Fröbel quotes with references from other passages in Kant's introductory lecture and likewise from Humboldt's statement of 1793. We may credit Fröbel therefore as the first writer—and so far as I can find, the only one prior to 1939—to have recognized the essential similarity of the statements of Kant and Humboldt. We know, however, from his autobiography that he had discussed geography personally with Humboldt a few years earlier in Berlin, so that he may have learned of the similarity from Humboldt. In any case, he was the first to put the two statements together.

No one, however, appears to have noticed his statement. Fröbel remained in the profession only a few years during which he established something of a reputation as a promising but immature critic of methodology—particularly as a result of a published debate with Ritter. Few readers, one may hazard, noted his statement of the concept hidden in the midst of nearly fifty pages of a new and elaborate structure for geography—an essay itself buried at birth by publication in a journal the author founded in Switzerland, which shortly died.

Some forty years later, Hermann Wagner called attention to this long-forgotten essay, but only as an example of the type of study that could have no effect on the development of geographic thought; Wagner did not mention its statement of this concept. Thereafter it appears to have been almost completely overlooked. The one copy which I have seen had rested in the Smithsonian Institution and the Library of Congress for over a century with its pages uncut.

In the Second Half of the Nineteenth Century

Throughout the second half of the nineteenth century the statements of Kant and Humboldt on the place of geography among the sciences appear to have been completely overlooked.

In part this reflects the complete discontinuity in training of geographers at the university level following the death of Humboldt and Ritter, both in 1859. Humboldt never held a teaching position and no successor was appointed to Ritter's chair in geography. When professorships in geography were established in most German universities after 1871, they were filled by men who had not been trained by geographers. For their understanding of the methodology of the field these new professors of geography were dependent on the published literature, particularly on the well-known essays of Karl Ritter. These were discussed at length by such students as Peschel, Marthe, and Ratzel. But while Ritter's thinking, as we have noted, was consistent with the concept which Kant and Humboldt had stated, he had not directly expressed that concept in his own writings nor had he referred readers to the statements of Humboldt or Kant.

Humboldt's work was regarded as of great importance, but primarily for its descriptions of the countries he had visited. Students endeavored to induce his methodology from those writings but overlooked his scattered statements on methodology itself. Thus as late as 1927, Hettner stated, in his history of geography, that Humboldt had never concerned himself with the methodology of geography and that the famous work of his old age, the *Kosmos,* was not expressly a geographic work since it combined general geography (systematic geography) with astronomy.

Fröbel's re-presentation of the concept, as we noted earlier, appears to have become well-nigh completely lost.

In view of the frequency of mention of Kant's name in modern discussion of the nature of geography, it may seem surprising that geographers of the nineteenth century paid so little attention to what he said on the subject. For this there were a number of reasons.

Students of the published works of Humboldt and Ritter would find no reason to look to the philosopher Kant for ideas about geography. If each of those masters, as we have suggested, used particular ideas and phrases from Kant in their writings, neither mentioned the source. The substantive materials of his lectures, as published in his name, offered nothing of value. Kant had also published a few individual research studies, on the origin of winds, of volcanism, etc., but neither Humboldt nor Ritter, so far as I have found, ever mentioned these.

Indeed there is strong negative evidence to indicate that both the founders of modern geography turned their backs on the geographic writings of the philosopher. Both were dominated in their thinking by the empirical approach to knowledge and distrusted the deductive thinking of *Natur Philosophie*. On the basis of a detailed examination of the many references to Kant in the *Kosmos*, Lind has demonstrated that while Humboldt spoke repeatedly of "the great philosopher," his concern was to attack Kant's scientific theories—frequently, Lind held, unfairly. Thus the astronomical theories which Kant had established or suggested on the basis of careful calculations, Humboldt described as having been "divined," "suspected," or "dreamed."

The personal explanation which Lind suggests, namely that this is an example of the jealousy of one great man for another, near contemporary, is mere conjecture and hardly plausible at that. The two were in fact not contemporaries, since Kant died before Humboldt became important. Further, Humboldt revealed no such characteristic in his relations with other men of high standing, as is shown particularly in his reflections on the work of Ritter.

Nevertheless if we combine the facts which Lind presents of Humboldt's disparaging reflections on Kant's scientific work, with the fact that when he used Kant's ideas concerning geography, even in quotation marks, he did not mention Kant's name, we can hardly escape the conclusion that Humboldt was motivated to belittle the scientific work of the philosopher. Why should he have done that?

In his earlier years, Humboldt had been strongly influenced by Goethe's philosophy of nature and at one time expressed interest in the system of the philosopher Schelling. But the subsequent development of a natural philosophy that would displace observation and experiment with pure reason and abstract ideas moved him to vitriolic condemnation of what he called a "mad saturnalia," a *"bal en masque* run mad." He could most effectively undermine that school by disparaging the scientific accomplishments of the eminent philosopher.

Whatever the reasons, Kant's work and interest in geography was largely ignored for nearly a century after his death. In the very detailed histories of the development of geography before the nineteenth century which Peschel, Wisotzki, and Günther published in the latter part of that century, the relatively few references to Kant's studies in geography place him as but one of the scores of scholars who had made minor contributions. Richthofen, writing in 1903, refers to Kant's work in philosophy and astronomy, but makes no mention of his work in geography. Hettner's historical essay of 1898 does not mention Kant. The fuller study of the "History of Geography" in his 1927 volume mentions Kant only as having preceded Laplace in presenting the nebular hypothesis of planetary origin and as having given a course in geography.

It may well be that in the conflict between the empirical scientists and the *a priori* natural philosophers, the former were completely triumphant in the second part of the nineteenth century and Kant's very fame as a philosopher tended to obscure his scientific work. When later it was demonstrated that his studies in astronomical theory had represented contributions of outstanding importance, several geographers were stimulated to examine his briefer studies in geography, but failed to find in them significant contributions to substantive knowledge. Hence they were not motivated to consider his statement of the position of geography among the sciences.

Nevertheless, even though the several statements of Kant and Humboldt, and that of Fröbel were not forced upon the attention of later geographers, they existed in the published literature. It is too much to assume that no geographer saw them; rather we must assume that anyone reading them failed to respond favorably. The reasons for this are to be found in the character of development of geography, and of science in general, in the second half of the nineteenth century.

As we noted earlier, when geography became permanently established in German universities, it was promoted largely by men trained in other fields—in a great variety of other fields. The consequence was methodological confusion—and vigorous methodological discussion. In part also the confusion was forced on geography by certain characteristics in the general development of science in that period—notably the emphasis on the arbitrary separation of nature and man, which earlier students had not accepted, and the short-sighted view that the end-purpose of science was the construction of scientific laws.

The new generation of geographers, bringing these concepts from the fields in which they had been trained, produced a double form of dualism in geography. Physical geography—notably in the study of the origin and development of land forms—could claim a place as a natural science constructing and applying scientific laws. Human geography, in contrast, not only had drifted farther from its physical base, but in focussing on the study of particular areas could construct no laws and hence appeared unscientific. Ratzel demonstrated that this contrast was unnecessary by laying the foundations of systematic human geography, but there still remained the dualism between physical geography as a natural science and human geography conceived as a sort of missionary bridge from the natural sciences to the less securely founded social studies. As long as this dualistic viewpoint prevailed, there was no place for the concept Kant and Humboldt had formulated. A Gerland could read Kant's statement and pass it on, as he did in 1905, without seeing anything of value in it.

These discussions, however, ultimately led to the replacement of the dualistic viewpoint by a unified orientation of geography. This was most effectively stated by Richtofen in his Leipzig inaugural address of 1883, which was recognized as restoring the viewpoint of the field that was common to the work of both Humboldt and Ritter and subsequently became widely accepted among German geographers as the programmatic statement of modern geography.

Neither in this nor in any other paper did Richtofen refer to the concept of the place of geography among the sciences, but his discussion of the nature and scope of geography is consistent with that concept. We know that he, and Hettner who studied with him, read widely in Humboldt's substantive works. To what extent was either of them influenced by Humboldt's methodological viewpoint absorbed in such study? We can hardly hope for an answer to that question. More significant is the logical effect of the re-establishment of the earlier orientation. For the reassertion of geography as a unified integral field independent of the division that had become established between the natural and the social sciences inevitably raised the question of how geography could be fitted logically into the total system of knowledge, in a logical classification of the sciences.

Hettner, 1895-1927

For Hettner, who had been trained in philosophy as well as in geography—and had even considered at one time going into philosophy—it was natural to seek an answer to this question. He had studied with Richthofen both before and after the latter's inaugural address at Leipzig, and in between had done field work in South America. While he accepted Richthofen's statement he found it provided no answer to this general question. He does not tell us the sources of his thinking but evidently he found in the concept of geography as a chorographic science, which Richthofen had taken over from Marthe and others, the essential comparison with history in contrast to the systematic sciences. Even before Richthofen's address, Wagner had distinguished between those geographers who found the basic concept of geography as an independent science in the "object" which it alone studied and those who found it in its "distinctive method of study."

In the methodological discussion of the latter part of the century, the nearest approach to Hettner's concept that I have found is in an address by the Italian geographer, Dalla Vedova, published in 1881 and discussed the following year by Wagner in the *Geographisches Jahrbuch*, a discussion which we may assume Hettner probably read. The individual sciences study their objects from three points of view: the "static" viewpoint, according to the character of the phenomena at a given moment; the "dynamic" according to the manner of their existence and development in time; and the "chorological," according to their collective existence in space. The third viewpoint presents the field open to geography. The original article, which is well documented, indicates no connection back to the statements of either Kant or Humboldt. Neither does it resemble Hettner's later statement save in the recognition of the three points of view.

There is no reason to suppose that Hettner would ever have examined the obscure essay in which Fröbel restated the concept of Kant and Humboldt. The only mention of that writer that I have found in Hettner's writings is in a footnote stating that he excluded methodological views that had no effect on later developments, such as "the methodological demands" of Fröbel—presumably those in his debate with Ritter.

According to his own statement, as noted earlier, Hettner in writing his basic statement in 1905 was unaware that Kant had recognized a similar viewpoint as the basis for recognition of geography as a separate science. Comparison of the two statements shows no similarity in organization or phrasing.

Likewise Hettner appears not to have known that Humboldt had presented essentially the same concept. He would have had no reason to look in Humboldt's study of subterranean vegetation, published in Latin, in which the concept is stated in a long footnote. In the later discussion, in the *Kosmos*, Humboldt was concerned to establish a single science of cosmology, including both astronomy and general (systematic) geography, whereas Hettner considered astronomy and geography as separate sciences each concerned with a different section of space. Further, Humboldt's concept of the terrestrial portion of his cosmology included the entire earth-body, whereas Hettner followed the practice of Ritter and most geographers in limiting the scope of the field to the thin outer shell of the planet—"the earth surface." Finally, Humboldt's cosmology separated general or systematic geography, which he included in his cosmology, from special or regional geography, whereas Hettner, following Richthofen and most geographers since Varenius, included both in the single field of geography.

Hence, though Hettner believed his view of geography was in general consistent with that expressed in Humboldt's substantive works, we can believe his statement (made to me later in correspondence) that his formulation of the concept of the position of geography among the sciences was independent of such statements by Humboldt. Certainly there is no similarity either in phrasing or in the organization of his presentation.

Hettner's own view of his over-all contribution to the development of methodology in geography no doubt applies to this specific case: "My own importance in the construction of the methodology of geography has been exaggerated; I believe only that I have clearly expressed and methodologically established what was actually present in the development of the field."

Re-discovery of the Concepts of Kant and Humboldt—1905–1939

The development of methodological thought in German geography toward the end of the nineteenth century no doubt contributed to the coincidence that Kant's long-forgotten statement was re-discovered just when Hettner was writing his basic statement of 1905. The observance of the hundredth anniversary of Kant's death caused Friedrich Hahn, professor of geography at Königsberg, who had earlier worked with Richthofen at Leipzig, to re-examine the geographic works of his famous predecessor. He sensed, and his student Kaminsky demonstrated in his doctoral dissertation, that Kant's importance in geography was not to be sought in his few substantive studies, but in his teaching, in particular in his presentation of the character of geography in relation to the whole field of knowledge. Kaminsky's dissertation came to Hettner's attention in time to be mentioned in a footnote; that the geographic philosopher had come to the same concept as the philosophic geographer was recorded as welcome confirmation of the validity of the concept. In incorporating this essay in his volume of 1927, Hettner repeated this confirming footnote and added a paragraph in the text quoting from Kant.

Three years after the publication of Hettner's volume of 1927, another doctoral dissertation, by Döring at Frankfurt, brought together for the first time the methodological statements that were scattered in Humboldt's various works. While Döring compared these particularly with the views of Hettner and found them essentially similar, he did not look back to Kant's statement. Shortly thereafter, Humboldt's lectures of the winter of 1827–28 were published for the first time.

With all these materials at hand, it was possible for me in 1939, in presenting Hettner's statement of his concept, not only to add Kant's complete statement but also to draw on Humboldt for additional confirmation. My conclusion that the three were in essential agreement in their view of the position and character of geography as a science has since been accepted by German writers.

Conclusion

Kant was the first, so far as we know, to state the concept we have been considering. But his statement has had no *direct* influence in modern geographic thought—other than as a form of confirmation. It may have had an indirect influence, through partial and uncertain connections: in slight degree only through Ritter, possibly in greater degree through an effect on Humboldt's thinking and only thereby, and only possibly, on the thinking of Richthofen and Hettner. In each case, however, it is quite possible that there was in fact no connection. On the whole it appears probable that Humboldt's original statement, published in 1793, was independent of the concept which Kant had been presenting in lectures since as early as 1775 but which was not published until 1802.

While Hettner indicated that his concept was intrinsic in the development of the field and hence was at least in part present in the thinking of his colleagues, he was not aware of any particular source nor is it possible to trace his concept back to that of either Humboldt or Kant. Rather, if we may paraphrase his thinking, the concept existed in the historic development of the field from very early times; several or many students may have formulated it independently. Its present importance in the thinking of geographers of the world, however, is most largely due to the work of Hettner.

Regardless of by whom or when formulated, the concept was ignored when geographers considered their subject in terms of views of science transferred from other sciences, in particular those of the individual natural and social sciences. It met with receptive response only when geographers considered their subject in terms of its own intrinsic characteristics.

The intrinsic characteristics of geography are the product of man's effort to know and understand the combinations of phenomena as they exist in areal interrelation in his world. These characteristics are therefore independent of any particular concept of the subject; rather they form the empirical fact on which such a sound concept must be based. Acceptance of the concept is in no way essential to work in geography, but it is of value to those students who wish to understand the nature of the field in which they work in relation and comparison with that of other fields of knowledge.

In particular, geographers from early times have observed that work in their field differs from that in many other sciences in the following respects: (1) the fact that geography has no one particular category of objects or phenomena as its specific subject of study but studies a multitude of heterogeneous things as integrated in areas; (2) geography cannot be classified as either a natural science or a social science, nor simply as a bridge between the two groups, but rather must study combinations in which both kinds of phenomena are intimately intermixed; (3) study in geography requires the use of two markedly different methods of study: the systematic examination of certain categories of relationships over the world or any large part of it, in general or systematic geography; and the study of the totality of interrelated phenomena in particular areas, in special or regional geography; and (4) while geography like all other sciences is concerned with the development and application of generic concepts and general principles or scientific laws, it is like history in that it is also concerned in large degree with the knowledge and understanding of individual, unique cases.

As I hope to have shown in detail in a forthcoming study, the concept stated by Kant and Humboldt and more fully expounded by Hettner provides a reasonable explanation of these empirical facts about the field of geography. Hence it is appropriate to suggest, with Hettner, that this concept is not to be considered as the invention of any one man or of any small number of scholars, but rather as the more or less conscious recognition of countless geographers seeking a common framework of reference for their work.

7. The Morphology of Landscape
Carl O. Sauer

Sauer's article is one of the landmarks in American methodological literature. Before him, Harlan Barrows had indicated in 1923 the nature of environmental determinism (this concept is also delt with in Part III), but his solution

*was unacceptable to the majority of geographers because it
eliminated by and large the physical aspect of the field.
Sauer's article appeared only two years after Barrows
enunciated his theory of "human ecology," and thus provided
a decisive influence against determinism. Drawing upon the
ideas of earlier American, French, and especially German
geographers, Sauer advocated a focus on geographic
association of facts in landscapes, areas, or regions and the
recognition of geographic phenomena as both physical and
cultural. The natural landscape was to be investigated
chiefly as the habitat of man.*

*Sauer's morphological approach, which placed the nature or
structures of regions or landscapes under analysis, developed
geographic theory by emphasizing objective observation
and classification of phenomena and meaningful
generalization. Not only did he succeed in sealing the doom
of environmental determinism; by restating the principle
that environment is a whole in which both physical and
cultural phenomena must be studied, he set the stage for
study of a new and highly significant phase of geography—
the impact of the cultural process as it is revealed in
historical and cultural geography.*

Diverse opinions regarding the nature of geography are still common. The label, geography, as is the case with history, is no trustworthy indication as to the matter contained. As long as geographers disagree as to their subject it will be necessary, through repeated definition, to seek common ground upon which a general position may be established. In this country a fairly coherent series of viewpoints has been advanced, especially through presidential addresses before the Association of American Geographers, which may be accepted as mirror and mould of geographic opinion in America. They are sufficiently clear and well known that they need not be restated. In Europeon geography a somewhat different orientation appears to be developing. In various quarters significant activity is being displayed, probably in some measure influenced by anti-intellectualist currents. At any rate a shaking up of some vigor is under way. It may therefore be appropriate to reexamine the field of geography, keeping current views abroad especially in mind, in order to attempt a working hypothesis that may serve to illuminate in some degree both the nature of the objective and the problem of systematic method.

SOURCE: *University of California Publications in Geography*, Vol. II, No. 2, pp. 19-54, issued October 12, 1925. The author is professor emeritus of geography at the University of California, Berkeley.

The Field of Geography

The Phenomenologic View of Science

All science may be regarded as phenomenology, the term science being used in the sense of organized process of acquiring knowledge, rather than in the common restricted meaning of a unified body of physical law. Every field of knowledge is characterized by its declared preoccupation with a certain group of phenomena, which it undertakes to identify and order according to their relations. These facts are assembled with increasing knowledge of their connection; the attention to their connection denotes scientific approach. "A fact is first determined when it is recognized as to limits and qualities, and it is understood when it is viewed in its relations. Out of this follows the necessity of predetermined modes of inquiry and of the creation of a system that makes clear the relation of the phenomena . . . Every individual science is naïve as a special discipline, in so far as it accepts the section of reality which is its field *tel quel* and does not question its position in the general scene of nature; within these limits, however, it proceeds critically, since it undertakes to determine the connection of the phenomena and their order." According to such definition of the grounds of knowledge, the first concern is with the phenomena that constitute the "section of reality" which is occupied by geography, the next with the method of determining their connection.

Geography as a "Naïvely Given Section of Reality"

Disagreement as to the content of geography is so great that three distinct fields of inquiry are usually designated as geography: (1) The study of the earth as the medium of physical processes, or the geophysical part of cosmologic science; (2) the study of life-forms as subject to their physical environment, or a part of biophysics, dealing with tropisms; and (3) the study of the areal or habitat differentiation of the earth, or chorology. In these three fields there is partial accordance of phenomena, but little of relation. One may choose between the three; they may hardly be consolidated into one discipline.

The great fields of knowledge exist because they are universally recognized as being concerned with a great category of phenomena. The experience of mankind, not the inquiry of the specialist, has made the primary subdivisions of knowledge. Botany is the study of plants, and geology that of rocks, because these categories of fact are evident to all intelligence that has concerned itself with the observation of nature. In the same sense, area or landscape is the field of geography, because it is a naïvely given, important section of reality, not a sophisticated thesis. Geography assumes the responsibility for the study of areas because there exists a common curiosity about that subject. The fact that every school child knows that geography provides information about different countries is enough to establish the validity of such a definition.

No other subject has preempted the study of area. Others, such as historians and geologists, may concern themselves with areal phenomena, but in that case they are avowedly using geographic facts for their own ends. If one were to establish a different discipline under the name of geography, the interest in the study of areas would not be destroyed thereby. The subject existed long before the name was coined. The literature of geography in the sense of chorology begins with parts of the earliest sagas and myths, vivid as they are with the sense of place and of man's contest with nature. The most precise expression of geographic knowledge is found in the map, an immemorial symbol. The Greeks wrote geographic accounts under such designations as periplus, periodos, and periegesis long before the name geography was used. Yet even the present name is more than two thousand years old. Geographic treatises appear in numbers among the earliest printed books. Explorations have been the dramatic reconnaissances of geography. The great geographic societies justly have accorded a place of honor to explorers. "Hic et ubique" is the device under which geography has stood always. The universality and persistence of the chorologic interest and the priority of claim which geography has to this field are the evidences on which the case for the popular definition may rest.

We may therefore be content with the simple connotation of the Greek word which the subject uses as its name, and which means most properly areal knowledge. The Germans have translated it as *Landschaftskunde* or *Länderkunde*, the knowledge of landscape or of lands. The other term, *Erdkunde*, the science of the earth in general, is falling rapidly into disuse.

The thought of a general earth science is impossible of realization; geography can be an independent science only as chorology, that is as knowledge of the varying expression of the different parts of the earth's surface. It is, in the first place, the study of lands; general geography is not general earth science, rather it presupposes the general properties and processes of the earth, or accepts them from other sciences; for its own part it is oriented about their varying areal expression.

With this preference of synthetic areal knowledge to general earth science the entire tradition of geography is in agreement.

The Interdependence of Areal Phenomena

Probably not even the adherents of other, recent schools of geography would deny place for such a view of the subject, but they deem this naïvely given body of facts inadequate to establish a science, or at the most would consider it an auxiliary discipline which compiles fragmentary evidence, to find its place ultimately in a general geophysical or biophysical system. The argument then is shifted from the phenomenal content to the nature of the connection of the phenomena. We assert the place for a science that finds its entire field in the landscape on the basis of the significant reality of chorologic relation. The phenomena that make up an area are not simply assorted but are associated, or interdependent. To discover this areal "connection of the phenomena and their order" is a scientific task, according to our position the only one to which geography should devote its energies. The position falls only if the non-reality of area be shown. The competence to arrive at orderly conclusions is not affected in this case by the question of coherence or incoherence of the data, for their characteristic association, as we find them in the area, is an expression of coherence. The element of time is admittedly present in the association of geographic facts, which are thereby in large part non-recurrent. This, however, places them beyond the reach of scientific inquiry only in a very narrow sense, for time as a factor has a well-recognized place in many scientific fields, where time is not simply a term for some identifiable causal relation.

Historical Development of Chorologic Relation into Scientific System

The older geography was troubled but little by critique. It was casually, even trivially, descriptive rather than critical. Yet though it is idle to seek in most of this literature a "system which makes clear the relation of the phenomena," we cannot dispose of all of it as accidental or haphazard in content. In some measure the notion of areal interdependence of phenomena as giving rise to areal reality was present, as any reader of Herodotus or Polybius knows. The *historia* of the Greeks, with its blurred feeling for time relations, had a somewhat superior appreciation of areal relations and represented a far from contemptible start in geography. However much it may have been embroidered by geophysical, geodetic, and geologic notes, classical geography in general, not cosmology subsequently interpreted by some as geography, gave primary emphasis to areal description, with frequent observations on the interrelation of areal facts. The culminating school, of which Strabo was chief, was by no means entirely naïve, and rejected vigorously other definition of geography than as chorology, with express exclusion of cosmologic philosophy.

During the period of great discoveries a bona fide but uncritical geography attained its greatest development in the numerous travel relations and especially in the cosmographies of that time. An ever increasing body of facts about countries was at that time being brought before the Western World, which took keen interest in the rapidly widening horizon. With such a deluge of newly acquired facts about parts of the world, attempts at systematic ordering were numerous, but often grotesque rather than successful. It is not surprising that dynamic systems of geography should have emerged only as the furore of exploration became spent. Yet it is perhaps even more difficult for us to judge the thought of this period than that of classical antiquity. Yule has helped us to better appreciation of the geographic acumen of some of the men of this period. Of the cosmographers, at least Varenius has been accorded a higher rank than that of a compiler. One very great step in synthesis certainly took place at this time, that of the development of cartography into a real chorologic discipline. Only through a large amount of classification and generalization of geographic data was it possible to consolidate the scattered and voluminous data of exploration into the geographically adequate maps that characterize the latter part of the period. To this day many of the maps of the seventeenth and eighteenth centuries are in some respects monumental. However much may have been added since in precision of measurement, in many ways we have retained the chorologic content as formulated in the maps of this period beginning the "Age of Surveys." "Every map which reproduces the form of the earth's surface is a kind of morphologic representation." Not only for physical morphology, but for the cultural expression of landscape, these maps represented a highly successful series of solutions that are still used. Without such a preliminary synthesis of the facts of geography the work of the next period would have been impossible.

In the nineteenth century the contest between the cosmologic and the chorologic views became acute and the situation of geography was much in doubt. Rationalism and positivism dominated the work of geographers. The milieu became a leading doctrine and thus continued through the century. Divine law was transposed into natural law, and for geography Montesquieu and Buckle were prophets of major importance. Since natural law was omnipotent the slow marshaling of the phenomena of area became too tedious a task for eager adherents of the faith of causation. The areal complex was simplified by selecting certain qualities, such as climate, relief, or drainage, and examining them as cause or effect. Viewed as end products, each of these classes of facts could be referred back fairly well to the laws of physics. Viewed as agents, the physical properties of the earth, such as climate in particular with Montesquieu, became adequate principles of explaining nature and distribution of organic life. The complex reality of areal association was sacrificed in either case to a rigorous dogma of materialistic cosmology, most notably in American physiography and anthropogeography. About twenty years ago the most distinguished American geographer took the position "that neither the inorganic nor the organic elements which enter into geographical relations are by themselves of a completely geographic quality; they gain that quality only when two or more of them are coupled in a relation of cause and effect, at least one element in the chain of causation being organic and one inorganic . . . Any statement is of geographical quality if it contains a reasonable relation between some inorganic element of the earth, acting as a control, and some element of organic existence . . . serving as a response." Indeed in this causal relation was, he said, "the most definite, if not the only unifying principle that I can find in geography." Cause was a confident and alluring word and causal geography had its day. The *Zeitgeist* was distinctly unfavorable to those geographers who thought that the subject was in no wise committed to a rigidly deterministic formula.

Latterly, Vidal de la Blache, in France, Hettner, Passarge, and Krebs, in Germany, and others have been reasserting more and more the classical tradition of geography as chorologic relation. It may be said that, after a period in which special, essentially physical disciplines were most in vogue, we are in process of returning to our permanent task and that this readjustment is responsible for the current activity of inquiry as to content of our field.

Summary of the Objective of Geography

The task of geography is conceived as the establishment of a critical system which embraces the phenomenology of landscape, in order to grasp in all of its meaning and color the varied terrestrial scene. Indirectly Vidal de la Blache has stated this position by cautioning against considering "the earth as 'the scene on which the activity of man unfolds itself,' without reflecting that this scene is itself living." It includes the works of man as an integral expression of the scene. This position is derived from Herodotus rather than from Thales. Modern geography is the modern expression of the most ancient geography.

The objects which exist together in the landscape exist in interrelation. We assert that they constitute a reality as a whole which is not expressed by a consideration of the constituent parts separately, that area has form, structure, and function, and hence position in a system, and that it is subject to development, change, and completion. Without this view of areal reality and relation, there exist only special disciplines, not geography as generally understood. The situation is analogous to history, which may be divided among economics, government, sociology, and so on; but when this is done the result is not history.

The Content of Landscape

Definition of Landscape

The term "landscape" is proposed to denote the unit concept of geography, to characterize the peculiarly geographic association of facts. Equivalent terms in a sense are "area" and "region." Area is of course a general term, not distinctively geographic. Region has come to imply, to some geographers at least, an order of magnitude. Landscape is the English equivalent of the term German geographers are using largely and strictly has the same meaning, a land shape, in which the process of shaping is by no means thought of as simply physical. It may be defined, therefore, as an area made up of a distinct association of forms, both physical and cultural.

The facts of geography are place facts; their association gives rise to the concept of landscape. Similarly, the facts of history are time facts; their association gives rise to the concept of period. By definition the landscape has identity that is based on recognizable constitution, limits, and generic relation to other landscapes, which constitute a general system. Its structure and function are determined by integrant, dependent forms. The landscape is considered, therefore, in a sense as having an organic quality. We may follow Bluntschli in saying that one has not fully understood the nature of an area until one "has learned to see it as an organic unit, to comprehend land and life in terms of each other." It has seemed desirable to introduce this point prior to its elaboration because it is very different from the unit concept of physical process of the physiographer or of environmental influence of the anthropogeographer of the school of Ratzel. The mechanics of glacial erosion, the climatic correlation of energy, and the form content of an areal habitat are three different things.

Landscape Has Generic Meaning

In the sense here used, landscape is not simply an actual scene viewed by an observer. The geographic landscape is a generalization derived from the observation of individual scenes. Croce's remark that "the geographer who is describing a landscape has the same task as a landscape painter" has therefore only limited validity. The geographer may describe the individual landscape as a type or possibly as a variant from type, but always he has in mind the generic, and proceeds by comparison.

An ordered presentation of the landscapes of the earth is a formidable undertaking. Beginning with infinite diversity, salient and related

features are selected in order to establish the character of the landscape
and to place it in a system. Yet generic quality is non-existent in the
sense of the biologic world. Every landscape has individuality as well
as relation to other landscapes, and the same is true of the forms that
make it up. No valley is quite like any other valley; no city the exact
replica of some other city. In so far as these qualities remain completely
unrelated they are beyond the reach of systematic treatment, beyond
that organized knowledge that we call science. "No science can rest at
the level of mere perception . . . The so-called descriptive natural sciences, zoology and botany, do not remain content to regard the singular,
they raise themselves to concepts of species, genus, family, order, class,
type." "There is no idiographic science, that is, one that describes the
individual merely as such. Geography formerly was idiographic; long
since it has attempted to become nomothetic, and no geographer would
hold it as its previous level." Whatever opinion one may hold about
natural law, or nomothetic, genetic, or causal relation, a definition of
landscape as singular, unorganized, or unrelated has no scientific value.

Element of Personal Judgment in the Selection of Content

It is true that in the selection of the generic characteristics of landscape
the geographer is guided only by his own judgment that they are characteristic, that is, repeating; that they are arranged into a pattern, or
have structural quality, and that the landscape accurately belongs to a
specific group in the general series of landscapes. Croce objects to a
science of history on the ground that history is without logical criteria:
"The criterion is the choice itself, conditioned, like every economic art,
by knowledge of the actual situation. This selection is certainly conducted with intelligence, but not with the application of a philosophic
criterion, and is justified only in and by itself. For this reason we speak
of the fine tact, or scent, or instinct of the learned man." A similar
objection is sometimes urged against the scientific competence of geography, because it is unable to establish complete, rigid logical control
and perforce relies upon the option of the student. The geographer is
in fact continually exercising freedom of choice as to the materials
which he includes in his observations, but he is also continually drawing inferences as to their relation. His method, imperfect as it may be,
is based on induction; he deals with sequences, though he may not
regard these as a simple causal relation.

If we consider a given type of landscape, for example a North
European heath, we may put down notes such as the following:

The sky is dull, ordinarily partly overcast, the horizon is indistinct and
rarely more than a half-dozen miles distant, though seen from a height. The
upland is gently and irregularly rolling and descends to broad, flat basins.

There are no long slopes and no symmetrical patterns of surface form. Watercourses are short, with clear brownish water, and perennial. The brooks end in irregular swamps, with indistinct borders. Coarse grasses and rushes form marginal strips along the water bodies. The upland is covered with heather, furze, and bracken. Clumps of juniper abound, especially on the steeper, drier slopes. Cart traces lie along the longer ridges, exposing loose sand in the wheel tracks, and here and there a rusty, cemented base shows beneath the sand. Small flocks of sheep are scattered widely over the land. The almost complete absence of the works of man is notable. There are no fields or other enclosed tracts. The only buildings are sheep sheds, situated usually at a distance of several miles from one another, at convenient intersections of cart traces.

The account is not that of an individual scene, but a summation of general characteristics. References to other types of landscape are introduced by implication. Relations of form elements within the landscape are also noted. The items selected are based upon "knowledge of the actual situation" and there is an attempt at a synthesis of the form elements. Their significance is a matter of personal judgment. Objective standards may be substituted for them only in part, as by quantitative representation in the form of a map. Even thus the personal element is brought only under limited control, since it still operates in choosing the qualities to be represented. All that can be expected is the reduction of the personal element by agreeing on a "predetermined mode of inquiry," which shall be logical.

Extensiveness of Areal Features

The content of landscape is something less than the whole of its visible constituents. The identity of the landscape is determined first of all by conspicuousness of form, as implied in the following statement: "A correct representation of the surface form, of soil, and of surficially conspicuous masses of rock, of plant cover and water bodies, of the coasts and the sea, of areally conspicuous animal life and of the expression of human culture is the goal of geographic inquiry." The items specified are chosen because the experience of the author has shown their significance as to mass and relation. The chorologic position necessarily recognizes the importance of areal extensiveness of phenomena, this quality being inherent in the position. Herein lies an important contrast between geography and physiography. The character of the heath landscape described above is determined primarily by the dominance of sand, swamp, and heather. The most important geographic fact about Norway, aside from its location, probably is that four-fifths of its surface is barren highland, supporting neither forests nor flocks, a condition significant directly because of its extensiveness.

Habitat Value as a Basis for the Determination of Content

Personal judgment of the content of landscape is determined further by interest. Geography is distinctly anthropocentric, in the sense of value or use of the earth to man. We are interested in that part of the areal scene which concerns us as human beings because we are part of it, live with it, are limited by it, and modify it. Thus we select those qualities of landscape in particular that are or may be of use to us. We relinquish those features of area that may be significant to the geologist in earth history but are of no concern in the relation of man to his area. The physical qualities of landscape then are those that have habitat value, present or potential.

The Natural and the Cultural Landscape

"Human geography does not oppose itself to a geography from which the human element is excluded; such a one has not existed except in the minds of a few exclusive specialists." It is a forcible abstraction, by every good geographic tradition a tour de force, to consider a landscape as though it were devoid of life. Because we are interested primarily in "cultures which grow with original vigor out of the lap of a maternal natural landscape, to which each is bound in the whole course of its existence," geography is based on the reality of the union of physical and cultural elements of the landscape. The content of landscape is found therefore in the physical qualities of area that are significant to man and in the forms of his use of the area, in facts of physical background and facts of human culture. A valuable discussion of this principle is given by Krebs under the title "Natur- und Kultur-landschaft."

For the first half of the content of landscape we may use the designation "site," which has become well established in plant ecology. A forest site is not simply the place where a forest stands; in its full connotation, the name is a qualitative expression of place in terms of forest growth, usually for the particular forest association that is in occupation of the site. In this sense the physical area is the sum of all natural resources that man has at his disposal in that area. It is beyond his power to add to them; he may "develop" them, ignore them in part, or subtract from them by exploitation.

The second half of landscape viewed as a bilateral unit is its cultural expression. There is a strictly geographic way of thinking of culture; namely, as the impress of the works of man upon the area. We may think of people as associated within and with an area, as we may think of them as groups associated in descent or tradition. In the first case we are thinking of culture as a geographic expression, composed of forms which are part of geographic phenomenology. In this view there is no place for a dualism of landscape.

The Application of the Morphologic Method

Form of Induction

The systematic organization of the content of landscape proceeds with the repression of a priori theories concerning it. The massing and ordering of phenomena as forms that are integrated into structures and the comparative study of the data as thus organized constitute the morphologic method of synthesis, a special empirical method. Morphology rests upon the following postulates: (1) that there is a unit of organic or quasi-organic quality, that is, a structure to which certain components are necessary, these component elements being called "forms" in this paper; (2) that similarity of form in different structures is recognized because of functional equivalence, the forms then being "homologous"; and (3) that the structural units may be placed in series, especially into developmental sequence, ranging from incipient to final or completed stage. Morphologic study does not necessarily affirm an organism in the biologic sense, as, for example, in the sociology of Herbert Spencer, but only organized unit concepts that are related. Without being committed in any sense to a general biogenetic law, the organic analogy has proved most useful throughout the fields of social inquiry. It is a working device, the truth of which may perhaps be subject to question, but which leads nevertheless to increasingly valid conclusions.

The term "morphology" originated with Goethe and expresses his contribution to modern science. It may be well to recall that he turned to biologic and geologic studies because he was interested in the nature and limits of cognition. Believing that there were things "accessible and inaccessible" to human knowledge, he concluded: "One need not seek for something beyond the phenomena; they themselves are the lore (*Lehre*)." Thus originated his form studies, and especially those of homology of form. His method of scientific inquiry rested on a definite philosophic position.

If therefore the morphologic method appears unpretentious to the student who is eager to come to large conclusions, it may be pointed out that it rests upon a deliberate restraint in the affirmation of knowledge. It is a purely evidential system, without prepossession regarding the meaning of its evidence, and presupposes a minimum of assumption; namely, only the reality of structural organization. Being objective and value-free, or nearly so, it is competent to arrive at increasingly significant results.

Application to Social Studies

Morphologic method is not only the introduction to the biologic sciences but it is steadily growing in importance in the social fields. In biology it is the study of organic forms and their structure, or the architecture of organisms. In the social field the continued synthesis of phenomena by morphologic method has been employed with greatest success perhaps in anthropology. This science can claim an honor roll of workers who have had the patience and skill to approach the study of social institutions phenomenologically, by the classification of forms, ranging from the concrete materials of clothing, housing, and tools to the language and customs of a group, thereby identifying step by step the complex structure of cultures. Spengler's recent brilliant and highly controversial thesis of history is far and away the most pretentious application of the method to the human field. Disregarding its elements of intuitionalism, it is in effect comparative morphology as applied to history, the second volume bearing that title. He characterizes the forms that, to his mind, compose the great historic structures, subjects them to comparison for different periods as homologies, and traces developmental stages. By however much the author may have exceeded his and our knowledge in his daring synthesis, he has shown the possibilities of a morphology of history, or of the study of history on a scientific basis other than the causal formula of historical rationalism.

The Introduction of Morphology into Geography and the Results

Method and term were first formally introduced into geography by Karl Ritter, whose restoration of geography succeded finally, not in the idealistic cosmology he had espoused, but because after all he laid the foundations for comparative regional study. Thereafter, perhaps because there was so much to do, the morphologic studies were rapidly narrowed so as to regard only the surficial form of the land. Grieseback's classic definition that "the morphologic system illuminates, by regarding the relationship of forms, the obscurity of their descent" was applied with fateful results to the field of geography. The restriction of forms to relief, and interest in the origin of these forms, shortly established, under the leadership of Peschel, v. Richthofen, and de la Noë, the genetic inquiry that was called geomorphology. At first relying on the naïve descriptive classification of surface forms, as for example in Penck's *Morphologie der Erdoberfläche,* which is chorologic morphology, increasingly the trend was to classify on the bas' of process, and to trace these forms back to more and more remote forms. The genetic historians of land form undertook increasingly the invasion of the field of geology. The final step was that some of these specialists lost sight almost completely of actual land forms and devoted themselves to the construction of theoretical forms deduced from individual physical processes. The defeat of geographic ends was therefore almost complete and such geomorphology became a separate branch of general earth science.

This autonomous genetic morphology inevitably led to an adverse reaction among the chorologically minded geographers, not because the work was not carefully done, nor because it failed to develop a valuable field of knowledge, but because it became unrecognizable as geography. Unfortunately a very general name was applied to a very specialized discipline. Under a misapprehension of the term there has been a tendency to disregard in consequence the possibilities of the morphologic method. Vidal de la Blache perhaps earlier than any one else realized the situation and reestablished morphology in its rightful position. The regional monographs that proceeded from his school expressed far more adequately than had been done before the full form content and structural relation of the landscape, finding in the cultural landscape the culminating expression of the organic area. In these studies, for example, the position of man and his works explicitly is that of the last and most important factor and forms in the landscape.

The perversion of geographic ends in the definition of morphology as the causal study of relief forms appears from the following considerations: (1) Relief is only one category of the physical landscape and ordinarily not the most important one; it almost never supplies the complete basis of a cultural form. (2) There is no necessary relation between the mode of origin of a relief form and its functional significance, the matter with which geography is most directly concerned. (3) An inevitable difficulty with a purely genetic morphology of relief forms is that most of the actual relief features of the earth are of very mixed origin. Behind the present forms lie processal associations, previous or ancestral forms, and almost inscrutable expressions of time. For the present at least, therefore, genetic morphology isolates those form elements that yield to causal analysis. In the selection of those relief facts that are legible as to genesis, it neglects some, even many, of the features of relief and abandons therefore the structural synthesis of even this segment of the landscape insofar as chorology is concerned.

In the late enthusiasm for studies of relief forms the climatologists were crowded into a relatively obscure position. Yet they, most largely, escaped the geographically sterile pursuit of the pure genetic method. Climatology has been phenomenologic rather than genetic. In spite of very scant knowledge of the origin of climatic conditions, the facts of climate have been summarized in terms of their geographic significance most admirably. In particular Köppen's series of trials at climatic synthesis, carefully developed as to biotically critical values, admirably restrained as to genetic explanation, are among the most important if not the most important contribution in this generation to a general geographic morphology. Yet such is the force of associations that few doubtless would name such climatic synthesis as a fundamental part of geographic morphology. It is more than a matter of mere nomenclature to object to the misapplication of the term morphology; it is a rut into which we have slipped and which has limited our range. Perhaps some of the cross-purposes in present-day geography may be traced to the failure to recognize that all the facts of the subject are to be organized by a general system, through which alone their relation may be determined.

Preparatory Systematic Description

The First Step in Morphologic Study

Historically "geography commenced by describing and registering, that is as a systematic study. It proceeded thereupon to . . . genetic relation, morphology." The geographic study is still thus begun. The description of observed facts is by some predetermined order that represents a preliminary grouping of the material. Such systematic description is for the purpose of morphologic relation and is really the beginning of morphologic synthesis. It is therefore distinguishable from morphology not at all in principle but in that it lies at a lower critical level. The relation is not dissimilar to that between taxonomy and biologic morphology.

Descriptive Terminology

The problem of geographic description differs from that of taxonomy principally in the availability of terms. The facts of area have been under popular observation to such an extent that a new terminology is for the most part not necessary. Salisbury held that the forms of landscape had generally received serviceable popular names and that codification might proceed from popular parlance without the coining of new terms. Proceeding largely in this manner, we are building up a list of form terms, that are being enriched from many areas and many languages. Very many more are still awaiting introduction into geographic literature. These terms apply as largely to soil, drainage, and climatic forms as they do to land surface. Popular terminology is a fairly reliable warrant of the significance of the form, as implied in its adoption. Such names may apply to single form constituents, as glade, tarn, loess. Or they may be form associations of varying magnitude, as heath, steppe, piedmont. Or they may be proper names to designate unit landscapes, as, for example, the regional names that are in use for most parts of France. Such popular nomenclature is rich in genetic meaning, but with sure chorologic judgment it proceeds not from cause but from a generic summation; namely, from form similarities and contrasts.

If systematic description is a desideratum for geography, we are still in great need of enlarging our descriptive vocabulary. The meagerness of our descriptive terms is surprising by comparison with other sciences. Contributing causes may be the idiographic tradition of unrelated description, and the past predilection for process studies which minimized the real multiplicity of forms.

The Predetermined Descriptive System

The reduction of description to a system has been largely opposed by geographers and not entirely without cause. Once this happens the geographer is responsible within those limits for any areal study he undertakes; otherwise he is free to roam, to choose, and to leave. We are not concerned here with geography as an art. As a science it must accept all feasible means for the regimentation of its data. However excellent the individualistic, impressionistic selection of phenomena may be, it is an artistic, not a scientific desideratum. The studies in geomorphology, in particular those of the school of Davis, represent perhaps the most determined attempt to oppose uncontrolled freedom of choice in observation by a strict limitation of observations and of method. Different observations may be compared as to their findings only if there is a reasonable agreement as to the classes of facts with which they deal. The attempt at a broad synthesis of regional studies by employing our existing literature immediately runs into difficulties, because the materials do not fit together. Findings on the most important theme of human destructiveness of natural landscape are very difficult to make because there are no adequate points of reference. Some observers note soil erosion systematically, others casually, and still others may pay no attention to it. If geography is to be systematic and not idiosyncratic, there must be increasing agreement as to items of observation. In particular this should mean a general descriptive scheme to be followed in the collection of field notes.

A general descriptive scheme, intended to catalogue areal facts broadly, without proceeding at this stage from hypothetical origins and connections, has been recently proposed by Passarge under the name *Beschreibende Landschaftskunde*. It is the first comprehensive treatment of this subject since v. Richthofen's *Führer für Forschungsreisende*, written just prior to the most flourishing period of geomorphology (1886). The work of Passarge is somewhat roughhewn and it is perhaps excessively schematic, yet it is the most adequate consideration by far that the whole matter of geographic description has had. Its express purpose is "first of all to determine the facts and to attempt a correct presentation of the significant, visible facts of area without any attempt at explanation and speculation." The plan provides

for the systematic observation of the phenomena that compose the landscape. The method resembles most closely the Chrie, a device for the collection of material in theme writing. It helps to see as much as possible and to miss as little as possible and has the further advantage that all observations are ordered. If earlier geographers had been familiar with a method of systematic observation of landscape, it would have been impossible for the characteristic red color of tropical residual soils to have escaped attention until v. Richthofen discovered that fact.

Passarge proceeds with an elaborate schedule of notes covering all form categories of the landscape, beginning with atmospheric effects and ending with forms of habitation. From these he proceeds to a descriptive classification of form associations into larger areal terms. For the further elaboration of the plan the reader is referred to the volume in question, as worthy of careful consideration.

The author has applied his system elsewhere to the "pure" as against the "explanatory" description of areas, as for example in his characterization of the Valley of the Okavango, in the northern salt steppe of the Kalahari. That he succeeds in giving to the reader an adequate picture of the composition of area will probably be admitted.

One may note that Passarge's supposedly purely descriptive procedure is actually based on large experience in areal studies, through which a judgment as to the significant constituents of landscape has been formed. These are really determined through morphologic knowledge, though the classification is not genetic, but properly based on the naïvely generic forms. The capacious dragnet which Passarge has fashioned, though disclaiming all attempt at explanation, is in reality a device fashioned by experienced hands for catching all that may be wanted in an areal morphology and for deferring explanation until the whole material is sorted.

Forms of Landscape and Their Structure

The Division between Natural and Cultural Landscapes

We cannot form an idea of landscape except in terms of its time relations as well as of its space relations. It is in continuous process of development or of dissolution and replacement. It is in this sense a true appreciation of historical values that has caused the geomorphologists to tie the present physical landscape back into its geologic origins, and to derive it therefrom step by step. In the chorologic sense, however, the modification of the area by man and its appropriation to his uses are of dominant importance. The area prior to the introduction

...sented by one body of morphologic facts. The
...ced are another set. We may call the former,
...original, natural landscape. In its entirety
...rts of the world, but its reconstruction and
...standing are the first part of formal morphology. Is it perhaps too
broad a generalization to say that geography dissociates itself from
geology at the point of the introduction of man into the areal scene?
Under this view the prior events belong strictly in the field of geology
and their historical treatment in geography is only a descriptive device
employed where necessary to make clear the relationship of physical
forms that are significant in the habitat.

The works of man express themselves in the cultural landscape. There
may be a succession of these landscapes with a succession of cultures.
They are derived in each case from the natural landscape, man expressing his place in nature as a distinct agent of modification. Of especial
significance is that climax of culture which we call civilization. The
cultural landscape then is subject to change either by the development of a culture or by a replacement of cultures. The datum line
from which change is measured is the natural condition of the landscape. The division of forms into natural and cultural is the necessary
basis for determining the areal importance and character of man's
activity. In the universal, but not necessarily cosmologic sense, geography then becomes that part of the latest or human chapter in
earth history which is concerned with the differentiation of the areal
scene by man.

The Natural Landscape: Geognostic Basis

In the subsequent sections on the natural landscape a distinction is
implied between the historical inquiry into origin of features and their
strictly morphologic organization into a group of forms, fundamental to
the cultural expression of the area. We are concerned alone with the
latter in principle, with the former only as a descriptive convenience.

The forms of the natural landscape involve first of all the materials
of the earth's crust which have in some important measure determined
the surface forms. The geographer borrows from the geologist knowledge of the substantial differences of the outer lithosphere as to composition, structure, and mass. Geology, being the study of the history
of these materials, has devised its classification on the basis of succession of formations, grouped as to period. In formations per se the
geographer has no interest. He is concerned, however, with that more
primitive phase of geology, called geognosy, which regards kind and
position of material but not historical succession. The name of a
geologic formation may be meaningless geographically, if it lumps
lithologic differences, structural differences, and differences in mass

under one term. Geognostic condition provides a basis of conversion of geologic data into geographic values. The geographer is interested in knowing whether the base of a landscape is limestone or sandstone, whether the rocks are massive or intercalated, whether they are broken by joints or are affected by other structural conditions expressed in the surface. These matters may be significant to the understanding of topography, soil, drainage, and mineral distribution.

The application of geognostic data in geographic studies is usual in a sense, areal studies being hardly feasible without some regard for the underlying materials. Yet to find the most adequate analysis of the expression of the underlying materials in the surface, it is probably necessary to go back to the work of the older American and British geologists, such as Powell, Dutton, Gilbert, Shaler, and Archibald Geikie. In the aggregate, of course, the geologic literature that touches upon such matters is enormous, but it is made up of rather incidental and informal items, because landscape is not in the central field of interest of the geologist. The formal analysis of critical geognostic qualities and their synthesis into areal generalizations has not had a great deal of attention. Adequately comparable data are still insufficient from the viewpoint of geography. In briefest form Sapper has lately attempted a general consideration of the relation of geologic forms to the landscapes of varying climates, to the illumination of the entire subject of regional geography.

Rigorous methodologist that he is, Passarge has not failed to scrutinize the geographic bearing of rock character and condition, and has applied in intensive areal study the following observations (somewhat adapted):

Physical resistance
  soft, easily eroded formations
  Rocks of intermediate resistance
    much broken (zerklüftet)
    moderately broken
    little broken
  Rocks of high resistance
    as above
Chemical resistance and solubility
  Easily soluble
    highly permeable
    moderately permeable
    relatively impermeable
  Moderately subject to solution and chemical alteration
    as above
  Resistant

In a later study he added provision for rocks notably subject to creep

a device for the connection of the forms, not as the end of inquiry. They lead toward the concept of the natural landscape which in turn leads to the cultural landscape. The character of the landscape is determined also by its position on the time line. Whether this line is of determinate or infinite length does not concern us as geographers. In some measure, certainly, the idea of a climax landscape is useful, a landscape that, given a constancy of impinging factors, has exhausted the possibilities of autogenous development. Through the medium of time the application of factor to form as cause and effect relation is limited; time itself is a great factor. We are interested in function, not in a determination of cosmic unity. For all chorologic purposes the emphasis of the diagram lies at its right hand; time and factor have only an explanatory descriptive role.

This position with reference to the natural landscape involves a reaffirmation of the place of physical geography, certainly not as physiography nor geomorphology as ordinarily defined, but as physical morphology which draws freely from geology and physiography certain results to be built into a view of physical landscape as a habitat complex. This physical geography is the proper introduction to the full chorologic inquiry which is our goal.

Forms of the Natural Landscape: Climate

In the physical structure of landscape, climate is first in importance. In the diagram it appears at the head of the list of forms and also as the major factor behind the whole category of forms. As a form, climate is an areal expression, the sum of the atmospheric features of the area. This is the sense in which it is treated in climatology. In American literature climates were first introduced prominently as areal forms, fundamental to geography in general, through Tower's chapters on climate in Salisbury, Barrows, and Tower's *Elements of Geography*. The value of this view has been demonstrated by the steadily increasing role which climatology has played in the fundamental courses of instruction. In no respect are we as near to general agreement as in this.

Climatology is areal reality; meteorology is general process. The contrast is that between physical geography and physiography.

Land Forms in the Natural Landscape

The land includes four edaphic elements or properties analogous to the climatic elements; namely, surface or land form in the narrow sense, soil, drainage, and mineral forms. In the case of surface forms we are deailng with a body of fact that is of interest to geomorphology, to physiography, and to geographic morphology. The first is concerned with history, the second with process, the third with description and relation to other forms. For our purposes surface forms are to be regarded as climates are in climatology. Strictly we are concerned with the character of relief only, that is, with expressions of slope and exposure in relation to the other constituent forms of the landscape. The topographic map, interpreted in terms of use significance of different slopes, is in principle the complete chorologic representation of surface form. The relation of surface form to climate is so close that the grouping of surfaces by climates is warranted generally. Geognostic relation of surface also lends itself well to the areal grouping of land forms. The further penetration into genesis of forms leads increasingly away from geographic ends. Restraint in this respect is necessary and is attained through a proper realization of the goal of areal reality.

The areal differentiation of soils fundamentally is based on differences of productivity, or their habitat significance. Soils as areal form constituents are primarily grouped by climates; the secondary classification is geognostic and therefore also chorologically satisfactory. The placing of soils into the structure of landscape therefore presents little difficulty, the soil survey being in fact a highly specialized form of physical geography. Unlike some physiographers and geomorphologists, the field student of soils is not pursuing a non-geographic end, but is limiting himself to a small part of the geographic field.

Drainage forms are of course direct expressions of climate, and the most feasible classification of streams, swamps, and bodies of standing water is in climatic terms. For instance, moors are a type of high latitude swamp, permanent features under conditions of low evaporation. Their growth is especially favored by the presence of certain plants, such as sphagnum moss. Their position is not restricted to lowlands, but they extend over fairly irregular surfaces by the expansion of a marginal zone of spongy vegetation. These swamps illustrate the interrelation of physical areal forms. Under them a distinctive soil is developed and even the subsoil is altered. This swampy covering also protects the land surface it has occupied from the attacks of running water and wind and moulds it into broadly rounded forms. Where climate conditions are not favorable to the development of such swamps, both in still higher and in lower latitudes, the forms of drainage, soil, and surface change markedly.

Mineral resources belong among the physical forms under the view of the physical landscape as a human habitat. Here the geognostic factor dominates genetically. The diagrammatic relation still holds in a measure, because of the concentration of minerals due to underground waters both at and beneath the surface. It would be pedantic to urge this point strongly, nor are we desirous to urge genetic relation as a necessary principle.

Forms of the Sea in the Natural Landscape

The relation of sea to land is organizable on the same basis of climate and geognosy. The seacoasts are in the main an expression of tectonic history and of climatic setting. Areally, climates afford the broader basis of classification, because elevation and subsidence of coasts have varied and are changing, as to direction and amount, so greatly, over short distances, as to make a tectonic classification of seashores chorologically unsatisfactory. The seas themselves are obviously as intimately related to climate as is the land. Their currents, surface conditions, density, and temperatures are as certainly to be classified in climatic terms as land forms.

Vegetation Forms in the Natural Landscape

A. v. Humboldt was first to recognize through systematic observations, the importance of vegetation in the character of the landscape. "However much the character of the different parts of the world depends on the totality of external appearances; though outline of mountains, physiognomy of plants and animals, cloud forms and transparency of the atmosphere compose the general impression: yet it is not to be denied that the most important element in this impression is the cover of vegetation." The bonds between climate and vegetation are so direct and strong that a large measure of climatic grouping of vegetation forms is possible. Some plant geographers have found the classification of vegetational associations most desirable in terms of thermal or moisture belts.

Summary of the Form Relations in the Natural Landscape

The large emphasis on climate in the previous statements does not mean that geography is to be transformed into climatology. The physical area is fundamental to any geographic study because it furnishes the materials out of which man builds his culture. The identity of the physical area rests fundamentally on a distinctive association of physical forms. In the physical world, generic character of area and its genesis are coupled so closely that the one becomes an aid to the recognition of the other. In particular, climate, itself an areal form, largely obscure as to origin, so largely controls the expression of the other physical forms that in many areas it may be considered the determinant of form association. An express disclaimer may be entered, however, against the notion of the necessity of a genetic bond in order to organize the phenomenology of the natural landscape. The existence of such bonds has been determined empirically. By regarding the relationship of forms we have discovered an important light on "the obscurity of their descent," but as geographers we are not enjoined to trace out the nature of this descent. This remains the problem of geomorphology, which indeed now appears more complicated than ever, the validity of climatic control and of great secular changes of climate being accepted.

Thus far the way is pretty well marked. We know the "inorganic" composition of landscape fairly well, and, except for a somewhat excessive aloofness existing between plant and general geography, the place of vegetation in the landscape is properly cared for.

The Extension of Morphology to the Cultural Landscape

The natural landscape is being subjected to transformation at the hands of man, the last and for us the most important morphologic factor. By his cultures he makes use of the natural forms, in many cases alters them, in some destroys them.

The study of the cultural landscape is, as yet, largely an untilled field. Recent results in the field of plant ecology will probably supply many useful leads for the human geographer, for cultural morphology might be called human ecology. In contrast to the position of Barrows in this matter, the present thesis would eliminate physiologic ecology or autecology and seek for parallels in synecology. It is better not to force into geography too much biological nomenclature. The name ecology is not needed; it is both morphology and physiology of the biotic association. Since we waive the claim for the measurement of environmental influences, we may use, in preference to ecology, the term morphology to apply to cultural study, since it describes perfectly the method that is involved.

Among geographers in America who have concerned themselves with systematic inquiry into cultural forms, Mark Jefferson, O. E. Baker, and M. Aurousseau have done outstanding pioneering. Brunhes' "essential facts of geography" represent perhaps the most widely appreciated classification of cultural forms. Sten DeGeer's population atlas of Sweden was the first major contribution of a student who has concentrated his attention strictly on cultural morphology. Vaughan Cornish introduced the concepts of "march" "storehouse," and "crossroads" in a most valuable contribution to urban problems. Most recently, Geisler has undertaken a synthesis of the urban forms of Germany, with the deserved subtitle: "A contribution to the morphology of the cultural landscape." These pioneers have found productive ground; our periodical literature suggests that a rush of homesteaders may soon be under way.

Diagrammatic Representation of the Morphology of the Cultural Landscape

The cultural landscape is the geographic area in the final meaning (*Chore*). Its forms are all the works of man that characterize the land-

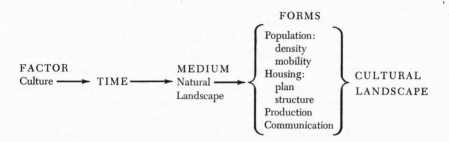

scape. Under this definition we are not concerned in geography with the energy, customs, or beliefs of man but with man's record upon the landscape. Forms of population are the phenomena of mass or density in general and of recurrent displacement, as seasonal migration. Housing includes the types of structures man builds and their grouping, either dispersed as in many rural districts, or agglomerated into villages or cities in varying plans (*Städtebild*). Forms of production are the types of land utilization for primary products, farms, forests, mines, and those negative areas which he has ignored.

The cultural landscape is fashioned out of a natural landscape by a culture group. Culture is the agent, the natural area is the medium, the cultural landscape the result. Under the influence of a given culture, itself changing through time, the landscape undergoes development, passing through phases, and probably reaching ultimately the end of its cycle of development. With the introduction of a different, that is, alien culture, a rejuvenation of the cultural landscape sets in, or a new landscape is superimposed on remnants of an older one. The natural landscape is of course of fundamental importance, for it supplies the materials out of which the cultural landscape is formed. The shaping force, however, lies in the culture itself. Within the wide limits of the physical equipment of area lie many possible choices for man, as Vidal never grew weary of pointing out. This is the meaning of adaptation, through which, aided by those suggestions which man has derived from nature, perhaps by an imitative process, largely subconscious, we get the feeling of harmony between the human habitation and the landscape into which it so fittingly blends. But these, too, are derived from the mind of man, not imposed by nature, and hence are cultural expressions.

Morphology as Applied to the Branches of Geography

The consolidation of the two diagrams gives an approximation of the total scientific content of geography on the phenomenologic basis by which we have proceeded. They may readily be expressed so as to define the branches of geography. (1) The study of the form categories per se in their general relation, the system of the forms of landscape, is morphology in the purely methodologic sense and is the equivalent of what is called, especially in France and Germany, general geography, the propaedeutic through which the student learns to work with his materials. (2) Regional geography is comparative morphology, the process of placing individual landscapes into relation to other landscapes. In the full chorologic sense, this is the ordering of cultural, not of natural landscapes. Such a critical synthesis of regions for the entire world is the latest contribution of Passarge, who has thereby nearly rounded out a critique of the entire field of geography. (3) Historical geography may be considered as the series of changes which the cultural landscapes have undergone and therefore involves the reconstruction of past cultural landscapes. Of special concern is the catalytic relation of civilized man to area and the effects of the replacement of cultures. From this difficult and little touched field alone may be gained a full realization of the development of the present cultural landscape out of earlier cultures and the natural landscape. (4) Commercial geography deals with the forms of production and the facilities for distribution of the products of areas.

Beyond Science

The morphologic discipline enables the organization of the fields of geography as positive science. A good deal of the meaning of area lies beyond scientific regimentation. The best geography has never disregarded the aesthetic qualities of landscape, to which we know no approach other than the subjective. Humboldt's "physiognomy." Banse's "soul," Volz's "rhythm," Gradmann's "harmony" of landscape, all lie beyond science. They seem to have discovered a symphonic quality in the contemplation of the areal scene, proceeding from a full novitiate in scientific studies and yet apart therefrom. To some, whatever is mystical is an abomination. Yet it is significant that there are others, and among them some of the best, who believe, that having observed widely and charted diligently, there yet remains a quality of understanding at a higher plane which may not be reduced to formal process.

Divergent Views of Geography

The geographic thesis of this article is so largely at variance with certain other views of the subject that it may be desirable to set forth in summary form what has been expressed and implied as to contrast in the several positions.

Geomorphology as a Branch of Geography

German geographers in particular tend to regard geomorphology as an essential division of geography, and use largely the term *Oberflächengestaltung*, or the record of development of surficial form. The forms considered are ordinarily topographic only. The content of geomorphology has been most broadly defined by Penck, who included the following forms: plains, hill surfaces, valleys, basins, mountains, cavernous forms, seacoasts, seafloors, islands. These descriptive topographic terms are studied by geomorphology as to their derivation, not as to use significance.

Geomorphology being the history of topography, it derives present surfaces from previous forms and records the processes involved. A study of the geomorphology of the Sierra Nevada is a history of the sculpturing of the mountain massif, concerned with the uplift of the earth block, and the stages of modification in which erosional processes, secondary deformations, and structural conditions are in complex relations. Relief features in this sense are the result of the opposition of orogenic and degraditional processes through geologic periods of time. Certain features, such as peneplains and terrace remnants, thus have high diagnostic value in reading the record of modification of surface. These elements of the landscape, however, may be of little or no significance in the chorologic sense. To geomorphology the peneplain has been extremely important; the trend of geography has not been notably affected by its discovery. Out of the topographic complex the geomorphologist may select one body of facts illustrative of earth history, the geographer will use a largely different set of facts which have habitat significance.

The geomorphologist, therefore, is likely to be a specialized historical geologist, working on certain, usually late, chapters of earth history. Conventional historical geology is mostly concerned with the making of rock formations. The geomorphologist directs attention to erosional and deformational surfaces in the record of the rocks. To such an extent has this been the American orientation that we have in our country little geomorphologic work of recent date that is consciously geographic in purpose, that is, descriptive of actual land surfaces.

The geomorphologist can and does establish a connection between the fields of geography and geology and his labors further our own work. He advances our studies of landscape materially where he has preceded the geographer, and we properly regard him potentially as much a collaborator in geography as in geology. One of the present needs in

American geography is a greater familiarity with and application of geomorphologic studies.

Physiography and Physical Geography

When Huxley reapplied the term physiography he disclaimed expressly the desire to reform physical geography. He was not lecturing, he said, "on any particular branch of natural knowledge, but on natural phenomena in general." The subtitle of his treatise read: "An Introduction to the Study of Nature." He chose the Basin of the Thames as the area for his demonstration, not through chorologic interest, but in order to show that any area contained abundant material for the demonstration of the general laws of physical science. Huxley said:

> I endeavored to show that the application of the plainest and simplest processes of reasoning to any of these phenomena, suffices to show, lying behind it, a cause, which will again suggest another; until, step by step, the conviction dawns upon the learner that, to attain to even an elementary conception of what goes on in his parish he must know something about the universe; that the pebble he kicks aside, would not be what it is and where it is, unless a particular chapter of the earth's history, finished untold ages ago, had been exactly what it was.

The two central ideas in his mind were the unity of physical law as shown by the features of the earth and the evolutionary march of the geologic record. It was the bright hour of dawn in scientific monism, with Huxley officiating at the observation of the lands. Physiography served in such a canonical role in elementary scientific education until a later age of machinery sent it into the discard in favor of "general science."

Physiography is still the general science of the earth, and concerns itself with the physical processes that operate at the surface of the earth and in the earth's crust. We still find the captions that Huxley introduced into his text: the work of rain and rivers, ice and its work, the sea and its work, earthquakes and volcanoes. These things have chorologic expression but they are studied as general processes. As an investigator the physiographer must be above all things a physicist, and increasing demands are made on his physical and mathematical knowledge. The way of the development of physiography as research is through geophysical institutes. Academically it fits in best as a part of dynamic geology. The geographer probably needs to know little more of it than he should know of historical geology.

One may question, therefore, the propriety of such terms as regional physiography and physiographic regions. They contradict the essential meaning of the subject and ordinarily mean rather a loose form of geomorphology, which of necessity has areal expression. Physiography was conceived as a purely dynamic relation and is categorically incapable of consistent areal expression unless it becomes also a name applied to physical geography or to geomorphology.

Geographic Morphology vs. "Geographic Influences"

The study of the physical environment as an active agency has recently been subjected to trenchant criticism by L. Febvre, with an equally incisive foreword by Henri Berr. Both thoroughly relish the chance to riddle this geographic ambition. Geography as they see it is "to give an example of the true task of synthesis . . . The effort of synthesis is a directed activity; it is not a premature realization." Questions of environment "may have for the geographer their interest; but they are not his end. He must guard well against acclaiming as 'scientific' verities theories of adaptation 'simpliste' in character which more competent people are in process of completing or correcting." "What is, then, the commendable attitude in human geography? It can consist only in searching for the relations which exist between earth and life, the rapport which exists between the external milieu and the activity of the occupants." Vidal de la Blache's thesis that in the relation of man to the earth there exists less of necessary adaptation than of "possibilisme" is worked out with skill and conviction. Excepting for their spirited devotion to the master of French geography, the authors are not really familiar with geographic thought. They do not fairly represent the tenets of geography because they know chiefly the publicists of environmentalism, against whom they consider Vidal as the outstanding bulwark. Vidal will have an honored place in the history of geography, but we are no longer much impressed by his concern to establish decently good relations with rationalistic thought. Rationalism has seen better days than these; we no longer need to come to terms with it by diplomatic compromise. In spite of the deficient orientation in geographic thought, the volume directs a quality of dialectic at one geographic school which entitles it to high rank in geographic criticism.

In this country the theme that geography is the study of natural environment has been dominant in the present generation. It has come to be advertised abroad that such is the American definition of geography. The earliest term was "environmental control." This was succeeded by "response," "influence," "adjustment," or some other word that does not change the meaning, but substitutes a more cautious term for the ringing declaration of control. All these positions are mechanistic. In some way they hope to measure the force that physical environment exerts over man. The landscape as such has no interest for them, but only those cultural features for which a causal connection with the physical environment can be established. The air, therefore, is to make of geography a part of biophysics, concerned with human tropisms.

Geographic morphology does not deny determinism, nor does it require adhesion to that particular faith in order to qualify in the profession. Geography under the banner of environmentalism represents a dogma, the assertion of a faith that brings rest to a spirit vexed by the riddle of the universe. It was a new evangel for the age of reason, that set up its particular form of adequate order and even of ultimate purpose. The exposition of the faith could proceed only by finding testimonials to its efficacy. To the true believer there were visible evidences of the existence of what he thought should be, which were not to be seen by those who were weak in the faith. Unless one has the proper temperament, the continued elaboration of this single thesis with the weak instruments at his hand becomes dreadfully monotonous. In such a study one knows beforehand that one will encounter only variants of the one theme of "influence."

The narrowly rationalistic thesis conceives of environment as process and of some of the qualities and activities of man as products. The agency is physical nature; man responds or adapts himself. Simple as the thesis sounds, it incurs continually grave difficulties in the matching of specific response to specific stimulus or inhibition. The direct influence of environmental stimuli is purely somatic. What happens to man through the influence of his physical surroundings is beyond the competence of the geographer; at most he may keep informed as to physiologic research in that field. What man does in an area because of tabu or totemism or because of his own will involves use of environment rather than the active agency of the environment. It would, therefore, appear that environmentalism has been shooting neither at cause nor at effect, but rather that it is bagging its own decoys.

Conclusion

In the colorful reality of life there is a continuous resistance of fact to confinement within any "simpliste" theory. We are concerned with "directed activity, not premature realization" and this is the morphologic approach. Our naïvely selected section of reality, the landscape, is undergoing manifold change. This contact of man with his changeful home, as expressed through the cultural landscape, is our field of work. We are concerned with the importance of the site to man, and also with his transformation of the site. Altogether we deal with the interrelation of group, or cultures, and site, as expressed in the various landscapes of the world. Here are an inexhaustible body of fact and a variety of relation which provide a course of inquiry that does not need to restrict itself to the straits of rationalism.

III. ENVIRONMENT AND DETERMINISM

In the early part of this century, a major stumbling block to meaningful objective research in American geography was the assumption that the physical environment largely determined the cultural landscape. This concept, inherited primarily from German geography, was introduced in the United States chiefly by William Morris Davis and Ellen Churchill Semple, both of whom had studied in Germany. The principle received additional impetus from the early leading geographers who, because they were trained in geology, were inclined first to investigate the physical environment to determine its effects upon man and his activities. Also influential was Darwin's law of natural selection, which was reflected not only in the development of geography, but in the development of all the sciences. Because of its late start as a university discipline, however, geography was delayed in its attempts to apply Darwinian thinking and slow to throw off its yoke once it did take hold.

Just before 1920, natural selection, and, consequently, environmental determinism, came under fire. The search for cause-and-effect relationships, particularly the control of the physical environment over man's activities, led investigators, teachers, and students down many blind alleys as they sought to develop meaningful generalizations and useful theory. From 1920 on, the movement away from the doctrine was so strong that it went to the opposite extreme to embrace cultural determinism.

One of the first steps away from determinism in general was the formulation of the theory of "possibilism." Developed largely in France by Vidal de la Blache and Brunhes in the late 1800's, possibilism holds that the natural environment does not simply impose itself on man and his activities; rather, it provides him with several options or possible choices. A further development was "probabilism," the notion that of the available choices, one is more advantageous for man and therefore more probable.

The emphasis today is on objective, rigorous investigation of all variables, both physical and cultural, of a problem. It is true, however, that in some situations, like that of the bushmen of the harsh Australian interior, physical environment does control man's activities. Many other cases could be cited in which it plays a significant if not a determin-

ing role. In Palm Springs, California, on the other hand, man has converted an environment similar to that of Australia into a flourishing,
luxurious landscape.

In the following articles, some aspects of the problem of determinism
are discussed. For another view, the reader might consult the article
by Sauer in the preceding section.

8. Determinism in Geography
Robert S. Platt

*Platt was a leader in the methodological battle to free
geography from the domination of determinism, and the
selection that follows states the case against the concept.
The role of physical geography was adversely affected by
the downgrading of environmentalism, but the physical
factor in the man-environment system is now assuming
its rightful place in the discipline.*

Determinism may persist as a false guide in geography even after
environmentalism has been banished from the field.[1] Long ago extreme
environmentalism was recognized as false, and now mild environmentalism also has been found misleading as an approach to geographic understanding.[2] But a complex kind of determinism may still
be detected frequently in geographic work. In some cases a combination of environmental and cultural factors is taken to account for geographic phenomena in a cause and effect relation. Some of the factors
are better defined than others, but all are supposed to be subject to
investigation and evaluation leading eventually to complete explanation
as scientific knowledge advances.

The primary question raised by this procedure is whether such an
approach leads immediately to understanding or to misunderstanding
in our present search for knowledge. A further question as to whether

SOURCE: *Annals of the Association of American Geographers,* XXXVIII (June,
1948), 126-32. Until his death, the author was professor of geography at the University of Chicago.
[1]Determinism, in the sense used here, refers to the idea that everything in human
life is caused inevitably by previous events or conditions. Extreme environmentalism
refers to the idea that everything in human life is caused by the natural environment; and mild environmentalism refers to the idea that human life should be
viewed as under the direct influence of the natural environment.
[2] R. S. Platt, "Environmentalism versus Geography," *American Journal of Sociology,*
LIII (March, 1948), 351-358.

the basic idea of determinism ultimately may be found true or false is not involved and need not be included except as a matter of coincidental interest.

Deterministic Approach

Consider the geography of Argentina from an explanatory viewpoint as an example of this procedure. Argentina may be characterized as a virile South American nation having a productive territory of over a million square miles, a vigorous population of about 15,000,000 people, a rich landed gentry, a highly commercialized economy, a centralized dictatorial government, and a militant nationalism at odds with the United States.

In explanation of these phenomena the following major factors may be cited:

(1) A fundament of fertile mid-latitude plains bordering on the Atlantic, and territorial unity unbroken by physiographic barriers from the east coast to the Andes.

(2) A racial heritage of white people from Europe, of colonial plus recent immigrant stock.

(3) A cultural heritage of Spanish land tenure and social organization.

(4) A reciprocal trade relation with Europe owing to the industrial revolution, particularly to the European demand for food in exchange for manufactured goods, and to steam transportation and refrigeration.

(5) A competitive relation with the United States, owing primarily to similar mid-latitude production.

(6) Military and political affiliations with Fascism in Spain, Italy, and Germany.

Failure to Explain

These factors are in effect and of significance. As historical and geographical circumstances associated with Argentine development, they may help toward an understanding of the country. But will this list or any similar list, however amplified, or any such approach to the subject explain Argentina or reveal cause and effect relations?

The approach is misleading rather than revealing. The value of the specified factors is unmeasured and immeasurable; multitudes of other factors also are present, many of them different, some of them opposite in effect; countless incidents and decisions of critical value are largely unknown and unknowable; and alternative tendencies are ignored.

Some factors of the Argentine fundament provide a basis for unity, but there is no self-evident pre-existent unity, and some natural features provide bases for disunity. Even the natural barrier of the Andes is not an unequivocal factor as an international boundary. At one time the line between Argentine and Chilean jurisdiction was drawn in the dry plains far east of the Andes, and western provinces of modern Argentina were eastern communities of colonial Chile.

White racial stock provides a basis for vigorous development, but factors other than immigration from Europe seem largely responsible for recent advance; and there are other significant racial strains.

The factor of Spanish culture is expressed in a landed gentry. But other factors are expressed in agrarian movements which have modified and may obliterate the old system.

Trade connection with Europe is a prominent factor in Argentine economy. But American big business has played a leading rôle in Argentine development; and the trade of the United States with Argentina is greater than with most other Latin American countries.

European fascism is an obvious factor in Argentine government and politics. But French, British, and American democracy has been another factor. Democracy has developed more in Argentina than in most other countries of Latin America, and is as much alive as fascism, and more deeply rooted. The Perón dictatorship came into power and has remained by hairbreadth decisions against contrary forces—through such incidents as the illness of a democratic president and Perón's fantastic release from prison.

So other factors appear, still without explaining Argentina fully. Minor incidents and critical decisions with their alternative possibilities pile up endlessly in the pursuit of causes.

Unknowable Causes

An illustration of a minor incident as a causal factor in great events is given in the old verse:

> For the want of a nail, the shoe was lost,
> For the want of a shoe, the horse was lost,
> For the want of a horse, the rider was lost,
> For the want of a rider, the battle was lost,
> For the want of a battle, the kingdom was lost—
> And all for the want of a horseshoe-nail.[3]

This illustrates the critical significance of an incident traced along one line of cause and effect. But what of all the other lines in the full

[3] "Benjamin Franklin, Poor Richard, 1758," B. E. Stevenson, *The Home Book of Quotations* (New York, 1934), p. 2041.

circle of causal factors bearing on these events? What of the critical decision of the blacksmith who failed to secure the nail, and the antecedents of that decision, and all the other decisions in a complete explanation of a kingdom or of Argentina?

The preceding list of major factors for Argentina is not an explanation but a rationalization, an ex post facto set of causes picked to fit corresponding events, including items apparently consistent with results, and excluding everything else. Determinism is branded as a false guide because it prompts a futile pretense of explaining—futile and misleading at least in our present state of knowledge.

Conceivably we might hope sometime to explain the present and the past. These have been determined and cannot be changed, all the returns are in, all the choices between alternative possibilities have been made.

Full explanation is conceivable; practically this may remain impossible, considering not only the general factors of unmeasured value but also the unnumbered incidents and decisions of critical value, the horseshoe nails and the blacksmiths' decisions, which we have no means of tracing. Full explanation, in fact, involves the whole world and everything that has happened in it.

Unforeseeable Future

If we cannot fully explain the present and the past, even more surely we cannot fully predict the future—not only because of ignorance regarding the effect of all current incidents, but also because innumerable decisions are being made and will be made between alternative courses of action, leading to different possibilities.

For the past, all such decisions have been made and are therefore definitely determined, even though we cannot trace them all to their sources. But for the future these decisions are not yet made, and there is no indication that we shall ever be able to make them in advance for our own future lives, to say nothing of our inability to make them in advance for the future lives of everyone else in the world.

In these decisions which form the chain of cause and effect in human affairs, the question of free will arises and is not proven pro or con. We may assume that there is no free will, that everything, past, present, and future, has been determined in a cause and effect relation beforehand, from the beginning of the world; and that we cannot really make choices between real alternative possibilities. But this does not seem to help us in our scientific search for knowledge. We seem to be just as far from full explanation of the present and past, in which all decisions already have been made, as from prediction of the future.

Since there is no proof against free will, it is unscientific to reject free will as if it were a closed question, and thus claim to know more about cause and effect than we can know.

But if for any reason we wish to make an unscientific practical choice between free will and pre-determinism, we had better make a consistent and harmless choice. In this case the consistent choice is to believe in free will, and to think and act in accordance with it, because free will is an assumption on which we all live every day—the assumption that we can choose what we do and that our choices are significant, not merely the gestures of puppets or new-born babes. This is also the only harmless choice in scientific thinking, because it leaves the consequences indeterminate to the same extent that a scientific refusal to choose between determinism and free will would leave them so.

The case against a deterministic approach in geography might rest at this point. There is sufficient evidence for leaving the approach indeterminate in our present search for knowledge, whether or not this is accompanied by belief in the ultimate truth of determinism.

Individual Indeterminism

However, the question of whether determinism is ultimately true or false has been mentioned as a matter of coincidental interest. This question has significance for geographers and may be pursued accordingly.

The following passages on the subject were written by William James:

[Determinism] professes that those parts of the universe already laid down absolutely appoint and decree what the other parts shall be. . . . The whole is in each and every part, and welds it with the rest into an absolute unity, an iron block, in which there can be no equivocation or shadow of turning. . . .

The stronghold of the deterministic sentiment is the antipathy to the idea of chance. . . . Many persons talk as if the minutest dose of disconnectedness of one part with another, the faintest tremor of ambiguity about the future . . . would ruin everything, and turn this goodly universe into a sort of insane sand-heap or nulliverse, no universe at all. . . .

[But] do not all the motives that assail us, all the futures that offer themselves to our choice, spring equally from the soil of the past; and would not either one of them, whether realized through chance or through necessity, the moment it is realized, seem to us to fit that past, and in the completest and most continuous manner to interdigitate with the phenomena already there? . . .

Decisions, for him who makes them, are altogether peculiar psychic facts. Self-luminous and self-justifying at the living moment at which they occur, they appeal to no outside moment to make them continuous with the rest of nature. Themselves it is rather who seem to make nature continuous; and in their strange and intense function of granting consent to one possibility and withholding it from another, to transform an equivocal and double future into an unalterable and simple past.[4]

Worldwide Indeterminism

So much for individual free will; but this does not answer the question of determinism in the general trend of history and the broad forms of social structure and civilization, which might occur in pre-determined order, even though individuals were free to participate in one way or another.

On this question William James has said:

The mutations of societies . . . are in the main due . . . to the acts or the example of individuals whose genius was so adapted to the receptivities of the moment, or whose accidental position of authority was so critical that they became ferments, initiators of movement, or destroyers of other persons whose gifts, had they had free play, would have led society in another direction. . . .

Nations . . . may be committed by kings and ministers to peace or war . . . by prophets to this religion or that, by various geniuses to fame in art, science, or industry. A war is a true point of bifurcation of future possibilities. . . . Just so does a revolution or any great civic precedent, become a deflecting influence, whose operations widen with the course of time. . . .

The community *may* evolve in many ways. . . . The accidental presence of this or that ferment decides in which way it *shall* evolve. . . . The ways are to a large extent indeterminate in advance. . . .

It is folly, then, to speak of the 'laws of history' as of something inevitable, which science has only to discover and whose consequences any one can then foretell but do nothing to alter or avert. . . . The utmost the student of sociology can ever predict is that *if* a genius of a certain sort show the way, society will be sure to follow. . . . The evolutionary view of history, when it denies the vital importance of individual initiative, is, then, an utterly vague and unscientific conception, a lapse . . . into the most ancient oriental fatalism.[5]

More recently the process of social development on the earth has been described by a sociologist, Lynd, as follows:

It is people who do things. . . . The pattern is what it is because of . . . the dynamic individual, creators and carriers of culture, struggling fiercely to feel "at home" with themselves and others in their world. . . .

Human motivation however conditioned . . . by the past, always operates in the present; and at the white-hot edge of decision, the stuff of behavior which

[4] William James, "The Dilemma of Determinism," *Essays on Faith and Morals* (N. Y., 1947), pp. 150, 153-155, 157, 158.
[5] William James, "Great Men and Their Environment," *Selected Papers on Philosophy* (N. Y., 1917), pp. 174-176, 188, 189.

the historian finds so rigid when cold, is continually bent and directed into new forms. Choices, limited to be sure by past conditioning and by the momentum of movement along habitual grooves, but still choices to an important degree, are being made as man lives along. And these choices, including the factors determining their constriction and their potential range, are the central part of the business of social science. . . .

We sail inevitably into the future, the sea is full of dangerous reefs and shoals, and drifting is more dangerous than choosing the course that our best intelligence dictates.[6]

The course of events in our world seems to be like a complex chain reaction into which new directive impulse, imperceptible in most cases, is injected by every human choice.

Status of Social Science

Where does this leave us with respect to social science in general and geography in particular?—unable to explain anything fully, unable to know and measure cause and effect in any complete way, unable to establish absolute laws, unable to predict the future with any certainty.

This should leave us in a much stronger position scientifically and better able to justify our existence as scholars. The indeterminism of alternative possibilities makes the efforts of science worth while and important—efforts in the pursuit of knowledge, and in planning, public policy making, and education.

What is science anyway? Only a narrow and shallow definition makes it merely a search for cause and effect, or for quantification, or for prediction, or universal laws. Science in the broadest sense, according to a geographer, Hartshorne, is "organized objective knowledge, . . . the pursuit of knowledge as reality by objective means." [7] Science according to a sociologist, Park, "is a systematic search for the facts about the world." [8] Science according to a philosopher, C. W. Morris, "is the record . . . of the more universal aspects of . . . a common world.' [9]

According to a German geographer, Alfred Hettner, as quoted by Hartshorne, "the common idea that generalizations and laws themselves are the purpose of science is an extraordinary adherence to medieval scholastic realism. On the contrary they are merely the means to the ultimate purpose which is the knowledge of actual reality, the individual facts, either conditions or events." [10]

[6] R. S. Lynd, *Knowledge for What?* (Princeton, N. J., 1939), pp. 38, 49, 134, 186, 187.
[7] R. Hartshorne, *The Nature of Geography* (Lancaster, Pa., 1939), pp. 134, 196.
[8] R. E. Park, *Outline of the Principles of Sociology* (N. Y., 1939), p. iii.
[9] G. H. Mead, *Mind, Self, and Society* (Chicago, 1934), p. xxix.
[10] R. Hartshorne, *op. cit.*, p. 379.

According to an anthropologist, Radcliffe-Brown,

the method of science in all instances is the analysis of a perceived analogy, an instance of perceived similarities and differences, which perceived and defined in the first instance rather vaguely, is in the end given a more precise definition. . . .

The modern theoretical scientist . . . excludes the concept of cause from his scientific investigation. . . . If . . . we were to define cause as the sum total of all necessary and sufficient conditions for a given event, then we could never exhaust the cause of anything. . . . When one is engaged in a system analysis, that which may be stated in superficially satisfactory causal terms can be more accurately stated in non-causal terms. . . . From the scientific point of view you are more accurate when you say there is a co-variation, and you can be still more accurate by defining that co-variation in quantitative terms.[11]

Procedure in Geography

Thus geography deals with perceived similarities and differences between areas, perceived in the first instance rather vaguely and in the end given a more precise definition, quantitative in some cases; tracing co-variation in space, and thus approaching "explanation in the only scientific way, that of observed coincidence."[12]

In any scholarly work there are clear-cut advantages in not claiming to do more than scholarship is able to do, not claiming to find cause and effect where this claim is misleading, not pretending to explain by rationalization. There are clear-cut advantages in admitting underlying assumptions, making explicit whatever is taken for granted, and then seeking accessible answers to appropriate questions.

In geography such questions as the following may well be included: What phenomena are observed? In what association of space and time? Under what conditions or circumstances? What patterns are discernible and what correlations? For the future what alternative possibilities appear within what known frame?

Our business is not to explain Argentina, but to discover and appreciate Argentina in the world pattern. We can even make conditional predictions or forecasts, which is all that any science can do. Taking for granted the history and geography of Argentina up to the present time, the immediate future appears narrowly limited. We can predict that if weather and economic conditions are good, a wheat crop will be harvested next season; and that if the provisions of the present

[11] A. R. Radcliffe-Brown, "The Nature of a Theoretical Natural Science of Society" (Transcribed notes, University of Chicago, 1937), pp. 35, 41, 42.
[12] R. S. Platt, "Items in the Regional Geography of Panama," *Annals of the Association of American Geographers*, XXVIII, No. 1 (March 1938), 35.

(1947) constitution are carried out, Perón will not succeed himself at the next election.

We can make broader forecasts with correspondingly less certainty. Very probably Argentina will export shiploads of foodstuffs in the next five years, although quantities are uncertain. Very probably public opinion will be less effective in shaping public policy in Argentina than in the United States during the next decade, whether or not successful revolution be accomplished.

For the far distant future, the possibilities appear more and more divergent, though still within limiting circumstances—under conditions of air, land, and water, and of human beings in social relations. One possibility is that Argentina may become a powerful threat to the United States. Another possibility is that Argentina may be wiped out in atomic war. Another possibility is that Argentina may become a staunch friend of the United States in a peaceful world.

Whatever faith we have in learning or in living seems to brand determinism as a pseudo-scientific sanction of vulgar belief in the inevitability of war or depression or any prospective event. If we avoid a deterministic approach and give our best efforts to the pursuit and use of knowledge, we can rightly hope to bend our common course in the direction of our desire, and to cause a trend of events (cause in a true philosophic and not in a pseudo-scientific sense) toward greater human welfare.

9. The Rise of Possibilism

George Tatham

Scientists are generally conservative when it comes to making changes in the basic methodology of a discipline. Well-established ideas are difficult to dislodge. The change from environmental determinism to possibilism, outlined here by Tatham, is an example of a slight modification toward a more tenable position, temporarily acceptable in a discipline in the process of evolving a defensible methodology.

[Some] geographers, particularly those who entered the field after training in history, instead of natural science, have tended to stress this freedom of man to choose. For them the pattern of human activity on the earth's surface is the result of the initiative and mobility of man operating within a frame of natural forces. Without denying the limits every environment sets to man's ambition, they emphasize the scope of man's action rather than these limits.

Febvre has named this point of view "Possibilism" and a very vigorous statement of its principles is to be found in his *Geographical Introduction to History*. The development of Possibilism is closely linked with the writings of Vidal de la Blache and Brunhes in France, and of Isaiah Bowman and Carl Sauer (among others) in the U.S.A. Some account of the growth of this philosophy will be found in later chapters, here only a statement of the main tenets will be given.

In common with the Determinists, the Possibilists start with the concept of the terrestrial "whole," and the interrelation of all phenomena on the earth's surface.

This (idea of relationship) must dominate every complete study of geographical facts. One cannot be content with the observation of a fact by itself or of an isolated series of facts. After this initial observation, it is important to place the series back in its natural setting, in the complex ensemble of facts in the midst of which it was produced and developed. We must investigate the manner in which it is connected with the series of facts which are its neighbours; we must ascertain in what measure it has determined them, and in what measure on the other hand it has been affected by their influence.[1]

The "geography of the whole—is in truth the highest goal of geographic study."

The dominant idea in all geographical progress is that of terrestrial unity. The conception of the earth as a whole, whose parts are co-ordinated, where phenomena follow a definite sequence and obey general laws to which particular cases are related was long confined to the dominion of mathematics. It did not become part of other branches of geography till our own day. . . . Friedrich Ratzel very wisely insists on such a conception making it the cornerstone of his *Anthropogeographie*. The phenomena of human geography are related to terrestrial unity by means of which alone can they be explained. They are related to the environment which is itself created by the combination of physical conditions in every part of the earth.

Geography getting its inspiration, like its kindred sciences from the idea of terrestrial unity, has for its special mission, to find out how far the physical and biological laws which govern the world are combined and modified in their application to different parts of the surface of the world.[2]

In this terrestrial unity (*ganzheit*), however, a greater emphasis is

SOURCE: Griffith Taylor, *Geography in the Twentieth Century* (New York: Philosophical Library, 1953), pp. 151-59. George Tatham, who wrote the portion of the chapter from which this reading was taken, is professor of geography at the University of Toronto.

[1] Brunhes, op. cit., pp. 14-15.
[2] Vidal de la Blache, *Ann. de Geog.*, 1913, p. 291; quoted by Febvre, op. cit., p. 62, and *Principles of Human Geography*, p. 7.

placed on the works of man than by the determinists. The works of man, not the earth and its influence, are the starting-point. This is strikingly brought out by comparing the form of Brunhes' book with that of Miss [Ellen Churchill] Semple's. Miss Semple's "simplified para-phrase" of Ratzel's *Anthropogeographie* is devoted to the study of how area, location, mountains, climate, &c. affect man. Brunhes attempts to classify the essential facts of human geography under three headings: Facts of Unproductive Occupation of the Soil (Houses and Roads); Facts of Plant and Animal Conquest (cultivation of plants and raising of animals); Facts of Destructive Exploitation (plant and animal devastation, mineral exploitation.)

Geographical influences are Miss Semple's chief concern, they are to be sought out and expounded. Brunhes' interest is focused on the facts of human occupation of the earth, irrespective of whether they show environmental influences or not. In the second part of his book, where the link between the earth and man is examined, it is not influences that are sought but "geographical relations between physical facts and hu-man destinies." His approach is certainly more conducive to unbiased research.

But not only are the works of man given more prominence, his activity is also stressed. Man is not looked upon as a passive being, he is seen as an active force, reacting on his environment and changing it.

Man is a geographical agent and not the least. He everywhere contributes his share towards investing the physiognomy of the earth with those 'changing expressions' which it is the special charge of geography to study. Through centuries and centuries, by his accumulated labours and the boldness and decision of his undertakings, he appears to us as one of the most powerful agents in the modification of terrestrial surfaces. . . . And this action of man on his environment is the part which man plays in geography.[3]

We must add to the group of material forces whose incessant interplay we have seen this new force, human activity; which is not only a material thing, but which also expresses itself through material effects.[4]

In this way we are in a position to appreciate better the role which should be assigned to man as a geographical factor. He is at once both active and passive. For, according to the well-known phrase 'natura non nisi parendo vincitur' (Vidal de la Blache, *Principles of Human Geography*, p. 19).

Human activity modifies both the inorganic and organic features of the earth.

Man utilizes not only inorganic agencies in his work of transformation. He is not content merely to make use of the products of decomposition in the soil by ploughing, not to utilize the waterfalls, the force of gravity brought into play

[3] Febvre, op. cit., pp. 63-4.
[4] Brunhes, op. cit., p. 27.

by inequalities of relief. He further collaborates with all living forces grouped together by environmental conditions. He joins in nature's game (*op. cit.* p. 20).

Vidal de la Blache returns to this point later and expands it as follows.

Civilization has appropriated its favourite crops. Their original habitats have been enlarged far beyond what could have been foreseen. From the original plant countless varieties have been perfected to suit the requirements of different climates, with the result that its importance is often greater in regions where it has been acclimatized, than in those where it originated. For instance, wheat does not today have the largest yield in regions where it was first cultivated; the harvests of Mediterranean countries cannot be compared with those of the plains of Central Europe. The largest ears of corn are no longer grown on tropical plateaux, but in the United States, on the prairies of the Middle West.

Bowman gives another illustration of this type of human activity.

As knowledge of the world spread, the associations of event or condition with place widened, they become more complex, they had less or more significance with respect to mankind. The potato and maize plants were unknown to pre-Columbian Europe. Their discovery raised the question, 'Are they useful to the rest of humanity and where can they be grown?' The whole known world was in a sense resurveyed by the rough processes of trial and error and the result has been astounding. These two plants largely changed the economy of Europe. The soil had not changed; man had gained a little more knowledge of it through a new plant. An element of one environment had been added to the elements, long fixed of many other environments.[5]

In this way man gradually replaces the variety of nature by uniformity.

The modern European is an indefatigable labourer at a task which tends to render uniform, if not the whole planet, at least each of the zones of the planet.[6]

The action of man raised to the level of one of the powers of nature leads to the core of the Possibilist philosophy, namely the contention that nature is not 'Mandatory but Permissive'.[7]

Nature is never more than an adviser.[8]

The unrelenting power of natural agents reigns in the physical world alone. Human geography is a field of compromise; nothing is absolute or definitive for the human species on the earth except these general laws and those fundamental conditions which determine the limits beyond which all life is excluded; and if men are not able to push back indefinitely all these limits in altitude, latitude, depth, &c. they are at least able somewhat to force or modify some few of them.[9]

[5] Bowman, *Geography and the Social Sciences*, p. 36.
[6] Vidal de la Blache, *Ann. de Geog.*, 1898; quoted also by Febvre, p. 157.
[7] Whitbeck and Thomas, *The Geographic Factor*, p. 12.
[8] Vidal de la Blache, p. 321.   [9] Brunhes, op. cit., p. 607.

The forces of physical nature are bound to each other in their consequences, in their relations and in the consequences of these relations. Man does not escape the common law, his activity is included in the network of terrestrial phenomena. But if human activity is thus circumscribed, it does not follow that it is fatally determined.[10]

There are no necessities, but everywhere possibilities; and man as master of these possibilities is the judge of their use. This by the reversal which it involves puts man in the first place, man and no longer the earth, nor the influence of climate, nor the determinant conditions of localities.[11]

It has been the custom for many years to speak of human society in the great climatico-botanical regions as adjuncts, so to speak, of plant and animal societies, which were themselves, it was assumed, strictly dependent on meteorological phenomena. But these regions, into which man was thrown as a kind of extra have nothing tyrannical or determinant about them. Although he reviews and criticizes them along with many others, there is no necessity for the historian or geographer to look on the facts, which he retains in his descriptions and on which his studies are essentially based, as component parts of a pre-established order.

Still less have those facts any determining value for men and their existence. Even plant societies, which are less adaptable to environment than human ones, do not suffer exclusion from external conditions, *a fortiori* human societies are capable of protecting their own existence from that tyranny.[12]

The geographical elements of the environment are fixed only in the narrow and special sense of the word. The moment we give them human associations they are as changeful as humanity itself. That is why modern geography has so definitely steered away from determinism and towards a study of types of actually working regional combinations of human and environmental conditions.[13]

Earth facts do not determine the form and nature of human society in development. They condition it. New earth facts are continually being discovered and old earth facts given new significance as human knowledge thought and social action develop. The relations are reciprocal.[14]

These quotations, to which numerous others could be added from Possibilist statements published during the last fifty years, make quite clear the contention that Nature does not drive man along one particular road, but that it offers a number of opportunities from among which man is free to select.

This number, however, is never unlimited, and environmental influence is definitely shown in this limitation. Possibilists do not, nor have they ever claimed, that man can free himself from all environmental

[10] Ibid., p. 27.
[11] Febvre, op. cit., p. 236.
[12] Febvre, op. cit., p. 172.
[13] Bowman, op. cit., p. 37.
[14] Ibid., p. 225.

influences. To attempt, to refute Possibilism by reiterating that "You can't grow bananas at the Pole, nor pineapples in Greenland," as is sometimes done, is to ignore the real character of the Possibilist thesis. Even Febvre, probably the most insistent on man's power of conscious choice, writes in this regard:

Men can never entirely rid themselves whatever they do of the hold their environment has on them. Taking this into consideration they utilize their geographical circumstances more or less according to what they are, and take advantage more or less completely of their geographical possibilities. But here as elsewhere there is no action of necessity.[15]

Brunhes strikes the same note:

The power and means which man has at his disposal are limited and he meets in nature bounds which he cannot cross. Human activity can within certain limits vary its play and its movements; but it cannot do away with its environment, it can often modify it, but it can never suppress it, and will always be conditioned by it.

At times Brunhes' statements are couched in language closely similar to that of Determinist writers, as for instance when he says, "Those who seem to be most independent of local conditions and who escape the geographical imprisonment of our sedentary life . . . the nomads, the shepherds, do not escape the tyranny of water." Vidal de la Blache speaks of the "sovereign influence of environment" and says:

Human societies, like those of the vegetable and animal world, are composed of different elements subject to the influence of environment. No one knows what winds brought them together, nor whence, nor when; but they are living side by side in a region which has gradually puts its stamp upon them. Some societies have long been part of the environment, but others are in process of formation, continuing to recruit members and to be modified day by day. Upon such, in spite of all they can do, surrounding conditions leave their impress, and in Australia, at the Cape, or in America, these people are slowly becoming saturated with the influence of the regions where their destinies are to unfold. Are not the Boers one of the most remarkable examples of adaptation?[16]

This final paragraph from Bowman:

While the 'physical laws' to which mankind responds are variable in their application and in degree of effect, yet this is also true that all men everywhere are affected to some degree by physical conditions. The drought of 1930 in the United States threw into strong relief the fact that it is only in regions of optimum climatic conditions that men may say 'I am free of those extreme

[15] Op. cit., p. 315.
[16] Op. cit., pp. 17-18.

conditions that have more nearly continuous effects upon man elsewhere.'
How circumscribed are such optimum areas, and how much history, and what
deep cultural relations have flowed out of the contrast between well-favoured
and ill-favoured regions.[17]

The limits set by Nature to man's action vary from place to place on
the earth's surface and from one historical period to another. In marginal environments, such as the hot and cold deserts, and at low stages
of culture man's choice may be extremely restricted. In the more favour-
able areas of the warm and cool temperate zones, and in periods when
man's techniques are highly developed the possibilities are more numerous. But however many skills man acquires he can never free himself entirely from Nature's control. This is emphasized over and over
again by Possibilists.

Thus Brunhes writes:

Is it not at least in part an illusion to believe that by increasing his means of
control and conquest of the earth man throws off its tyranny and increases his
own independence? Is it not on the contrary a sort of contract with more exact,
and one might almost say, more Draconian terms that is signed by civilized
men as they make their relations with the earth closer and more productive?

Thus everything on the surface of the globe is for men a matter of habit, of
sound understanding, of physical facts, and of skilful adaptation to these facts.
Moreover, the adaptation must take place promptly, and at the right time,
preceded, prepared for, and brought about by exact scientific investigations.

These investigations should also tend to moderate our ambitions and turn
us away sometimes from undertakings that would mean such bold opposition
to the forces of nature that men would run the risk of seeing sooner or later his
patient work annihilated at a single stroke. The more imposing and glorious
man's conquest the more cruel the revenge of the thwarted physical facts.

Brunhes illustrates this with the example of the drainage of coastal
lowlands causing the land to sink and to be reflooded by the sea, or
the bursting of dykes, &c.

Bowman similarly points to the experience of the farmers on the
High Plains, who having crossed the isohyets that fixed the boundary
of agriculture by breeding better seed and using dry farming methods
find topography setting a limit to the use of agricultural machinery
on which the new technique depended.[18]

Great emphasis of this element in Possibilist thought is necessary in
view of the misunderstanding of some critics who appear to think a
Possibilist denies that environment influences man at all. What is
important is to realize that a recognition of the power of environmental influence is very different from an acceptance of the full deter-

[17] Op. cit., p. 161.
[18] See also Whitbeck and Thomas, *The Geographic Factor*, Chap. I.

minist thesis. Carl Sauer has given this point masterly treatment in his papers on methodology.[19]

Conscious of the selective power exercised by man Possibilists are cautious in approaching the problem of environmental factors in history. Though Brunhes sees "human history deeply rooted in the material things of the earth" he does not believe that all history can be explained by geography. "History evolves upon the earth, but it is made up of complex and involved elements, that are removed as far as possible from elementary geographic conditions." He also asks if geographers are to be satisfied "with indicating some large and obvious relationships, exact though it be, between the general geographic situation of a country and its general historical destiny," which is so obvious that anyone with an open mind can perceive it.

Yet if more precise investigation is to be undertaken it is an exceedingly delicate task. The search for causal relations is always hazardous unless there is a repetition of circumstances with identical results. But no two parts of the earth's surface are identical; each region presents a unique combination of physical and human features and therefore each region must be separately studied when the intricate interrelations of man and his environment are to be analysed. This is the *raison d'être* of regional geography. Brunhes bases his work on studies of island regions; Vidal de la Blache, inspired by his teaching, the brilliant regional monographs of Demangeon (*La Plaine Picardie*), Blanchard (*La Flandre*), Vacher (*Le Berry*), and Gallois (*Régions naturelles et noms de pays*).

Precisely the same problem is met in history. Attempts continue to be made to distinguish cycles or patterns in history, and critics continue to point out that such cycles can only be established by an arbitrary selection of facts in each period; a different standpoint, resulting in a different selection, and the pattern is spoiled or another established. Each historical epoch is in fact a unique succession of events. This does not mean that causal relations or cycles cannot be found, it merely stresses the difficulties inherent in the search.

One factor stressed by Possibilists in the study of historical geography is the importance of habit. Man is a creature of habit and habits once established become a part of his environment and exert considerable influence on his later development.

Nature does not act on the needs of man [writes Febvre], it is man who by choosing two or three out of several means of satisfying his needs, and by clinging obstinately to what he has chosen, acts in the long run on nature, digs into it a trench, so to speak, always the same and in the same direction, of no

[19] "Recent Developments in Cultural Geography," in *Recent Developments in the Social Sciences*, ed. Hayes, 1927. Morphology of Landscape, Univ. of California Publications in Geography, II, No. 2.

great volume at first perhaps, but evergrowing deeper and wider. In other words what has to be brought out clearly is the manner of life of the various human societies.[20]

Habits, especially mental habits, modes of thought, long cherished ideas, may hamper man quite as seriously as deficiency in the physical environment. "Between the desires and needs of man and everything in nature that can be utilized by him beliefs, ideas, and customs interpose. The origin of cultivation and of animal domestication is intimately bound up with religion and magic." [21]

Ideas may even enclose a developing civilization in man-created isolation.

But there is also another isolation, one which man forges about himself by his own acts, by whatever structures he builds upon his own achievements. His feelings, prejudices, and all his conceptions of social life are wrought into his inventions, into which he has put much of himself, and the modes of life which absorb his entire activity. To these may further he added a religious consecration through ancestor-worship and respect for a past which is shrouded in mystery. The result is that he weaves a thick shroud which envelops and paralyses him.[22]

In a most significant paragraph, Bowman refers to the part habits of thought play in precipitating crises in civilization.

It may be shown that there has never been a civilization that declined because it exhausted the possibilities of the land. No nation ever declined because it exhausted the possibilities of the land. No nation has ever fully developed its 'frontier'. The earth has never gone back on man, but man has found himself entangled in 'the unpredictable effects of his system'. What really happens is that knowledge at the moment of strain, is not great enough to control the forces of nature and of systems of government combined.[23]

[20] Op. cit., p. 239.
[21] Febvre, p. 167.
[22] V. de la Blache, p. 327.
[23] Bowman, *The Pioneer Fringe*, pp. 42-3.

IV. GEOGRAPHICAL DESCRIPTION

The principal task of the geographer is to present "what areas or places are like." Man has attempted to describe his surroundings from his very beginnings, but it has been one of his most difficult undertakings. The chemist in his laboratory is able to add known elements to an experiment and describe his results. The geographer, however, does not have such an advantage; he must describe the earth's surface without exact knowledge of the physical and human variables that comprise it. In addition, his task is complicated by the difficulty of measuring many of the human factors.

Nevertheless, description has been and still is of vital importance to the geographer. Even though his tools and methods have become more rigorous, the job of rendering into understandable language the results of his observations and research still remains. Through sophisticated mathematics and statistics, a high degree of accuracy can be applied to problems, but the results of complex formulas and models must still be described. Thus, the written word is still the most important means the geographer has of conveying to both layman and scholar the results of his efforts.

In dealing with the dilemma of the geographer in an article entitled "The Problem of Geographical Description" (*Institution of British Geographers*, No. 30, 1962, pp. 1-14), the British geographer H. C. Darby considers geography and history part science and part art; both rely on good writing to convey the importance of a "time" or "space." Darby summarizes five methods of providing an explanatory element in geographical description: (1) the sequent occupance of space, (2) the introductory narrative or "an account of the processes of change leading up to the geography of the present day, (3) retrospective reference to describe and explain a present landscape only by looking back to significant points in time, (4) combining a geographical description with explanatory or significant historical footnotes, and (5) utilizing cross-sections but beginning with the present and going back through time.

The first selection in this part presents present-day attitudes toward descriptive writing, and is followed by three good descriptions of England, the American West, and Brazil.

10. Mere Description

Lester E. Klimm

*Klimm's short editorial on "mere description" outlines
a problem in today's scientific world with its emphasis
upon finding theories and laws. New information must
be described, and much description and empirical
research often precedes (and follows) the formulation
of hypotheses, theories, and laws.*

"Description" has become a dirty word. This is evidenced by the adjectives with which it is usually modified; strangely enough "mere" and "pure" have the same derogatory meaning when used in this connection. This jade comes from a very respectable family, "Exploration," but values have changed, and what was never "mere" when it was roughly measured by day's journeys is prostitution of the geographic art when it results in detailed maps of observed and measured phenomena. The tradition of literature and drama is that fallen women are sterling characters at heart and are redeemable by love and understanding: perhaps geographers may do as much for "mere description!"

The objections to mere description most commonly advanced are that, by itself, it generates no theories and that, actually, a certain amount of hypothesis is necessary before it can be decided what and how to describe. There is a modicum of validity to both of these objections, but experience is also replete with evidence to the contrary. It is true that the routine compiler of measurements or observer of phenomena *may* derive no theories from his data, but how often he does just the opposite!

That description is impossible without theories to start with is one of those widely-accepted statements that deserves more examination than it has gotten. We do, of course, owe the collection of a great deal of our stock of information to the necessity to test a hypothesis. It may or may not support the hypothesis, but the information remains.

A quarter of a century ago V. C. Finch described a methodology for urban geography in the following words: ". . . It puts to the fore that aspect of the subject upon which the writer speaks with authority; the present city. It puts in its proper place that body of deductions . . . which, however well they may have been developed, . . . still are

SOURCE: *Economic Geography*, XXXV (January, 1959), p. ii. The author (deceased) was professor of geography at the University of Pennsylvania.

deductions. A century hence the recorded observations of landscape may be worth much, the deductions little."

If the description promises to be the only part of many studies that will stand the test of time, shouldn't every effort be made to do it very well indeed? And, if the data gathered to test our hypotheses are going to be used as grist for other mills, shouldn't its gathering and presentation be a disciplined procedure with its potential users in mind?

These questions are raised anew, here, because the need and opportunities for useful non-theoretical descriptions are greater than ever. The amount of data becomes overwhelming. Air-photo coverage, for example, is available for large areas, especially in the United States. From this it is possible to determine, with great accuracy, the distribution of urbanized areas, forests, agricultural areas, etc. Boundaries may be located and measurements made on scales from 1:20,000 down.

Indeed, this embarrassment of riches may necessitate new methods of thinking by geographers. Their descriptive generalizations (regionalizations) until now have often been based on assumed relationships. Some of this has been more or less unconscious, with economic or cultural phenomena poured into a mold of geologic—or political—regionalization. Now that there is detailed information, the challenge is to come up with non-theoretical descriptive generalization at usable, smaller scales, yet retain as much as possible of the form and pattern of the actual distribution.

It is *not* being argued here that theories, hypotheses, relationships should not be diligently sought. It *is* being argued that non-theoretical description—"mere description"—is respectable because it may well be the ultimate "truth"; and it tends to keep us honest in our theorizing.

11. The English Landscape
David Lowenthal and Hugh C. Prince

"The English Landscape" is an example of description that succeeds by selection of details and highlights and interpretation of the most significant aspects of the countryside. The authors convey a feeling for England through their emphasis upon typical aspects of the people and the land that give character to this particular country. Many novelists have this ability but it is all too rare in scholars. Thomas Hardy, for instance, gives

some of the best descriptions available of English heaths
and other areas where his stories take place. Geog-
raphers need to have similar abilities of description to be
effective in making known to their readers what places
are like.

What are the visual qualities of the English landscape? How do the
English people look at England? What do they see or want to see?
As with any country and any people, the answers to these questions
depend partly on what is there, partly on the history and characteristics of the inhabitants, partly on how they interact with their surroundings. We begin with a view of the English scene as it appears
to us.

The English Scene

Variety

The visitor accustomed to sameness over space finds in England a
remarkable and preeminently characteristic degree of variety. Smallness of scale, a highly varied surface geology, and an accidented terrain have led countless observers, native no less than foreign, to note
how rapid the transition is from one landscape to another.[1] Few English views do not afford a glimpse of contrasting scenery.

The diversity of the landscape is enhanced by the intricacy of the
paths leading through it. A maze of roads and boundaries twist and
turn to reveal a succession of new vistas, now near, now distant; each
turning confronts the traveler with sudden breaks in slope, changes
in vegetation and land use, contrasts in the man-made landscape
between features created at various times in the past—a cultural
palimpsest in which historical change is as strongly marked as regional
difference.

Density of texture is a social as well as a visual feature of the English
landscape. The intricate mosaics of both town and country slow the
runner to a walk; he traverses only half the expected distance in the
time intended. There are few blanks on the map of England; almost
everywhere is a *place*, with a meaning and a character of its own. In
city, town, and village the haphazard and the accidental reinforce a
taste for heterogeneity, an abhorrence of straight lines and uniform

SOURCE: *The Geographical Review*, LIV (July, 1964), 304-46. Dr. Lowenthal is a
research associate at the American Geographical Society, New York City; Mr.
Prince is a lecturer in the Department of Geography, University College, London.
[1] A. E. Trueman: *Geology and Scenery in England and Wales* (Pelican Books, A
185; Harmondsworth, Middlesex, 1949), Chap. 1; O. J. R. Howarth: *The Scenic
Heritage of England and Wales* (London, 1937), Chap. 1.

spaces, to produce an abundance of intimate detail; only an overriding sense of proportion and notable restraint and conformity in the use of color rescue many places from chaos.

The quality of intimate idiosyncrasy derives also from the feeling of belonging, of connectedness in time, in place, and in a social order, that much of England still evokes. "Density of feature," wrote that most appreciative of visitors, Henry James, "is the great characteristic of English scenery. There are no waste details; everything in the land-scape is something particular—has a history, has played a part, has a value to the imagination." [2] Despite industrialization and the mass circulation of standardized goods and ideas, England remains a country of *pays*, where one can hardly help being struck by local differences in building materials, shapes of houses and fields, ways of material life in general, and that feeling of community which makes for a height-ened sense of locality. [3]

This is not to say that there are no monotonous or anonymous stretches. A walker soon wearies of the largely featureless surface of Salisbury Plain, as the motorist tires of mile after mile of suburban streets. But such experiences need be neither usual nor prolonged. Salis-bury Plain is no more than thirty miles across, and most suburbs lie within a few miles of open, or at least nonresidential, landscapes.

Smallness of scale also enhances scenic contrast. Unlike the Alps, the mountains of the Lake District can be seen as a whole from nearby. That theirs is a "little land" with "little rivers, little plains . . . little hills, little mountains" [4] the English often remain unaware until they confront the unnerving bigness of abroad. But the sense of inhabiting a miniature has inspired English poets for centuries. (Smallness of scale is not a matter of size. There are small countries, such as the Netherlands, with large-scale scenery. Nor is variety all a matter of scale.) The basic structure of some countries can be grasped in a drive across them at high speed, but in Britain "hills and rivers, chalk downs and heaths, coalfields and fens go by too quickly, and are not re-peated." [5] Single physical features seldom monopolize the whole ho-rizon, but are made more distinctive by their contiguity. Thus the flatness of the fenland is underscored by the Isle of Ely and the dark pine forests of the Breckland margin.

The sense of variety is heightened, finally, by the abrupt transitions

[2] Henry James: *English Hours* (2nd edit.; New York, 1960), p. 141.
[3] W. G. Hoskins: The Heritage and an Historical Account of Its Disfigurement, *Journ. Royal Soc. of Arts,* Vol. 105, 1956-1957, pp. 78-84.
[4] William Morris, as quoted in W. A. Eden: The English Tradition in the Country-side: III, The Re-Birth of the Tradition, *Architectural Rev.,* Vol. 77, 1935, pp. 193-202; reference on p. 202.
[5] John Dick Scott: *Life in Britain* (New York, London, Toronto, 1956), p. 28.

between areas of different land use, the sharp definition of moorland and pasture, of arable and meadow, of parkland and wasteland, above all of town and country. These contrasts are intensified by the strong outlines of roads, hedges, walls, cliffs, ridges, and rooftops, and by the counterchange of textural patterns—rough trees against smooth grass, brick against stone or plaster, paving stone against road surface. But the range of variation in shape and size is small, in color smaller still. The landscape can be depicted faithfully in pencil and wash; it is a draftsman's rather than a painter's scene.

Openness

The English landscape not only *is* varied; in most places it *looks* varied because it is open and can be viewed at a distance: foreground contrasts with middle distance and background. England is one of the most sparsely forested countries of Western Europe, with only 6 percent of its area wooded, as compared with 20 to 30 percent in France and Germany and 34 per cent in the United States.[6] Even places denominated as forests—the New Forest, Sherwood Forest, Epping Forest—are forests in a legal and historical sense only, often remnants of royal game reserves, and may contain more open land than woods.

Yet it is not so much a paucity of trees as their disposition that defines the English landscape. Except for new forestry plantings, trees in England do not obscure the view; they lie within it. Between one-quarter and one-third of the country's timber stands in scattered hedgerows and in parks. On the ground, the visual effect of well-wooded hedgerows can be strikingly deceptive. "The eye seems ever on the verge of a forest, which is, as it were by enchantment, continually changing into inclosures and hedgerows," commented an eighteenth-century observer of the Norfolk scene. But "there is not, generally speaking, a piece of woodland or a coppice in the whole District." [7]

The effect of a more extensive prospect is similar. Standing on a hilltop almost anywhere in the Home Counties, one might well suppose the landscape to be mostly wooded, but the comprehensiveness of the view itself belies this impression. The trees are mostly grouped together in small clumps, spinneys, and copses, and in hedgerows enclosing cultivated fields. Trees scattered singly over meadows and parks are

[6] "Hedgerow and Park Timber and Woods under Five Acres, 1951," *Census Rept. No. 2*, Forestry Commission, London, 1953, p. 65; Stephen Haden-Guest, John K. Wright, and Eileen M. Teclaff, edits.: A World Geography of Forest Resources, *Amer. Geogr. Soc. Special Publ. No. 33*, New York, 1956, pp. 156 and 270. For changes in Britain's woodlands, see H. L. Edlin: *Trees, Woods & Man* (London, 1956); and Robin H. Best and J. T. Coppock: *The Changing Use of Land in Britain* (London, 1962), Chap. 4.

[7] William Marshall: *The Rural Economy of Norfolk* (2 vols.; 2nd edit.; London, 1795), Vol. 1, p. 4.

usually browsed to a height of six feet, leaving clear lines of sight beneath them; in close-canopied beechwoods the ground is free from undergrowth and seedlings. By contrast, the cutover and neglected woodlots of New England not only interrupt, but frequently obliterate, the view.

Extensive tracts of open country occur at all elevations in England, from the Fens at sea level through the lowland heaths of Dorset, Bagshot, Breckland, and the Suffolk Sandlings to Salisbury Plain and the Downs, the moors of Dartmoor and Exmoor, the Pennines and the fells of Northumberland. It is the open uplands that make the greatest impact. Above 1000 or 1500 feet, England is almost entirely bare of trees, whereas in America most hilltops are forested. In highland England one looks out to a horizon bounded by ground that is vegetated but treeless, and the open skyline strengthens the impression of a generally open countryside.

It also makes the scene higher, grander, and more spacious. "Densely wooded slopes appear to lose height just as they lose grandeur," as Trent remarks in condemning recent afforestation in the Lake District.[8] Small-scale, dark in color, and vertically aligned in detail, forests are discordant against most skies. But bare ground and grassland, like most cloud patterns, are large-scale, layered, and light-colored. In England open land and sky often meet without trees intervening; their similar forms and textures blend, leading the eye to cross the horizon and embrace the whole.

The gently rolling surface of many English uplands furthers their union with the sky. The broad expanse of Dartmoor matches that of the cumulus clouds above to encompass the visual field.[9] The chalkland Downs similarly harmonize with their skies. "These mountains," as Gilbert White termed the Downs, are living things, "somewhat analogous to growth in their gentle swellings and smooth fungus-like protuberances, their fluted sides, and regular hollows and slopes . . . [as they] swell and heave their broad backs into the sky." [10]

Atmosphere

Climate, weather, and sky affect the appearance of landscapes everywhere. In some parts of the world the atmosphere is an inert, transparent background against which a skyline of terrestrial forms is silhouetted. In England sky and weather are active and tangible, impossible to disregard. "Such a country!" exclaimed the American land-

[8] Christopher Trent: *The Changing Face of England: The Story of the Landscape through the Ages* (London, 1956), p. 183.
[9] Vaughan Cornish: *Geographical Essays* (London [1946]), p. 68.
[10] Gilbert White: *The Natural History of Selborne* [1789] (Doubleday Dolphin Book, C 96; Garden City, N. Y., n.d.), p. 136. See also H. J. Massingham: *English Downland* (3rd edit.; London, New York, etc., 1949).

scape architect Olmsted, "—green, dripping, glistening, gorgeous!" [11]
Gorgeous or horrendous, the atmosphere plays a principal role in it.

The English landscape takes on the shade and color of the sky.
Atmospheric conditions are seldom the same from day to day; indeed,
they commonly alter every few minutes. "One seldom, if ever, hears,
'It's a nice day' from the lips of the English," asserts Mary Ellen Chase
with more poetic license than strict truth. "Instead they wisely comment solely on the brief hours at hand: 'It's a bright morning.' 'A fine
afternoon.' 'A pleasant evening.'" [12]

The English countryside rarely suffers extremes of heat or cold,
drought or deluge, but it frequently experiences most of the range
between them; and so do the English people. Sustained sunshine is so
rare, indeed any kind of "good" weather so evanescent, all predictions
so unreliable, that one learns to take the weather as it comes, to be
prepared for almost anything, and to be at home outdoors under all
conditions. In the absence of central heating, staying indoors has a
limited appeal except in the worst weather.

Sudden transitions from light to shade, from warm to cold, from wet
to dry, not only lend additional variety to the landscape, they make it
more dynamic; shifting shadows and patches of light, Constable's
"chiaroscuro of nature," [13] impart a sense of movement to the ground
beneath. The atmosphere adds an altogether new dimension to the
English scene. Sky is part of landscape; cloud cover is low, broken,
variegated, rapidly moving, seldom too bright to be looked at directly;
horizons are blurred; the sense of vertical relief is thus greater than in
countries much more mountainous. One tends always to look up. The
importance of sky in the view is confirmed by the sketches of English
watercolorists who laid wash upon wash to capture those fleeting rays
and passing shadows. For Constable the sky was always "the keynote,
the standard of scale, and the chief organ of sentiment." [14] Moreover,
his skies were generally rain-laden. "I am going to see Constable,"
gibed the painter Fuseli, "bring me mine ombrella." [15]

But the painter hardly exaggerates the climate. For all its variety, the
English atmosphere is prevailingly moist; when it is not raining it is
often threatening to. Landscapes are most often seen through a veil of

[11] Frederick Law Olmsted: *Walks and Talks of an American Farmer in England*
(rev. edit.; Columbus, Ohio, 1859), p. 70.
[12] Mary Ellen Chase: *This England* (New York, 1936), p. 11. The best general
work on this subject is Gordon Manley: *Climate and the British Scene* (The New
Naturalist [Series], London, 1952; The Fontana Library, London, 1962).
[13] Kenneth Clark: *Landscape into Art* (Pelican Books, A 369; Harmondsworth,
Middlesex, 1956), pp. 87-88.
[14] Constable to John Fisher, quoted in Kurt Badt: *John Constable's Clouds* (London, 1950), p. 55.
[15] John Ruskin: *The Lamp of Beauty: Writings on Art* (selected and edited by
Joan Evans; London, 1959), p. 37, footnote 1.

haze, or floating miraculously on a bank of mist, or as gaunt shapes filtered dimly through dun-colored fogs, the "London particulars" that Dickens immortalized. The characteristic view of anything is apt to be suffused with moisture; outlines are blurred, colors are softened, the whole appearance of things is more subtle, more mysterious, more romantic, than if seen under direct sunlight. Instead of standing out clearly separated, objects melt into one another as in a dream.

Because rain, fog, and haze are more tangible than dry air and have a color and texture of their own, landscapes seen through them tend also to look more unified. Their diversity notwithstanding, English scenes often look composed and organized. So Gilpin describes haze as "that thin, dubious veil, which . . . hides nothing. It only sweetens the hues of nature—it gives a consequence to every common object, by giving it a more indistinct form—it corrects the glare of colours—it softens the harshness of lines; and above all, it throws over the face of landscape that harmonizing tint, which blends the whole into unity, and repose." [16]

The effect of moisture finally is to throw things into the distance. Thus the London atmosphere, in James's words, "flatters and superfuses, makes everything brown, rich, dim, vague, magnifies distances and minimizes details." [17] Even when seen close up, objects in England frequently seem to be far away; detail is lost, foreground vanishes, the distant prospect dominates. As Gilpin put it, "English landscape affords a species of *rich distance*, which is rarely to be found in any other country." [18] This is the dominant aspect of English scenery; indeed, without distance there would be no scenery, only objects. "Why do those cliffs of shadowy tint appear / More sweet than all the landscape smiling near? / 'Tis *distance* lends enchantment to the view." [19] Openness admits distance, atmosphere emphasizes and organizes it, variety and regularity are both subsumed by it.

Recurrent Themes

Diverse as it is, the English landscape is largely made up of cultural features whose configurations are everywhere alike, or at least so similar that they are instantly recognizable. Among the most important of these elements are hedged and walled fields, which provide a general matrix; villages and council estates; suburban and semi-detached houses; seaside resorts; coalfield industrial districts; and parklands. Some of

16 William Gilpin: *Observations, Relative Chiefly to Picturesque Beauty, Made in the Year 1772, on several Parts of England; Particularly the Mountains, and Lakes of Cumberland and Westmoreland* (2 vols.; London, 1786), Vol. 1, p. 11.
17 Henry James: *Essays in London and Elsewhere* (New York, 1893), p. 14.
18 Gilpin, *op. cit.* [see footnote 16 above], Vol. 1, p. 8.
19 Thomas Campbell, "The Pleasure of Hope" (1799), as quoted in Norman Nicholson: *The Lakers: The Adventures of the First Tourists* (London, 1955), p. 45, footnote 1. (Our italics.)

these features are small in size and countrywide in distribution; others
are large-scale and more regionally distributed; the descriptions below
proceed from the specific to the general but otherwise follow no particular order.

The fabric of rural England is composed of fields and pastures enclosed by rectilinear hawthorn hedges. To be specific, some 616,000
miles of hedgerows enclose 80 percent of England's agricultural land. [20]
Hedgerows lend the countryside an air of "orderliness without sever-
ity," [21] of composition without constraint. The large, rectangular fields
of the English Midlands, with hedges neatly trimmed to a height of
five feet and planted at regular intervals with oak, ash, and elm, were
created by Parliamentary enclosures in the late eighteenth and early
nineteenth centuries. Elsewhere the pattern differs. In the southwest,
in the Welsh borderlands, and in parts of Kent, Essex, and East Anglia
hedges are older and denser, fields much smaller and less regularly
shaped. In the limestone and sandstone country of the north and west
fields are bounded by stone walls. But hedges and stone walls together
so dominate the countryside that one feels something is missing when
fields stretch without interruption, as in the Fens—where hedges were
never planted—or on open moors.

Over most of rural England far more people live in compact villages
and hamlets than on isolated farms. But the village is characteristic of
the English countryside in a more important sense. It is not a mere
incident on the highway; the road through it bends or turns or halts.
The English village is a definite structured place with a distinct focus
and a recognizable beginning and end. [22] Local building materials and
vernacular styles of architecture make coherent the remnants of centuries and give visual expression to parochialism.

Not all rural villages rest content with simple harmony. In many
winding streets pride of place is occupied by furniture borrowed from
an urban scene—concrete lamp standards, monumental bus stations,
fortresslike public conveniences, pompous war memorials, and beds of
geraniums in municipal traffic circles. Other villages assume an urban
appearance from the style and arrangement of their buildings: here,
houses are substantially built, bold in scale, with harsh facades or
ostentatious decoration; there, unsoftened by trees or shrubs, geometrically placed residential rows disrupt the informal order of a rural
setting.

In country as well as in town, houses built by local authorities have
an uncompromising urban look. No two council estates are exactly

[20] Norman U. Moore: Our Disappearing Hedgerows, *Country-Side*, N.S. Vol. 19,
1962, p. 321.
[21] Edmund Blunden: The Landscape in *England's Heritage* (by Adrian Bell and
others; London, 1961 [paperback]), pp. 13-39; reference on p. 27.
[22] Thomas Sharp: *The Anatomy of the Village* (Harmondsworth, Middlesex, 1946),
pp. 7-9.

alike, yet the type is unmistakable. Whether as terraced rows in a village street or as large, self-contained communities, they are everywhere arrayed in curved regularities. Predominantly of red brick and tile, buildings are similar in height, proportions, and color, and—despite superficial differences in decor—are bleak, regimented, and monotonous. [23]

No feature of the English architectural landscape is more characteristic, or more incongruous, than the semi-detached house. This compromise between row or terraced housing and separate or detached houses first appeared about three centuries ago as improved dwellings for farm workmen on estates. It commends itself today as a way of combining privacy (each family has its own roof over its head; access to back door and garden is around the side of the house) with space saving (less land is needed than for detached houses), but the enduring popularity of the semi-detached probably owes more to habit, lethargy, and snobbery.

Visually these houses have little to commend them. Indeed, British architects have long viewed the semi-detached as an obdurate anomaly, the form least capable of arrangement into satisfactory patterns, or of conformity with any preexisting landscape. [24] "Semis" stand out more than solitary houses: they are up to twice as large, more angular, generally taller. Almost all English semis are twins—houses divided vertically into two symmetrical halves. The individuality of each half depends on the fences, on the style of porch or windows, more often on the decoration. One half may be half-timbered, the other pebbledash. But the division straight down the middle makes the structure more emphatic than if the two halves were identical. Efforts to make each pair of semis distinctively unlike its neighbors are more successful, but the most elaborate contrivances, the most strenuous facade work, do not obliterate the inherent uniformity of the type. Even the fantastically differentiated semis strung along many major highways can at once be recognized by their siting and by their pretensions to be different from one another and anything but contemporary. [25] All over

---

[23] So the largest housing estate in the world is described; see Peter Willmott: *The Evolution of a Community: A Study of Dagenham after Forty Years* (London, 1963), p. 1. Other examples are illustrated in Stanley Gale: *Modern Housing Estates: A Practical Guide to their Planning, Design and Development* (London, New York, etc., 1949).

[24] Patrick Abercrombie: *Greater London Plan 1944* (London, 1945), p. 181.

[25] ". . . here are some quaint gables culled from Art Nouveau . . . ; there the twisted beams and leaded panes of Stockbrokers Tudor are happily contrasted with bright green tiles of obviously Pseudish origin; next door some terra-cotta plaques, Pont Street Dutch in character, enliven a white wood Wimbledon Transitional porch, making it a splendid foil to a red brick garage that is vaguely Romanesque in feeling" (Osbert Lancaster: *Here, of All Places* [Boston, 1958], p. 152). For illustrations of typical suburban semis see Olive Cook and Edwin Smith: English Suburban, *The Saturday Book*, Vol. 22 (edited by John Hadfield) [London], 1962, pp. 120-140.

England stand these ungainly symmetrical buildings, marshaled in serried rows, in pairs, or occasionally even in rural isolation.

Another persistent theme in the English townscape, a companion feature to village borrowings from the urban scene, is *rus in urbe*—in detail, the rustic residence; in mass, the dormitory suburb. The garden-city idea germinated in England, and a rustic ideal dominates the architecture and layout of much of the urban and suburban scene. It takes several forms. In London, royal parks form broad green vistas leading to the center of the capital. Georgian squares give surrounding houses views into private gardens, and Nash's spectacular terraces are ranged around four hundred acres of landscaped Regent's Park. In effect, "one is in the country. It is difficult, anywhere, to be more than fifty yards from a tree." [26] In Belsize Park, Hampstead, Wimbledon, and the Surrey sand country, Victorian mansions and villas are set in spacious grounds shaded by tall trees and dense shrubbery. In most English cities rural nostalgia—or at least the suburban notion of rural—displays itself in log benches and wooden fences, roughhewn surfaces, small-scale floral displays, and other attributes of the municipal rustic style. Finally, millions of small houses, each with securely hedged back and front gardens, give substance to the aspiration that an Englishman's home should be his castle, most desirably a castle commanding a rural principality.

The rural ideal is also manifest in low-density housing, in building layout, in gardens stuffed with jungly trees and ceramic gnomes and toadstools, and in rustic styles of ornament. Houses incorporate real or fancied features of rural buildings: gabled fronts, half-timbered and diminutive upper stories, clustered chimneys, leaded panes in windows, lanterns at the door, dovecotes over the garage. And like country houses, they bear names, not street numbers, to emphasize their individuality and to rescue their occupants from suburban anonymity.

In its own inimitable jolly way the English seaside resort is as distinctive and pervasive as the rural village. England has a long, deeply indented coastline. Tidal waters penetrate far inland, seagulls follow the plow above fields in Leicestershire, and no part of the country lies a hundred miles from the sea. Coastal resorts are approached through acres of caravans and lanes of bungalows and chalets. The seafront, with its cast-iron pier, its pavilion and promenade, is lined with grandiose hotels parading gaily painted Moorish balconies, striped awnings, emerald cupolas, and palm-court interiors. In the side streets, ice-cream parlors and fish-and-chips shops jostle with amusement arcades and novelty bazaars. On the beach, peddlers, donkey carts, Punch-and-Judy shows, and bathing huts crowd among deck chairs and throngs of children. From Blackpool to Brighton, from Torquay to

[26] V. S. Pritchett: *London Perceived* ([London and] New York, 1962), p. 8.

Skegness, all seaside resorts sell their "special" rock candy and cater to crowds who seek a little sunbathing, less swimming, and solitude not at all, but rather the English image, of which the Brighton pavilion is the exemplar, of an essentially urban Oriental pleasure ground.[27]

One reason seaside resorts are so gay is perhaps that many other English towns are so drab. Fully four-fifths of the population live in cities, most of them the creation of the past two centuries and numbingly dreary to look at. Most blatant are the coalfield industrial districts, compared with which all other English scenes are gardens. In the tormented landscapes stretching from Wolverhampton to Wallsend and from St. Helen's to Sheffield live almost as many people as in Greater London. They are hemmed in by jagged skylines of slag heaps, pit mounds, piles of scrap iron, belching stacks, and blast furnaces; slippery paths of mud and cinders tread their way through tangles of coal tramways, inky canals, and back alleys; row upon row of grimy slate-roofed dwellings huddle between railway embankments and factories. "This mournful place" is Dickens' Black Country, whose "dark depressing influence . . . filled them with a dismal gloom. On every side, and as far as the eye could see into the heavy distance, tall chimneys, crowding on each other, and presenting that endless repetition of the same dull, ugly form . . . poured out their plague of smoke, obscured the light, and made foul the melancholy air".[28] All the grim elements of that era are still to be seen, further brutalized by decay and dereliction.

What makes this battlefield so forbidding is the concentration of these elements to a degree hardly imaginable even in the industrial wastelands of, say, New Jersey. The squalor of the Black Country and its outliers transcends the merely ugly; the whole landscape seems torn apart by some demonic force, and a perverse and noxious climate suitably embellishes the corrupt creations of man and nature. The Black Country, which many view as an almost unbelievable fantasy, is in its own way exhilarating.[29]

The "sense of unknown horror in this weird gloom" is enhanced, as Henry Adams recognized a century ago, by "the violent contrast be-

[27] See Yvonne Cloud, edit.: *Beside the Seaside: Six Variations* (London, 1934); John Piper: *Buildings and Prospects* (London, 1948), pp. 11-34 ("The Nautical Style"); Barbara Jones: *The Unsophisticated Arts* ([London] 1951), pp. 69-92 ("Beside the Sea"). A British Travel and Holidays Association survey showed that 72 percent of the people who took holidays in the United Kingdom in 1955 went to seaside resorts ("Holidays in 1955" [London, 1956], p. 8).
[28] Charles Dickens: *The Old Curiosity Shop* (London and New York, 1907), pp. 326-327. For a good contemporary picture see Walter Allen: *The Black Country* (London, 1946), p. 14.
[29] George Orwell: *The Road to Wigan Pier* (Harmondsworth, Middlesex, 1962 [paperback]), p. 94; *idem: England Your England and Other Essays* (London, 1954), pp. 27-29; J. B. Priestley: *English Journey* (London, 1934), pp. 336 and 398-399.

tween this dense, smoky, impenetrable darkness, and the soft green charm" of the countryside in some places within a stone's throw.[30] The industrial conurbations of the north "all abut on paradise."[31] Discontinuities between town and country are particularly striking where lines of back-to-back tenements loom up suddenly in an area of abandoned mines, as crowded and noisome in their lonely desolation as if they were in Birmingham or Stoke on Trent.

The "dark Satanic mills," however, are not what lovers of the English landscape nowadays principally curse. "'This sceptre'd isle, this earth of majesty, this something or other Eden.'" quotes a character in "Vile Bodies." "Nina looked down and saw inclined at an odd angle a horizon of straggling red suburb; arterial roads dotted with little cars; factories . . .; a disused canal; some distant hills sown with bungalows; wireless masts and overhead power cables . . . 'I think I'm going to be sick,' said Nina."[32] This is twentieth-century urban England, of glass, aluminum, chrome, and the pink bungaloid of bypasses and arterial roads, the standardized monotony of the New World. It is perhaps less apparent to a visitor because it is still less widespread than elsewhere. And its importance in the landscape has perhaps been exaggerated by the postwar shift from railways to roads, on which an increasing proportion of the English now travel. Many of Britain's railways traverse countryside so pristine that nature lovers seek to turn derelict railroad lines into footpaths. But because the roads go from town to town, the automobile traveler sees a predominantly built-up matrix. Not realizing that much of the land in between is still almost as it was, he overestimates the recent encroachment on rural England.

While urban England often seeks to appear in a rustic guise, much of rural England dresses in quaint or decorative costume—it is a tourists' land, full of minsters and manors. In thousands of landscaped parks the spectator can easily identify the "superimposition of a 3-D diorama after Claude on an acreage of agriculture."[33] Despite war and austerity, income taxes and death duties, parklands still cover much of the English landscape. Their clumps of trees on shaven lawns, stretches of ornamental water, cascades, temples, folly towers, vistas sweeping up to great houses, drives and imposing entrance gates, model villages, and highway diversions are all contrived to create a visual impression.[34]

[30] Henry Adams: *The Education of Henry Adams: An Autobiography* (Boston and New York, 1918), p. 72.
[31] Joseph Fry: Look, Stranger, at This Island Now, *Sunday Times*, London, Jan. 5, 1964, p. 35.
[32] Evelyn Waugh: *Vile Bodies* (Harmondsworth, Middlesex, 1938) [paperback], pp. 199-200.
[33] Rayner Benham: Kent and Capability, *New Statesman*, Dec. 7, 1962, p. 842.
[34] See Hugh C. Prince: Parkland in the Chilterns, *Geogr. Rev.*, Vol. 49, 1959, pp. 18-31.

Some park landscapes are firmly separated from the surrounding countryside by belt plantings and high fences, but others blend with the ornamental farmland, the *ferme ornée*, designed as a garden for visual pleasure while operating as a farm for profit. "Why may not a whole estate be thrown into a kind of garden by frequent plantations?" asked Addison; [35] many landowners, small as well as great, have taken up this challenge with some degree of success. They have planted stands of timber on hillcrests, clothed disused quarries and marl pits with majestic beeches, restored—or built—ruins as diverting eye-catchers, sited farmhouses with an eye for the picturesque, placed livestock so as to animate the landscape, and, on occasion, selected miniature fawn Channel Island cattle to increase the sense of distance. [36]

Other farmers ornament the countryside less self-consciously: in early summer their hedges of hawthorn and dog rose are laden with white and pink blossoms, in autumn ablaze with hips, haws, and scarlet holly berries, in winter neatly cut and laid; snowdrops, bluebells, and celandines grow in copses and in the corners of fields; cedar and chestnut adorn grounds around farmhouses.

The English landscape is altogether so tamed, trimmed, and humanized as to give the impression of a vast ornamental farm, as if the whole of it had been designed for visual pleasure. Hedgerows, stone walls, and roads contain vistas, model contours, reinforce contrasts between textures and colors of adjacent fields, and link contrasting landscapes, as in the Yorkshire Dales, where limestone wall, "unbroken and continuous from every tram terminus to the last wilderness of bog and cloud," [37] carry the eye from grassy valley bottom up to untenanted heath and rocky cliff. Riverbanks and roadsides are trimmed and grass-verged; villages are self-contained, street facades unbroken. Although it has few strong vertical lines, the English landscape looks both architectural and tidy. Even suburbs that spread into open countryside are seldom scattered at random but are arranged neatly along roads or contours.

In an issue devoted to "Man-Made America," the editors of the *Architectural Review* term the American landscape "a universe of uncontrollable chaos inhabited by happy accidents." [38] To an American visitor the English landscape seems a world of ordered beauty obscured only here and there by sad contrivances.

· · · · ·

[35] Joseph Addison in the *Spectator*, 1712, quoted in James Lees-Milne: *Earls of Creation: Five Great Patrons of Eighteenth-Century Art* (London, 1962), p. 141.
[36] Dorothy Stroud: *Humphry Repton* (London, 1962), p. 107; Derek Clifford: *A History of Garden Design* (London, 1962), p. 139; Humphry Repton: *Observations on the Theory and Practice of Landscape Gardening* (London, 1803), p. 6.
[37] Priestley, *op. cit.* [see footnote 29 above], p. 154.
[38] *Architectural Rev.*, Vol. 108, 1950, pp. 339-343.

Amenity—The Key

To summarize the relationships between the English people and their landscape, the word "amenity" offers a key. Few terms are so loosely employed in England, yet every usage carries some overtone of its Latin root, connoting pleasure. "Amenity" serves to denote almost any kind of interest in a place and any inherent value that transcends purely economic considerations. It is attached to whatever seems to need protection. In one town the "amenities" are historic buildings and the flavor of the past, in another open spaces, in a third views and vistas, elsewhere facilities for recreation or access to nearby points of scenic interest. The portmanteau quality of the term gives the public a sense of common cause against those to whom land is merely a marketable commodity. Why restrict caravan sites? To preserve seashore amenities. Why place electric pylons here rather than there? To preserve the amenities of the landscape. Not everything done for amenity's sake is well done or unanimously liked, but it is all thought to be well meant.

Most amenities in this small and densely populated country depend for their existence on the English talent for compromise. Clashes of interest over land use are not only tolerable but endlessly negotiable. Owners and nonowners, producers and consumers, recognize that their interests dovetail as well as differ, and generally settle disputes without undue stress. In Wordsworth's day the Lake District was regarded as "a sort of national property in which every man has a right and an interest who has an eye to perceive and a heart to enjoy."[39] That concept now extends to almost the whole English countryside.

Government departments are in general highly sensitive to amenity interests. For example, naturalists oppose a plan for a power-booster station on the bank of the Severn near Gloucester on a spot containing an acre of bladderwort, "an extremtly rare plant with pretty yellow flowers that eat insects. ... We have also a pair of marshwarblers nesting on the site and would like them left alone if possible." This mild plea causes great concern at the Central Electricity Generating Board: "We didn't know there was bladderwort on the site when we bought it, but we always try to be as helpful and as co-operative as possible in cases like this."[40]

To keep the local scene wire-free, the Friends of the Lake District recently fought to get an electricity line through Upper Borrowdale placed underground, offering to defray part of the additional cost. After a public inquiry, the Minister of Power gave permission for overhead lines along only about one thousand yards of the route. But

[39] William Wordsworth, as quoted in Bracey, *Industry and the Countryside*, p. 182.
[40] "The Bladderwort at Bay," *Guardian*, Nov. 2, 1962.

the North-Western Electricity Board was so "impressed by the extent of the anxiety aroused" by this threat to the beauty of Upper Borrowdale that it put the whole line underground on its own initiative.[41] By contrast, the residents of a New England village recently offered to pay the entire cost of undergrounding in order not to disfigure a fine local landscape; the power company admitted that the underground line offered no technical problem and would outlast an overhead grid, but rejected the proposal as unwarrantable interference with its affairs.

No English concern, private or public, could afford to treat the public as outsiders in any landscape. Practical men concerned with affairs of moment seem positively beleaguered sometimes by lovers of the countryside. "Whenever and wherever the Air Ministry want to establish a range," complained an Air Marshal, "one always finds that the site selected is the only habitat of some rare bird, or the only place where someone can train racehorses, or that there is some other excellent local reason" for leaving it alone.[42] But the compromise is not all on one side. Those anxious to preserve the landscape have learned not to expect too much. "How do you get rid of dandelions?" asks a gardener ruefully surveying his domain. "You can't get rid of dandelions," comes the answer. "You must learn to love them." [43]

It is not weeds, however, but man-made objects that the British have had to learn to live with. They do not always succeed. Mais relates how he finally came to admire the electricity pylons he once abominated, but doubts whether he could ever come to love gosometers.[44] Yet there are those that do. And landscape architecture helps roads, power lines, dams, and other technological paraphernalia fit into, and even enhance, the landscapes they traverse.[45] There is room even for those dandelions of the human landscape, automobiles and trailers, as long as they conform in location, color, and layout to the requirements of the local scene.[46]

Just as they accommodate industrial artifacts to attractive rural landscapes, so the English find something potentially worthwhile in the dreariest wastelands. In worked-out mining country subsidence pits become lakes and ponds, noxious marshes are drained to create pasture and heathland, and colliery tips, when pioneer vegetation colonizes

[41] *Thirty-Fifth Ann. Rept. Council for the Preservation of Rural England, 1960-1961,* Vol. 17, No. 3, p. 22.
[42] J. C. Slessor: *Proposed Range in the Hebrides, The Times,* Sept. 20, 1955, p. 9.
[43] R. J. Taylor, in *Report of Proceedings,* Conference of National Park Authorities, May 4-5, 1961, p. 25.
[44] S. P. B. Mais: The Plain Man Looks at England, in *Britain and the Beast,* pp. 212-224; reference on p. 221.
[45] See Sylvia Crowe's "The Landscape of Power" (London, 1958) and "The Landscape of Roads" (London, 1960).
[46] Caravan Sites and Control of Development Act, 1960.

their distinctive topography, embellish flat terrain as intriguing landmarks.[47] No landscape is abandoned as beyond hope.

It is in their general attachment to amenities that the English best
display the commingling of private and public interests, of local and
national values, that makes England a settled and comfortable land.

12. The American West

Walter Prescott Webb

*Some historians, particularly frontier historians, have been
concerned with describing the natural environment as a factor
in history. One of the best of these from the geographic
point of view is Walter Prescott Webb, whose description of
the West gives one as clear a word picture of the area
as the previous selection does for England.*

This is an attempt to discover what the West is and why it is that way.
We shall not approach it from the outside; we shall begin in the
middle, because that is where its dominating force—The Desert—re-
sides.

Fortunately the West is no longer a shifting frontier, but a region
that can be marked off on a map, traveled to, and seen. Everybody
knows when he gets there. It starts in the second tier of states west of
the Big River. A line drawn from the southern tip of Texas to the
farther boundary of central North Dakota marks roughly its eastern
boundary. It starts almost in the tropics; it reaches almost to the
northern limits of the Temperate Zone. Hemmed in by Canada on the
north and Mexico on the south, it runs with the sun to the Pacific. It
comprises more than half of the nation's area—all or part of seventeen
very large states. The air-line distance around it is one-fifth the distance around the earth. This is the West, as distinguished from the
other two great regions, the North and the South.

Internally the West is divided into three strips, laid one beside the
other on a north-south axis—a mountain strip in the center flanked by
the Great Plains strip to the east and the Pacific slope strip to the west.
These gigantic natural features give variety and part of the character
to the country; but they do not explain it, either separately or in

SOURCE: *Harper's Magazine*, CCXIV (May, 1957), 25-31. The author (deceased)
was professor of history at the University of Texas.
[47] Kenneth Browne: Dereliction, *Architectural Rev.*, Vol. 118, 1955, pp. 305-311.

combination. One can never understand the West—all of it—in terms of the rolling plains, the craggy mountains, or the slope to the sea, for none is common to the entire region. They divide rather than unify; they do not bind the West to its inevitable destiny.

The overriding influence that shapes the West is the desert. That is its one unifying force. It permeates the plains, climbs to all but the highest mountain peaks, dwells continuously in the valleys, and plunges down the Pacific slope to argue with the sea.

The desert is the guest that came to dinner, never to go away. It has stripped the mountains of their vegetation, making them "rocky"; it has dried up the inland seas, leaving Death Valley completely dry and Lake Bonneville a briny fragment in Great Salt Lake. It is the great designer of the American West, painting the landscape with color, chiseling the mesas and pinnacles, building the plains with soil washed down by perishing rivers such as the Platte and Canadian. It shortened the grass on its borders before destroying it in the interior. It never permitted trees on the plains it built, and where it found them it beat them down to sage and brush, reducing the leaves to thorns and the

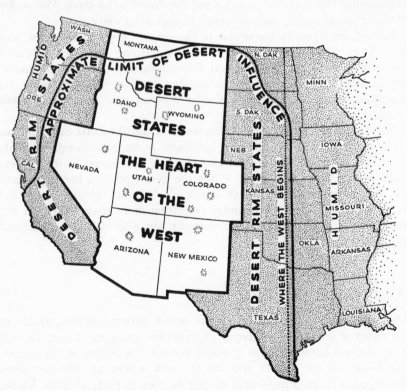

The Dominance of the Desert.

sap to grease and oil. The trees it could not destroy it shriveled, and those it could not shrivel it petrified.

The desert designed the animals as it shaped the land. It compelled its creatures to conform to its colors, put horns on toads, made snakes travel sidewise to keep from sinking in the sand, created grasshoppers that fly five miles for a sprig of grass. It made them all parsimonious of water. The rabbits require little if any, the antelope do without for long periods, some rodents and plants (like the Joshua tree) manufacture and store their own. The little prairie dog is a desert masterpiece. He is a misnamed squirrel, because the Americans who named him could not believe that a squirrel would live in a dugout. As for water, he will not touch the stuff. What is *at the heart* of the West? Where is the center from which the shaping force and power radiate? The answer is simple if we would only see and accept it. The heart of the West *is* a desert, unqualified and absolute. Draw a line anywhere from the region's eastern boundary to the Pacific, stand on its midpoint, and you will find yourself either in the desert or near it.

If we do not understand the West it is because we perversely refuse to recognize this fact; we do not want the desert to be there. We prefer to loiter on its edges, skirt it, avoid it, and even deny it.

Instead, let us go to the center of the desert's greatest intensity, and from there measure the radius of its diminishing influence. There it lies around us in all its terror and desolate beauty, its sands shimmering in the distance, its mirages playing tricks with our vision, its mountains etched against the sky, a crosscut saw with some teeth knocked out.

This is the best of the desert, the worst of the West. Its radius varies because the desert expands and contracts, as its enemy—rain—retreats or advances. Always at its margins there is dampness, at its borders moisture, at its limits wetness. When the desert pokes a hot finger into the border regions, the people speak of drought; when it pulls the finger back, they say "the country is getting more seasonable." At the heart of the desert there is no drought, there is only an occasional mitigation of dryness.

What Nobody Mentions

The influence of the desert from the center outward is comparable to the effect of a fire. If we keep a gigantic fire going for a long enough time, we will have where it was and around it a replica of the American West. In the center will be an area where all life has been destroyed, a charred mass such as may be seen in parts of Utah, Idaho, and Nevada. Beyond that will be a series of concentric circles where the destruction decreases as the distance grows. While the fire is burning you can escape its heat by going outward from it, or by going upward. So today, in the mountain state, you may go above it.

For a million years a fire of low intensity has been burning, and is still burning, in the West. It is broader and more intense in the south, narrower and somewhat cooler in the north. It covers the eight central states marked "desert states" on the map, and it scorches the near side of their flanking neighbors—the rim states, east and west—giving all nine of them large desert areas.

This analogy of the fire is useful because fire, like the desert, is a positive thing. We have usually explained the West in negative terms, lack of wetness, rather than by the presence of dryness. We have adopted a series of progressively wetter terms, arid, semi-arid, and subhumid—to describe the relative distance from the devil of dryness. Our aversion to deserts has led us into deceitful euphemisms, the lifted verbal hand shielding off the uncomfortable heat of reality. Let us here be realistic and divide the West in two categories, Desert States and Desert-rim States.

We have not always been dishonest about the presence of the desert. The early explorers thought they knew one when they saw it. They called it by name, and until after the Civil War they put it on school maps. Before the middle of the sixteenth century, Coronado wrote: "It was the Lord's pleasure that, after having journeyed across these deserts seventy-seven days, I arrived at . . . Quivera." From Montana territory, Ordway of the Lewis and Clark expedition confided to his journal that "this country may with propriety be called the Deserts of North America." Zebulon Pike, farther south, said, "These vast plains . . . may become as celebrated as the sandy deserts of Africa." In 1859 Horace Greeley wrote from the buffalo range that "we are in a desert indeed." By 1835 the school maps showed the Great American Desert in block letters east of the Rockies. By 1850 such men as Daniel Webster and Jefferson Davis conceded its existence, and staked their political fortunes on their belief.

After the Civil War the Great American Desert was abolished. It has hardly been mentioned in polite Western society since, and *never* by the Chambers of Commerce. Of course, there were some small tourist deserts left, such as the Mohave and the Jornada Del Muerto, but nothing of consequence. The desert did not know it had been abolished; it waited patiently as puny men moved in from all sides to conquer it. Enough time has now elapsed to reveal the results of this impertinence.

While the annual rainfall for each state has not been found in the reference books, we do have it for selected cities, at least one in each state. These figures are a little high, because the larger cities are likely to be in the region of most rainfall. Though the figures are not exact, they are significant.

AVERAGE ANNUAL PRECIPITATION

8 Desert States	12.00"	semi-arid
6 Eastern Rim States	24.20"	subhumid
3 Western Rim States	26.48"	subhumid

The Desert States barely escape the true desert mark of 10 inches. The rim states are subhumid. The average for the entire West is 20 inches, the upper limit of the semi-arid.

The significant thing about these figures is that they form a pattern which matches nearly all the yardsticks we use to measure the assets of a civilization. The pattern of precipitation is relatively high in the rim states and low in the desert states. The same is true of people, bank deposits, factories, cities, horses, mules, cattle, and all farm crops. (One exception is sheep; there are more sheep per square mile in the desert states than in either rim. The same is true of hard minerals.)

When this pattern is drawn, the West, especially in its desert part, appears as a depressed region. The rim states are populous and rich as compared to the vast interior. The rim states of Texas and California have about twenty million people as against less than six million for the eight desert states. Texas has about thirty persons per square mile, California about sixty-eight, but the desert states have only six. Texas and California combined had as of 1951 bank assets or liabilities of about $25 billion, as against less than $6 billion for the eight desert states with nearly twice the area.

These figures indicate what the desert has done to those who set out to conquer it. It emerges in its true character as a great interior force—repelling to people and repulsive to wealth in nearly all forms. Though surrounded and beleagured, the Great American Desert has not been conquered; instead it has shaped the lives and destinies of those who went against it. That is what Major John Wesley Powell saw when he wrote in 1878 that "a new phase of Aryan civilization is being developed in the western half of America."

The First Defeats

If the figures above have given the impression that the rim states have escaped the desert or conquered it, and are now safe beyond the danger line, that impression must be corrected. To correct it, we need to look at man's first general attack, that of the 1880s, which coincided with a wet cycle in the West. Since the attackers came from the humid country, they struck the eastern rim states first. They went single-handed, with high hopes; they returned before the onslaught of the drought, empty-handed. A. M. Simmons summed up the campaign in these words:

From the 98th meridian west to the Rocky Mountains there is a stretch of country filled with more tragedy and whose future is pregnant with greater promise than perhaps any other equal expanse of territory within the confines of the Western Hemisphere.

The disorderly charge and the ensuing rout were thus described:

Following times of occasional rainy season, the line of social advance rose and fell with rain and drought, like a mighty tide beating against the wall of the Rockies. And every such wave left behind it a mass of human wreckage in the shape of broken fortunes, deserted farms, and ruined homes.

Later, Frederick H. Newell said: "The Great Plains can be characterized as a region of periodic famine."

The attackers withdrew, but returned with two new allies, science and invention. By ingenuity they would destroy the desert in spite of hell and without water. They made headway in the rim-land by inventing barbed wire, adapting the windmill, learning about dry farming, importing desert plants, reshaping their plows, and revising their laws.

Their hopes always outran their accomplishments. What was discovered today would enable them to complete the conquest tomorrow. In the face of tragedy they became superstitious or religious, and called in the rain-makers with magic, dynamite, and prayer, and later with a chemical calculated to make a dry cloud give water.

The federal government enlisted on the side of The People *vs.* The Desert. It sought dam sites and blocked the rivers to create tiny islands of water in a sea of aridity. In the meantime the well-drillers were probing the earth to discover every aquifer, or underground water deposit. Pumps were installed to bring up water for homes, cities, and irrigation, and every source of water—whether from river, lake, or well—was declared to be "everlasting."

Regardless of the source of the water, its major effect was to create an oasis, a lovely word implying a pleasant place in the midst of a larger and less pleasant one. In and around the oasis people came to build towns and cities, establish industry, and open irrigated farms. This has happened all over the West, so that the West is today virtually an oasis civilization.

The concept of the oasis has not apparently been used in reference to the West, and cannot be used as long as we persist in denying the desert. The Chambers of Commerce would not be pleased if we referred to such oases of elevation as Denver, Boulder, and Rapid City; of such river oases as Santa Fe and El Paso; of the spring-made oasis of San Antonio; of the man-made oasis of Boulder City, Nevada; or of the well-based (and probably temporary) oasis of Lubbock, Texas. Los Angeles is the greatest oasis of them all.

One of the paradoxes of the West is that with its excess of land and dearth of people, it is already an urban society. The eight desert states are 54.9 per cent urban. Only Montana, Wyoming, and Idaho are rural. Utah, with only 8.4 people per square mile, is 65.3 per cent urban; Nevada, with only 1.5 persons per square mile, is 57.2 per cent urban. The desert has driven the people in to the oasis.

Within the desert states, the people have not overdrawn their water supply. They have struck a balance with their possibilities. This is not true in the rim states where the great cities are. Today most of these cities have outgrown their water supply and are in crisis. They have exhausted the water that made the original oasis, and their problem now is to find more at any cost. They go farther and farther to get it, and bring it in at increasing expense. Here are some examples.

Los Angeles is in an area of about 16 inches of rainfall. "Fresh water issuing from the hills led to the choice of the original site." It was begun on the little river of its name. The people congregated here and consumed the original supply of water. In 1913 the Los Angeles aqueduct was completed across the Sierra Nevada range to a new source 233 miles distant. The original cost for the aqueduct alone was $25,-000,000. The city outgrew this supply, and in 1939 an aqueduct was built to the Colorado, 242 miles away at a cost of $200,000,000. But this is not enough, and a plan is afoot to tap the waters of the Columbia, in the northwest, to enlarge or save the oasis of southern California.

El Paso began as a river oasis on the Rio Grande. As it grew the upstream water was pumped out, and the river failed. The underground water was tapped, to fail in turn. The government built Elephant Butte Dam to catch the floodwater, but it cannot keep the river running. Today El Paso is acquiring dam sites in the Guadalupe Mountains, one hundred miles east; it is leasing underground water from the University of Texas lands in Hudspeth County, forty miles from the city.

San Antonio, a real rim city with close to 30 inches of rainfall, was created by the living springs that gushed out to form the San Pedro and San Antonio rivers—tiny but dependable streams. Later the city got its water from artesian wells of tremendous head and volume. Today San Pedro Springs are completely dry; the San Antonio Springs are reduced to a token, and the rivers they fed are gone. The water table has fallen, the artesian wells no longer flow. The city has few good dam sites in its territory, and is desperately pleading with the state water board to let it acquire water from the Guadalupe River basin fifty miles away.

The visitor is always shown the San Antonio River which winds through the heart of the city. The river is, so far as the visitor can see, an exotic thing; its sides are curbed, its low banks a riot of tropical plants. Boats ply back and forth carrying tourists to points of interest. The river flows full here, almost level with its curb—full of water now being pumped from the wells which are no longer artesian. This is the price a proud and beautiful rim city is paying to perpetuate its oasis-like character.

Dallas never shows anybody the little river on which it was born, the rat-tailed Trinity that served it well for a time. Dallas too is a proud city, consciously cultured, not joyously relaxed and playful like San Antonio, or boisterous and natural like its own near-neighbor, Fort Worth. Dallas will probably deny that it is an oasis, what with its 30-plus inches of rainfall. But let us look at its water problem: Before it outgrew the Trinity, it found an "everlasting" supply in artesian wells which have now failed or become inadequate. It began to build dams, but not in time to meet the drought. In desperation Dallas built a pipeline to the Red River, which gathers its waters high up on the salty plains and semi-desert. Today a glass of Dallas water left overnight has a saline scum on the surface in the morning. Peddlers of potable imported water have done well at fifty cents a gallon.

The last example is the underground oasis of Lubbock, Texas. There is no spring near, and it is many miles to a river. Lubbock stands on the High Plains where the annual rainfall is about 18 inches. It grew like a mushroom because a state college was built there, oil was discovered, and an "everlasting" supply of water was found underneath the fertile soil. This High Plains aquifer is of enormous extent, making possible a giant oasis covering several counties. Turbine pumps whir day and night, pouring out streams from 4 to 8 inches in diameter. Crop yields are enormous. This is the story of the rise of an oasis based on ground water.

The story of the fall cannot be told because it has not happened. Lubbock sees the crisis coming, and is trying to avert it by acquiring water rights in the sandhills to the west. The water table is falling as new wells go down and old ones are deepened.

The story of the five cities could be continued with variations all around the semi-arid rim of the arid region. It is a story of cities that got a little too close, all haunted now by a growing consciousness that in every oasis the desert rides outside. What lies outside was described by a real authority, none other than Moses. "And thy heaven that is over thy head shall be brass, and the earth that is under thee shall be iron. The Lord shall make the rain of thy land powder and dust: from heaven shall it come down upon thee, until thou be destroyed."

What the West Hasn't Got

Once we recognize the desert as the major force in the American West, we are able to understand its history. With our feet planted firmly on a desert base, what hitherto seemed strange, irrational, bizarre, becomes logical and reasonable. Granted the prevailing influence of the desert, it is obvious that the West is in comparison to the East a land of deficiencies. It is full of negatives and short on positives. This obvious fact was first noted by examining ten standard school histories to see the relative amount of space devoted to the western three-fifths of the country occupied by a little more than one-fifth of the people.

The results were unbelievable. At one extreme the West got one and one-half pages out of a hundred: at the other extreme it got fifteen. The average for the ten books was six or seven pages out of a hundred. This disparity could not be explained by either bias or ignorance or prejudice of the authors, but it had to be explained, made logical and reasonable.

Below is a list of the positives and negatives of the West:

NEGATIVES	POSITIVES
Water	Land
Timber	Grass
Cities	Minerals
Industry	Natural Wonders
Labor	Indians
Negroes	Orientals

A study of these columns give a clue to the brevity of Western history. The scarcity of water, timber, cities, industry, labor, and Negroes in the desert means the absence of many problems about which historians write. Their presence in the rim states is considerable. For example, practically all the timber is in East Texas, Oklahoma, and the three Pacific states. The Negro problem exists only in Texas and California, and it did not come to California until after World War I. Manufacturing amounts to only 14 per cent of the national total—and since there is little manufacturing, there is little to say about labor.

The column of positives gives us the main subjects about which the historians must write. Three of them—land, minerals, and natural wonders—cannot be destroyed by the desert. Many of the natural wonders, the Petrified Forest, the Painted Desert, and the Grand Canyon it created. The grass it tolerated on its rim. On the land men laid down dry farming and irrigation; on the grass they established the Cattle Kingdom; and on the minerals they built mining. All have been producers of raw products, and each destructive. The farmers with the help of the wind destroyed the soil, the cattle the grass, and the miners removed an irreplaceable resource. The natural wonders, in which the West abounds, have produced annually an increased crop of tourists, whose emblem is the desert water bag. They may prove the West's most dependable asset.

Uncle Sam's People

The West is the home of four-fifths of the surviving Indians, and nearly all their reservations. It is the domicile of four-fifths of the Japanese and three-fifths of the Chinese in this country. It is the home of nearly all people of Spanish-Mexican descent. Paradoxically, contrary to the general opinion, it is in the Toynbeean sense the most cosmopolitan region of the nation. The North is peopled by many nationalities, but nearly all belong to the Western civilization. The West has all these plus the Indian civilization and the Oriental.

The concentration of the Indians in the West suggests how the desert has been used as a place to discard what is unwanted elsewhere. In their rush westward, the Americans drove the Indians toward the desert to be the wards of Uncle Sam. In the same movement they took the land from Uncle Sam, all they considered worth taking. The refuse—mainly in the desert—they left in the hands of the government. Here Uncle Sam is the biggest landholder; he owns 47.7 per cent of the land in the eight desert and three Pacific states. He owns 87.4 per cent of Nevada, 65.3 per cent of Idaho, 64.6 per cent of Utah, 51.8 per cent of Oregon, 47.7 per cent of Wyoming, 46.2 per cent of California. He owns it mainly because nobody wanted it. Here he established the national parks and forests. The Mormons, like the Indians, fled to it because they were not wanted, and all inland atomic explosions are touched off in the desert. (But ancestors of many of the best people in the West today went there because they were "wanted" elsewhere in another sense.)

In the columns above we listed six negatives and six positives. We now must add a seventh negative indicated by the short shrift the West gets in the standard histories. There the historian is deprived of that indispensable ingredient of history, chronology. Aside from the Spanish effort which resulted in failure, everything that happened there occurred yesterday—almost within the long life of one man. Historically, the West has no depth, no long background of slow development. It's story is told in current events. It came on the scene too late to participate in the founding of the nation or to prevent its dissolution in the Civil War. The result is that it has not yet produced a great statesman. Only two Presidents, Herbert Hoover and Dwight Eisenhower, have come from the region; only one was born there, and he rarely mentions it except at campaign time, and in the state of his birth.

Aside from the Battle of San Jacinto, there has never been a military conflict on Western soil that had the slightest influence on national affairs.

The twenty-volume *Dictionary of American Biography* gives a sketch of every American who has had significance in our history. An examination of the 1,252 names listed under the letter B revealed that only 99 (8 per cent) had any connection with the West. The current *Who's Who* lists 45,227 biographies, but only 7,369 (16.7 per cent) are from the West. These percentages run far below the 22 per cent of the population now in the West.

Eighty-six people have been voted into the American Hall of Fame, but there is not a Western man among them.

The federal government has set up fifty-seven sites of national historic character, and of these only two are in the West, one commemorating Theodore Roosevelt and one in the Black Hills honoring Washington, Jefferson, Lincoln, and Theodore Roosevelt—not notable for being Westerners. All national *historical* parks and sites, battlefields, and cemeteries are in the East, the boot hills of the West not yet having attained national recognition.

What is the biographer going to do for a region that has so few men of distinction? What is the historian going to do with a country almost without chronology or important battles or great victories or places where armies have surrendered or dead soldiers were buried? How can he make a thick history out of such thin material?

Brief and Bizarre

Two characteristics of Western history emerge from the situation: Western history is brief and it is bizarre. It is brief because the time is so short and its material deficient.

Western history is bizarre because of the nature of what it has got. The historians and other writers do what men have always done in the desert. They make the best of what little they do have. Westerners have developed a talent for taking something small and blowing it up to giant size, as a photographer blows up a photograph.

They write of cowboys as if they were noble knights, and the cowmen kings. They do biographies of bad men, Billy the Kid, the Plummer gang, and Sam Bass, of bad women like Calamity Jane, of gunmen like Wyatt Earp and Wild Bill Hickok, of cowmen like Goodnight, of miners like Death Valley Scotty and Silver Dollar Tabor. They blow the abandoned saloon up into an art museum, and Boot Hill into a shrine for pilgrims. In Montana Charlie Russell is better than Titian, and in the Black Hills Frederick Remington is greater than Michelangelo. Custer, who blundered to his death, taking better men with him, found a place in every saloon not already pre-empted to that travesty on decency and justice, Judge Roy Bean.

This talent for making the most of little has produced two strange Western societies, one good and one bad. The good society is that of the Mormons in Utah, a rejected people with a bizarre religion who sought peace in the desert, took the bee as their symbol, and created by their hive-like industry something admirable.

The other society of more recent vintage sprang up in a similar desert, but took a different direction. No state has less to recommend it than Nevada. It is all desert and, once its minerals were depleted, it had little chance of prosperity and hardly enough people to maintain a state government. It solved its problem by creating an oasis of iniquity and license in a sea of moral inhibitions. It provided a haven in the desert to which all could come who wanted to gamble, divorce, or fornicate and have it quick and legal. Then it found it could have a monopoly only on the first two, and so substituted for the third the abolition of state income tax to attract the millionaires who make good customers at the casinos. Nevada was revolutionized, its population shortly doubled, and it has had the highest income per capita of any state in the Union. Nevada is what it is today because of what it did not have yesterday. In compensating for what the desert denied it, it has created the most bizarre society in the nation.

As we look at the West with its dry center and rims of less dryness, we see that the desert is the unifying force. True, the people have moved into the oases, some of them man-made, but for the most part they dwell around its moist edges where they struggle for water with all their ingenuity. They are a normal people trying to create and maintain a normal civilization in an abnormal land.

They are like a musician performing on a giant stringed instrument with many of the strings missing. The missing strings put extraordinary demands on the performer. He must make the best of what he has; he must compensate by ingenuity, agility, and improvisations for the missing strings. His range is limited, his repertoire reduced. He cannot follow the musical conventions, will try anything, and we should not be surprised that the effects are sometimes odd. We can understand him better if we remember that he is seeking to conquer the Great American Desert. As the Preacher said: "One generation passeth away, and another generation cometh: but the earth abideth forever." And so does the desert in the heart of the American West.

13. Brazil: Complex Giant
H. O. Sternberg

To determine the factors responsible for the character of a country so diverse as Brazil is indeed difficult, but Sternberg succeeds in presenting "the personality" of this South American giant. He rightly places emphasis upon the attitudes and customs of the people that result in part at least from their cultural backgrounds. The role of the natural physical and biotic attributes of an area, as well as man's interpretation of the environment, accounts for regional differences such as the contrasts between the undeveloped north and the populous south.

For the *caboclo* of the Amazon flood-plain, jabbing the blade of his paddle into the silty waters of the wide main stream, or gliding through a tunnel of trees and vines in some small black-water tributary, there is one Brazilian reality. Quite another exists for the northeastern *vaqueiro*, riding in leather armor through the thorny bush of his drought-smitten land. Different images of their country are held by a gold-miner in Minas Gerais, a *herva-mate* gatherer in Mato Grosso, a sheepherder in Rio Grande do Sul, a coffee planter in São Paulo or another of the many regional types of rural Brazil. The factory hand or the construction worker may think back with nostalgia to the countryside from which he came, but now Brazil is to him a throbbing manufacturing center, an urban sprawl, perhaps a hillside shanty town inserted in a beautiful landscape and overlooking luxurious apartment buildings.

There is, indeed, an extraordinary diversity in the land and in the peoples of Brazil. This diversity separates regions of different latitudes, geological structures, land forms, climate and vegetation. It also separates people who live side by side but in different cultural ages— some whose only tool may be a simple hoe, others employing the most advanced technology. And it is precisely in the light of this cultural

SOURCE: *Foreign Affairs*, XL (January, 1965), 297-311. Copyright by the Council on Foreign Relations, Inc., New York. The author is a Brazilian geographer and currently a visiting professor of geography at the University of California, Berkeley.

diversity, interacting with a complex pattern of physical and biotic features, that Brazil's unity appears so surprising.

II

The personality of the country—so hard to pin down—is being molded by the combination and assimilation of very heterogeneous ethnic and cultural components. Inhabited until the sixteenth century by a Stone-Age people, Brazil has been the physically diversified stage for a unique and impressive mingling of Europeans, Africans and Orientals— among themselves and with the aboriginal stock.

Whereas the Spaniards, at the time of the Conquista, were able to cram their galleons with treasures accumulated by the subjugated na- tives, the Portuguese had to turn to the more prosaic chores of agri- culture. In this they were handicapped by the fact that the total population of the mother country was only of the order of 1,300,000 inhabitants and that their overseas colonies in Africa and the Orient quite often represented a tremendous drain on arms, money—and men. Under these circumstances, it is understandable that the keynote of expansion and settlement came to be miscegenation. Portuguese blood was spread thin, but half-breeds—like the Portuguese-Indian *mamelucos*, fanning out from São Paulo—established the sovereignty of Portugal over literally millions of square miles.

After four centuries, there are still some isolated tribes of Indians, part living in unexplored regions, part being intruded upon by civiliza- tion. Sometimes this contact involves bloody conflicts, such as the massacre of July 1962, when the Apuranã, considered to be "pacified" and more or less integrated, butchered seven whites and left more than one hundred wounded in a rubber-gathering area along the Purus river. Notwithstanding such guerrilla warfare, the Indian is being rapidly assimilated and disappearing as an individualized component of the Brazilian population, of which he represents, according to liberal esti- mates, considerably less than 0.2 percent.

As the Amerinds soon proved to be uncooperative and inefficient workers—from the point of view of the Portuguese, that is—settlers resorted to slave labor imported from Africa. According to the last available census data, Negroes represent roughly 10 percent of the present population. But four centuries of intermarriage have resulted in innumerable shadings from white to brown to black, and not too much reliance should be placed on this figure or others pertaining to classi- fication by ethnic groups. They are certainly not of much concern to the vast majority of Brazilians, used to a free and easy association among the races.

Starting in 1808, when foreigners were assured the right of land ownership, immigration from Europe and the Orient has occurred in more or less well defined waves, each characterized by the predominance, but not exclusiveness, of one ethnic group. Thus, there was a German, an Italian, a Japanese phase. Some immigrants came to settle as freeholders, like the Germans and Italians in Rio Grande do Sul. Others, like the Italians in São Paulo, arrived to pick up the rudimentary implements which the plantation Negroes dropped upon abolition of slavery. In some cases, small contingents of immigrants caused a cultural impact out of proportion to their numbers. An extreme case is perhaps that of the French cultural influence, which has put such a lasting stamp on sophisticated circles of Brazilian urban society and which has practically no substratum of French immigration. Throughout all these periods, Portuguese immigrants continued to disembark in what had been their largest colony.

Regardless of the complexity of Brazil's ethnic and cultural composition, one feels there is a unique Brazilian theme ringing through the country—for all the fascinating variations which are played upon it. It is interesting to notice that the fisherman of the Northeast put out to sea in *jangadas,* a version of the aboriginal raft, or that in many parts of Brazil popular music reflects rhythms harking back to Africa. But such cultural characteristics cut across the different ethnic groups, just as, for instance, certain African religious rites have been adopted by members of the white-skinned population—even by some upper-class whites.

The importance of some immigrant groups derives first and foremost from the fact that they are bearers of culture, capable, even in relatively small numbers, of enriching the Brazilian heritage. It does not derive from their limited contribution to the very rapid growth of the Brazilian population. In fact, it is doubtful if non-Portuguese immigrants and their Brazilian-born offspring represent more than 10 percent of the present population, whose upsurge is mainly due to natural increment. The main factor here is a very high birth rate, which more than offsets a high but rapidly declining death rate.

In 1850, the citizens of Brazil numbered a mere 7,200,000, well below the population of France, Italy or Spain. In 1960, Brazil, mustering 71,000,000 people, had far outstripped these countries and had become, in number of inhabitants, the foremost country of Latin language and—with various enrichments—Latin culture. Should the rate of decennial increase continue around the 37 percent observed in the period 1950–60, Brazil will be pushing the 100,000,000 mark by 1970.

The age structure of the Brazilian population shows a very high proportion of young people in relation to those in the productive ages, who thus have to bear a heavy burden of dependency. This situation is, of course, unfavorable to the accumulation of capital and the economic development of the country. Furthermore, with so many mouths to feed, children and adolescents are called on very early to work as helpers, especially in the rural areas, and are unable to finish—or often even to start—schooling. A high rate of illiteracy is, therefore, an added obstacle to the raising of living standards.

To say that the average density of population in Brazil is around 25 inhabitants per square mile (1960 census) is hardly very illuminating, since the people are most unequally arranged over the vast land, with a remarkable concentration along the coast. An outstanding feature of the geographical distribution of Brazil's people is the existence of an immense area which has less than two and a half persons per square mile and which comprises practically all the Amazon region, a large part of Mato Grosso state (along the border with Bolivia and Paraguay) and a section of northern Goiás state in central Brazil. Within this area, one may find single *municípios,* like Caracaraí (in the far north) or Diamantino (Mato Grosso state), each with an area about equal to that of Arkansas, supporting a population of 3,321 and 4,148, respectively; this means a density of merely 0.05 and 0.08 inhabitants per square mile.

Most Brazilians, in fact, live in a belt some 300–400 miles wide, skirting the coast from the eastern bulge of Brazil to Rio Grande do Sul in the far south (where it occupies the entire width of the country) and presenting a major protrusion into southern Goiás. Densities within the belt vary considerably and the involved distributional patterns which result are explained by a web of physical and historical factors. Although some rural patches in this belt may boast densities in excess of 200 people per square mile, they are exceptional, and one still finds considerable areas—some almost literally within earshot of the Atlantic surf—which support scarcely more than a dozen people per square mile.

The pattern of population distribution is not only intricate but rapidly changing, as areas with exhausted soils become relatively depopulated and new pioneer fronts are opened up (as in the state of Paraná, south of São Paulo, whose population increased by over 100 percent in the 1950s). While some "islands" of denser population are relics of former economic cycles, others are at the receiving end of an unceasing stream of migrants.

One important change, which is occurring all over Brazil—but is obviously not peculiar to the country—is the intense shift of the population toward the city. According to data from the last two censuses (1950 and 1960), it far overshadows, in sheer numbers involved, the push into previously unoccupied or sparsely settled areas. In effect, Brazil's urban population increased during that decade at more than three times the rate of the rural population. The most striking illustrations of this fantastic urban growth are offered by Brazil's two largest metropolitan areas, São Paulo and Rio de Janeiro, each of which now has more than 5,000,000 people. The phenomenon is observable all the way down the line and does not stop at the level of the state capitals. And, of course, each city has its sibling shanty town, perching impudently on steep slopes, like the *favelas* of Rio; advancing on stilts into tidal ooze, like the *mocambos* of Recife; or swaying gently on the surface of the waters, like the *cidade flutuante* (floating city), which has recently sprouted on more than a thousand rafts, log-jammed in front of Manaus on the upper Amazon.

This mass movement of people from the rural areas to the cities obviously has profound social, economic and political implications. For, as pointed out recently by Professor T. Lynn Smith, the millions of humble folk transplanted from the countryside represent precisely that part of the Brazilian population which is least prepared educationally, economically, culturally and politically to cope with the problems of life in the nation's great metropolitan centers.

Varied are the motives for the farm to city migration. Some are factors of attraction: as Professor Charles Wagley has said, Brazilians are profoundly urban in their hopes, being seduced by the glitter and vivacity of the city. But the value attached to the urban way of life is further enhanced by the dismal prospects facing the majority of rural dwellers. And the majority of Brazilians—notwithstanding the existence of 31 cities of more than 100,000 inhabitants—are still rural, 55 percent of the population being thus classified as late as 1960.

III

The way in which a substantial part of the farmlands of Brazil were occupied has resulted in the erosion, not only of the soil, but of man's legitimate aspirations of finding, in a parcel of good earth, a reasonable living for himself and his family. In effect, when the threshold of the New World was crossed, habits of thrift, learned from thousands of years of agriculture in the limited confines of Europe, were cast aside. Such habits involved a type of agriculture where diversified farming was coupled with the keeping of livestock, and both integrated an unbroken biological cycle. But on the new shores, land was, or appeared to be, unlimited. And fertility of the soils was, or appeared to be, assured by the age-old accumulation of forest detritus. Instead of crop rotation, shifting agriculture was adopted and has remained dominant to this day. Under this system, land is cleared, cropped, exhausted and abandoned, and new forests are destroyed and their soil plundered. As the pioneers slash and burn their way through virgin territory, the belt of agricultural production is pushed farther and farther from the markets. The depleted lands are usually given over to extensive grazing, while the settlement of new areas obviously exacts fresh investments and compounds the problem of inadequate and costly transportation.

It is true that certain favorable trends may now be discerned, not the least important of which is the shift from an essentially one-crop economy to relatively diversified farming. The job of applying science and technology to farming has begun; here and there, agricultural "know-how" is changing the traditional landscape of rural Brazil. In the interior of Pernambuco in the Northeast, for instance, contour cropping has been used in one commercial enterprise to conserve soil and precious water; in São Paulo there is increasing acceptance of conservation practices and irrigation of coffee orchards is also receiving recognition, while mechanized wheat farming is producing a sophisticated pattern of agriculture in Rio Grande do Sul.

However, inhibiting customs and attitudes and an unsound institutional framework still prevent the full application of available agricultural technology to the major part of Brazilian farmlands. Thus, for instance, although owners of many big estates are personally wealthy, their agricultural undertakings are for the most part undercapitalized, as shown by inadequacy or absence of farm machinery and insufficient or non-existent storage facilities. Such operators may stretch their financial resources in order to own more land or to take a plunge in non-agricultural enterprises, but rarely consider plowing back a significant portion of their returns into the land they already own, with a view to improving it.

When such questions as low productivity in agriculture, prevalent rural poverty and widespread destruction of natural resources are reviewed, the very root of the problem is sometimes overlooked— that is, the institutional framework of agricultural production. The dominant features of Brazil's agrarian structure are large estates and extensive agriculture. Properties of over 2,500 acres hardly add up to more than 2 percent of the total number of establishments; yet, some of them are so immense that together they comprise more than 50 percent of the country's farmland.

Areas dominated by the large *fazendas,* or *latifúndios,* where land is used much less intensively than on the small farms, represent effective barriers to cultural, social and technological change. Coöperatives do not thrive there. Illiteracy and mortality rates are high. Vertical mobility is difficult and horizontal mobility the rule.

In a country where 80 to 90 percent of the population active in agriculture do not possess the land they work on, and receive a pittance for their labors, it is not surprising that social unrest should flare up in widely scattered incidents. Tremendous social injustices in the rural areas have offered an ideal medium for the development of great tensions and have favored a climate of subversion, skillfully exploited by agitators and opportunists.

There is crying need for measures which will lead to a more equitable distribution of land and the establishment of a rural middle class in Brazil. Few topics have consumed more ink or spittle during recent years than that of agrarian or land reform. It has been a favorite plank for politicians, and the philosophical-political approaches to the theme range through the entire spectrum, from promoting middle-class family farms to advocating state take-over. What Brazil needs is certainly not a mere redistribution of land, nor letters of marque for indiscriminate invasion of property. A land reform which will permit the greatest possible number of people to own, manage and work their piece of ground must assure the farmer clear title to the land and water rights, credit, technical assistance, coöperative organization and the possibility of developing rural industries—among other things. Meticulous attention to such "prosaic" details—a hallmark of the professional, as opposed to the soapbox approach—will make the difference between accomplishment and utter, demoralizing failure.

Take, for instance, the matter of clear-cut titles of ownership. A profitable lesson can be learned from what is perhaps the most successful of all large-scale pioneering settlement ventures in Brazil— that carried out by a railroad and colonization company in northwestern Paraná state. In order to guarantee future purchasers clear title to the land, the enterprise bought up all titles presented—even if it meant acquiring the same tract five or six times. This procedure has paid off handsomely and the development stands out in sharp contrast to most pioneer areas, where land grabbing and unending disputes represent an impediment to rural stability.

In considering a reform desiged to oppose at one time the idle, unproductive *latifundium* and the ineffectual *minifundium,* one might ask if it is possible to find in Brazil any real-life situation capable of proving that the proposed targets are actually feasible and not a mere pipedream.

The answer is in the affirmative. There are, indeed, in existence, quite a few undertakings capable of furnishing useful guideposts for such a program. This is the case, for example, with several agricultural enterprises in southern Brazil, like Holambra, a successful Dutch community of more than a hundred families, enjoying a high standard of

living in São Paulo, some 75 miles from the state capital. This venture
has shown that reclamation of exhausted lands can be turned to good
account. Founded on diversified crop and livestock farming and
handled on a coöperative basis, the enterprise has recovered a derelict
estate and is now establishing a second development. Holambra is
recognized as a remarkable success. To find the reasons for this success is the first step in assessing the possibility of its being repeated
on a large scale.

One important factor was the attitude of the farmers in regard to
the land. Although inexperienced with the problems of subtropical
agriculture, they preferred to come to grips with the many difficulties
encountered and bend every effort in mastering them, rather than
breaking camp and moving on to some other site over the hill. Being
literate and accustomed to using the results of scientific agronomic
research, they made good use of the information available in the re-
nowned Agronomic Institute, located 25 miles away, in Campinas
(1960 pop. 180,000).

Equally important was their ability and willingness to invest capital
in their venture. Of course, the choice of a propitious site, with a
topography suited to mechanization, and good roads connnecting
the enterprise with a rapidly expanding urban market (also a source
of fertilizer, in the form of garbage) were not irrelevant to the success
achieved. Finally, cultural unity has permitted the group to maintain,
develop and make good use of their common heritage, and an effective
coöperative organization has enabled them to combine the benefits of
a system of privately owned, family-sized farms (averaging 90 acres)
with those of a large and aggressive concern.

IV

One result of the low productivity levels still prevalent in most
Brazilian agricultural ventures has been the negligible purchasing
power of the rural population. This prevents the country's industry
from cashing in on what could otherwise be a significant domestic
market. And industry is hungry for expanded markets, for it has grown
at a tremendous pace in recent years; in the 1950s industrial income
overtook that produced by agriculture.

As manufacturing develops, and diversifies, it tends to become more
and more concentrated in the southeastern region, long the political
heartland of Brazil. Three-fourths of the national labor force is employed in this developing industrial belt, which reaches across parts
of the states of São Paulo, Guanabara (the former federal district),

Rio de Janeiro, Minas Gerais and Espírito Santo. In fact, the growth of the southeastern manufacturing heartland has to some extent been at the expense of the inhabitants of other regions.

Regional contrasts in growth rates between the underdeveloped northern and the vigorous southern halves of the country have long been denounced, and there is even reference to a *paralelo fatídico*, an "ill-omened parallel," which is supposed to partition Brazil into "have" and "have-not" areas. Lest lack of advance be equated with low latitude, in a facile rationale of climatic determinism, it may be added that Rio Grande do Sul, the state of Brazil farthest from the equator, recently showed acute signs of economic imbalance. According to a study carried out by the National Council of Economy, this proved to be the effect of price controls adopted by the federal government which affected farm products and agriculturally oriented industries, the foundation of Rio Grande do Sul's economy.

Deliberate efforts to spread the benefits of industry and counteract its increasing concentration in the Southeast have been embodied in legislation enacted for the Northeast and subsequently extended to the Amazon region. It permits a reduction of income taxes proportionate to amounts invested in industries considered useful in promoting regional development. On the other hand, what promises to be one of the most effective means of stimulating the healthy development of medium and small manufacturing centers in the backlands is now getting under way in the Cariri Valley of semi-arid Ceará state, in the Northeast. Here more than 150 springs, issuing from a vast sandstone tableland, permit the concentration of about half a million people in the oasis-like area, where a number of small cottage industries have gradually developed, producing cutlery, fishhooks, leather goods, clocks, muzzle-loading firearms, lace, hammocks and similar handcrafts.

In 1961, Morris Asimow, a professor of industrial engineering at U.C.L.A., became interested in the potentialities of the area, which is now receiving energy from the important Paulo Afonso hydroelectric plant on the Rio São Francisco. With the help of Brazilian and North American students, he made feasibility studies and designed specific small-industry projects for the area. Included were such diversified establishments as a corn-processing plant, a powdered-milk factory and small-scale engineering manufactures with facilities for building sewing machines, electric motors, radios and similar equipment. The ways and means by which these projects were set up and are being implemented are instructive in more ways than one. Plans were not based merely upon the natural resources of the area, but also upon assets which are only too often neglected: human resources—with consideration for the previous training in, and attitude toward, handcrafts already developed by workers and artisans in the Cariri.

The Asimow approach is essentially a grass-roots one and makes for the widest possible participation of the parties most directly interested in the development of the area. The people of the Cariri were not handed something on a platter by a remote authority, paternalistic and, at heart, skeptical about their capacity to go it on their own. The study team, playing a purely catalytic role, pointed out opportunities and the people of the Cariri were quick to take them.

And in so doing they appear to have unwittingly shaken a widely prevalent planning philosophy, by which the initiative of government in the capital-forming process is prerequisite to closing the gap between the two economic halves of Brazil. For people in the Cariri—merchants, farmers and professional groups—proved to have savings which they were willing to invest after being convinced of the viability of the new ventures. Although conditioned to the idea of individual or family-owned enterprises, they were willing to try corporative ownership. Forming corporations with from 20 to 300 stockholders, they raised the amazing total of almost one million dollars, about half the necessary capital to get started (the other being underwritten by the federal Bank of the Nordeste).

It is true that implementation of the plan has encountered more difficulties than appear to have been anticipated by its promoters: some individual projects had to be shelved and others are lagging behind schedule. Quite typically, sharply accelerated inflation—freely condoned by a "developmentist" government—has been one of the major obstacles encountered in this attempt to develop a backward part of Brazil. While the working capital was being collected from the individual stockholders, and emissaries shuttled back and forth with never ending paper work, trying to obtain the government bank's approval—and matching loans—prices of required machinery and equipment spiraled out of reach of the nascent industries. When the writer visited the area last summer, additional capital was being underwritten and other adjustments were being made in the light of experience gained since the feasibility studies were completed. Not only were some projects getting into the production stage, but several new industries, totally independent of Professor Asimow's program, had been spawned or had found nurture in the climate of optimism generated by his plan.

If the Cariri pilot project proves to be successful, the basic approaches adopted, with indispensable attunement to local conditions, may blaze the way for accelerating the economic development not only of the Brazilian Northeast but of other underdeveloped areas of Latin America. By providing non-agricultural jobs in rural areas, decentralized industrialization of this type can prevent the inevitable movement of labor out of agriculture from becoming a catastrophic exodus. The shift from the agricultural to the industrial sector can thus take place without a major geographical displacement, without further crowding of the big cities.

V

The natural physical and biotic attributes of an area may be considered, for practical purposes, invariable, but not so man's interpretation of that environment: technological advances may play down disadvantages and maximize assets. Conversely, inadequate techniques may allow valuable resources to lie idle or, even worse, promote their accelerated destruction. The relations of people to land, therefore, are conditioned by a number of cultural, man-made factors: scientific, technological and administrative tools, which are theoretically accessible to all mankind, and the specific institutional framework of a given region or country, which favors or hinders the use of such levers for development.

Time and again, the student of Brazilian geography is made to realize that obstacles arising from the natural environment may be less significant in narrowing the economic capability of a nation than are, for instance, sins of omission and commission on the part of its leaders. And yet, when backward areas are considered—and there are many in Brazil—only too often there is a tendency to explain them in terms of milieu or race. Since nine-tenths of Brazil's territory lies within the inter-tropical belt, the country's future has frequently been assessed in the light of all the still current prejudices concerning the humid low latitudes. Now, Brazil's natural endowments are far from niggardly. There are vast tracts of good arable land, and recent studies have shown that a large part of even the poorest soils—such as the Amazon uplands or the west central plateau—although extremely low in fertility, often have good natural structure and by no means should be written off as useless. They constitute potential farmland, which may be brought into production some day, when it becomes economically feasible to make additional investments in the form of fertilizer and good husbandry. On the other hand, the mineral deposits of Brazil—with metallurgical ores in the front rank—and its vast hydroelectrical potential form an ample basis for the continued development of a powerful domestic industry. In fact, in terms of many leading minerals and of power resources, Brazil's reserves easily place it among the four or five best endowed countries in the world.

In so far as human resources are concerned, it seems hardly necessary here to refute such racial prejudices as conceive some direct relation between underdevelopment and negative innate characteristics of the local population. It is true, however, that the human factor will become fully effective only when girded with the proper cultural and economic equipment. In this connection, the writer always thinks of one particular group of farmers in the Northeast who were observed wreaking great havoc on the semi-arid landscape with improper farming methods; their unusual capacity for destruction derived not from some fault, such as laziness, but precisely from a virtue, diligence.

What, then, is missing for the harmonious development of the country's various economic sectors and its varied geographic regions—a development so essential to political stability?

Brazil has undergone the changes from colony to monarchy to republic and has weathered several revolutions in the course of its history. None of these movements effectively demolished the archaic social and economic framework carried over from colonial times. The revolution of 1930 might have ushered in profound structural changes, but Vargas and his successors left virtually untouched the economic and political privileges of the *bem nascidos,* the "well born," in the apt expression used by José Fernando Carneiro, one of the sharpest and best informed observers of the Brazilian political scene.

Consider the case of agrarian reform, which recently ousted President Goulart appeared to champion, much to the distress of absentee landowners who trembled for their latifundia. A 48-page report, now released by the Brazilian National Security Council, reveals the fact, long suspected in some circles, that Vargas' political heir had been going about a little agrarian reform of his own. In his name or in that of members of his family or business associates, he had collected some 1,750,000 acres of land, an area equivalent to seven times that of Guanabara state! And, since this property was made up of widely scattered establishments, Air Force planes were sometimes employed to link the *fazendas* and transport everything from cattle to building materials. Here, then, is another instance of the long line of frauds which have been perpetuated upon the Brazilian people by self-styled champions of the unfortunate.

Instead of prying loose, from an overprivileged minority, control over the actual and potential riches offered by a generous earth, they have woven a mesh of restrictions which have progressively worsened the relation of men and the land. One example of the way in which administrative incompetence added to political manipulation has adversely affected geographical patterns and relationships is that of shipping. With a shoreline of some 4,000 miles, endowed with several excellent harbors, and a population concentrated near the coast, seaborne trade would appear to be a natural and vital link in Brazil's economy. However, the assets of geography were practically cancelled out, as ships and cargo-handling equipment became obsolete and harbors were allowed to silt up. Even more important than such physical impediments to shipping are the institutional distortions resulting from the astute selection of longshoremen and merchant seamen as one of the mainstays of demagogical, "populist" governments. The last few years have witnessed the development of a domestic shipbuilding industry and some improvement of port facilities, but at the same time the new caste of "dockside maharajahs," as they have been called, grew in power and ruthlessness. Exerting a complete monopoly of the ship-side labor market, they demanded and obtained from an obliging government extravagant privileges, which set them entirely apart from other, politically less strategic members of the working class. For princely pay, as little work as possible. With ships spending less time at sea than standing by for loading and unloading, with cost of dockside operations increasing day by day, and with pilferage rampant, the sea routes were destined to be abandoned by shippers, largely in favor of quicker, safer—and, all things considered, more economical—transportation by truck. A striking example of this state of affairs was reported in Rio's *Jornal do Brasil* when a certain corporation invited truckers to bid for the job of hauling 20,000 tons of common salt from its salterns on the Coast of Rio Grande do Norte to southeastern Brazil. The corporation was: Companhia Comércio e Navegacão, one of the largest coastal shipping companies in the country.

VI

Those students of Brazilian geography who include in their considerations the role of governments in changing the fate of the earth—for better or for worse—will find an overwhelming number of items to set down on the negative side of the ledger, starting with agrarian reform (or rather, lack of same), proceeding to Brasília and going on down the line to a zigzagging, irresponsible economic policy. And yet there are those who believe that the revolution which broke out last March, in the midst of almost complete chaos, actually cut short Brazil's march toward the redemption of the common man. It is certainly a pity that some otherwise judicious observers should be so unwilling to face the facts of life; that they should so naïvely fail to distinguish between the claims of the group recently toppled from power (who basked in the image of a progressive government, devoted to social welfare and jousting with the evil knights of reaction), and the reality of corruption, opportunism and political nest-feathering, which so disgusted reform-minded democrats in Brazil. Partly to blame, perhaps, for such lack of perspective is a sort of tacit "conspiracy of silence" on the part of certain intellectuals, lest in recognizing the true character of Brazil's "populist" leaders of recent years they should appear hostile to the banners which the latter so enthusiastically unfurled. Many of these banners are just and worthy, and since they fell into soiled hands, it is time they were retrieved and carried forward.

Of course, there are those who would like to see such motifs safely out of the way and forgotten. These people regarded the recent revolution as having saved them definitely and permanently from the danger of Communism, thus assuring them of the right to continue peacefully to exploit their fellowmen, while proclaiming the end of safeguarding "Christian civilization." They may have rejoiced too soon. For it does not look as if the present government intends to limit its action to a mere house-cleaning, but is bent on effecting structural changes, from the basement up.

In his first half-year in office, President Castello Branco has sent close to 150 messages to Congress, almost half propounding reforms of a social, fiscal and administrative nature. Five of these reforms will require changes in the 1946 Constitution. With respect to agrarian reform, for instance, the proposed amendment would permit payment of expropriated latifundia in government bonds, thus removing the effective barrier represented by the existing constitutional requirement that such payments be made in cash.

Brazil's new leadership seems to have avoided the unforgivable sin of ignoring the count-down and to have understood that the archaic structure inherited from colonial times must be replaced without delay, so that resources—and technology wherewith to exploit them—may become available to the greatest number of people, in all regions of the half-continent.

V. GEOGRAPHICAL TOOLS AND TECHNIQUES

In order to make their generalizations about the spatial diversity of the earth as accurate as possible, geographers have developed tools and techniques and adapted those of other disciplines. A gradual evolution in the sophistication and complexity of technology as well as of method has taken place. As indicated in Section IV, these supplement but do not replace subjective observation and the written or spoken word, which earlier geographers depended heavily on.

The map was discovered long ago as an excellent device for portraying data concerning the earth's surface, and it remains the major tool of the geographer. With the advent of the airplane, the aerial photo became increasingly important in the interpretation and recording of data. The computer is a recent and important device for the analysis of geographic data fed into it by the researcher, and its importance undoubtedly will increase. Orbiting satellites and other electronic devices are just beginning to be utilized for remote sensing of various phenomena of the earth's surface. Thus, increasingly automated technology is changing and often simplifying data collection and analysis, but the results are no better than the ability of man to plan how and what to collect, and to know what techniques will give the most accurate results. The following articles examine some of the most important tools and techniques of spatial analysis.

14. The Role of Field Work
Robert S. Platt

S. W. Woolridge, a senior British geographer, once indicated the importance of field work in geography with a parody of eighteenth-century British poet William Wordsworth:

> *One traverse in a Yorkshire Dale*
> *Will teach you more of Man,*

Of Man in his terrestrial home,
Than all the text-books can!

He went on to urge that training in field work in the local
area was vital to effective teaching in geography. The
laboratory of geography is the "out of doors," and the
ability to decide what and how to observe, record, and
analyze is critical in the training of a geographer.

In this article, Platt, one of the deans of American field
geography, seeks to clarify the ideas and objectives of
geographical field study for both geographers and
nongeographers. A fifth question should be added to Platt's
four: How can field data help develop generalizations,
theories, and laws in the discipline of geography? Rigorous
methods of analysis with the aid of the computer, when
appropriate, may greatly facilitate the analysis of field data.
But even as technology grows, field training, as Platt
demonstrates, remains an important source of our knowledge.

A preliminary taste of field study belongs at an early stage of orientation. A first question is: Why is this so? It is because in the field students
confront directly the basic phenomena of geography. The empirical evidence is in the field. Answers are found to basic questions: What are
we talking about in geography? What are we trying to understand?
What phenomena do we perceive in geographic space? Along with this
opportunity, unmatched in the classroom, field study does not preclude
the devices available in the classroom, of saying anything in words and
displaying maps and other materials that reach beyond the visible
landscape.

A second major question is: What is to be studied at the orientation
stage? In general, the appropriate object of study is the areal association, the complex pattern of things together in place. Geography deals
essentially with things in place, as seen in the field and not as gathered
in the classroom. Geography is an integrative subject first and last,
dealing with things in association, not merely elements taken separately
or items listed in inventory form.

Field study cannot include everything existing in a place. Geographers cannot give attention to totality without discrimination—to all
molecules, all insects, all aspects of bird plumage, tree bark and surface irregularities—in microscopic detail, or even in large aggregation.
Attention is focussed on a coherent group of things under an organizing theme. Following historic precedent, the theme chosen here con-

SOURCE: Robert S. Platt, "Introductory Field Study," *Perspective in the Study of Geography*, Department of Geography, University of Chicago, 1951, pp. 12-15. The author (deceased) was professor of geography at the University of Chicago.

cerns the areal pattern of occupance made by human endeavor in the earthly setting, the enterprise of people living and making a living in this place, directed by human will.

A specific need is for objective evidence of this human enterprise from a geographic viewpoint. For purposes of orientation such evidence is found at the outset most clearly observable in simple units of functional organization, particularly in basic rural units of productive enterprise, each comprising the areal pattern of activity of one man or a small group of people—a farm, for example.

In field study, consideration of such a unit may begin appropriately with its functions in the human enterprise: What is done here? What activities take place within the site? What active connections does it have with other areas? What system of operations for purposes of living and making a living is reflected in the visible pattern of buildings, roads, fields, and fences, stationary forms understandable in terms of a living pattern?

But consideration of functions is not enough. The pattern of forms and functions represents a complex system inherited from the past, not invented by the present operators to fulfill current needs in direct response to nature but developed by predecessors in a long sequence of historic cultural invention, brought here from far-off places of origin and applied to this place, possibly on foundations laid by an older system here before, and still being modified in the ecological contacts of life in this setting. The significance of the cultural heritage is to be recognized for Illinois as well as for China or Peru, including both concept of cultural origin, (of a pattern originating elsewhere in the past and spreading to this place) and the concept of sequent occupance (of this pattern succeeding a different previous pattern in this place).

Thus the object of study is recognized as a pattern of occupance, functionally organized and using an old system set down in a natural environment suitable enough for its continued operation. The natural environment has been mentioned but not emphasized. This now finally deserves close attention as no less important than preceding topics. It is left to the last for better understanding than seems possible under the theory of environmental influence, which emphasizes first the active role of nature as against other factors. In proper perspective, as providing the setting of functional organization and cultural development, the natural environment appears to have even more pervasive and universal importance. Every human activity is in a setting of natural environment, and so is every cultural system at every stage of development—not just occasional activities influenced by conspicuous environmental factors. At this point students are introduced to aspects of nature analytically categorized.

So much for the objects to be studied. A third major question is:

What mode or means of field study is to be used? Obviously a primary means is by direct sense impressions, mostly by sight, observation.

Another means, by inquiry or interview, is needed almost as soon as observation. This tool for learning in the field has lagged behind observation and has been regarded as inferior. Perhaps this is due to the example set by geology, with which geography was until recently associated in the field, and in which inquiry is unimportant. In geography inquiry is important: The major objective is to understand occupance as an expression of human enterprise, and the best evidence on this is from the people engaged in the enterprise. Informants need not be big authorities but may be anybody engaged in the enterprise—a hired hand for example, just as, in observing the landscape, the student looks at any hill and not only at the biggest hills in sight. Moreover, the ideas of local people about their enterprise may be no less helpful than objective facts of occupance for purposes of understanding.

Inquiry need not depend on a formal questionnaire but involves conscious grasp of objectives, to find out: What is here and what goes on here? What is the system of operations and what are its internal and external connections? Where did it come from? What was here previously? What natural conditions does it enjoy or suffer from?

Field study also requires means for recording findings. The outstanding device is the map, which shows things in two or three dimensions, as they are wanted in geography, instead of in the one dimension of words (suitable enough for expressing a sequence of time). Another device is the photograph, also showing objects in two or three dimensions, but ordinarily more useful for showing individual features of the pattern than their space relations (except in the case of air photographs, which serve as a kind of map). Finally the device of field notes is indispensable, as an easy substitute and a necessary supplement to maps and pictures.

In connection with maps, pictures, and notes, certain useful devices have been invented. The device of analytical classification is so old and well known that it is occasionally mistaken for something inherent in objective reality and not recognized properly as a device of the human mind for dealing with a complex world. The student is already familiar with common categories (of buildings, crops, and livestock) and may proceed directly to systems of farming and types of land, soil, and climate.

A device more distinctively geographical is that of generalized areal uniformity, of choosing criteria on which areas are recognized as uniform or homogeneous and different from adjacent areas. Small unit areas visible in the landscape or large regions visible on a map may be recognized either on the basis of a single criterion (such as slope) or on multiple criteria expressed in such symbols as those of the fractional code.

Areal units of functional organization need to be clearly distinguished from those of uniformity, though allied with them and similarly useful. Units of organization, already discussed as objects of study, are characterized by a pattern of lines of movement, boundaries of movement, and points of focus.

Conventions and devices for field study form an arbitrary framework which may be interposed between the student and the geographic landscape. Geographers differ as to whether students at the outset should be presented with explicit directions and a full set of categories or whether they should first confront the landscape and discover their own problems and need of categories.

A fourth and final question is: What ideas from the progress of geographic thought are helpful for field-study orientation? In answer it may be said that each stage has made a valid contribution. (1) The residual contribution of environmentalism is simple: There are relations between occupance and nature. (2) The contributions of the inventory stage are basic and substantial: Empirical data are needed and are gathered by means of various devices, particularly that of mapping unit areas based on uniformity in multiple categories. (3) Functional organization as a unifying concept remains of primary significance. (4) Cultural origin as a concept needed in interpretation completes the series to the present.

15. Microgeographic Sampling
J. M. Blaut

At the macro-scale, geographers deal with spatial phenomena for the entire earth. Because inquiry and generalization at this scale are difficult, the researcher has sought to study small or micro-areas in such a way that the results are indicative of the nature of larger regions. The micro-regional approach has been applied to an entire continent by Robert S. Platt in his book Latin American Countrysides and United Regions *(1943). More recently, geographers have attempted to obtain results that are valid for a large area or statistical universe by applying other sampling techniques involving quantitative methods.*

Blaut has experimented with microgeographic studies in

various cultures and regions. In this article, he evaluates
case studies and sampling as methods of obtaining more
accurate research results in agricultural geography. His
findings may be even more valuable in the development
of improved approaches to regional geography.

The possibility of using formal statistical sampling in geographic research has recently received a certain amount of attention, but no statement of the degree or limits of usefulness of the procedure has appeared.
It would seem that our task at this stage is to demonstrate specific areas
of geography in which the sampling approach may be fruitfully employed.

The present paper deals with one phase of the subject: the application of representative probability sampling, in combination with microgeography, to a problem in applied regional geography which as yet
seems not to have been solved by any other means. While the method
—termed for convenience the "micro-regional sample survey"—is discussed here in relation to a specific type of problem, it is clearly
adaptable to somewhat wider use. It may, in fact, illustrate the basic
approach needed to quantify regional geography and generalize microgeography.

Regional Geography and Agricultural Development

Attempts to incorporate regional geography in basic research programs preceding agricultural development, especially in underdeveloped areas, have encountered serious obstacles. These have arisen
primarily from the discrepancy between geographic field methods and
the ordinary focus of regional geography, and have resulted in a
failure to provide the kind of precise and intensive data needed as a
prerequisite to development.

In applied research the essential aim is prediction, and the test of
adequacy is simply whether action taken on the basis of our conclusions will succeed or fail. We should, therefore, be able to supply
information having high predictive value in determining the probable
effects and aftereffects of alternative policies. This requirement estab-
lishes threshold criteria of accuracy and breadth: accuracy must be
sufficient to allow precise determination of norms and variations, and
breadth should be sufficient to include all relevant factors. The latter
will follow logically from the regional approach, but the former can
only come with a scheme of research combining *intensity of treatment*
with *representativeness of coverage*.

SOURCE: *Economic Geography*, XXXV (January, 1959), 79-88. The author is a
geographer at the College of the Virgin Islands.

The field methods of geography are sufficiently detailed to satisfy these criteria. Geography has evolved as a field science, seeking to build its regional descriptions and interpretations on a solid foundation of particular knowledge, much of which derives from field investigation of individual phenomena and their local areal associations. In line with this approach a set of careful field techniques has been worked out for analysis on a level essentially coextensive with the visual horizon of the field investigator. While the goal may be macro-regional synthesis, the means preferred are microscopically intensive—in a real sense microgeographic. Incorporating techniques borrowed from such neighboring disciplines as pedology, farm management, and ethnography with our own, we should currently be in a position to obtain the required data at any specified level of intensity.[1]

Clearly, perhaps inevitably, regional geography has not made optimal use of these available methods. To obtain an immense volume of field data, adequate for full understanding and prediction in the absence of reliable secondary data, would be prohibitively difficult under normal circumstances for any moderately large area. Yet just such areas provide the usual scope for provincial, national, or "regional" agricultural development programs. Furthermore, while reliable secondary sources would reduce the need for field work, the pre-existing data available in underdeveloped areas are inadequate, outdated, or even absent entirely, and dependence on primary-data collection is correspondingly greater if usable results are to be achieved.

Thus the problem becomes one of discovering some means of adapting the field approach to moderately large areas, of obtaining the intensity and detail of microgeography for a macro-region as a whole. Regional geography, by virtue of its breadth of scope and precise field techniques, should qualify for a central role in agricultural development research in underdeveloped areas—more so than any specialized discipline. So far it has largely failed to participate in such work, except by contributing systematic surveys on limited phases and by integrating the data supplied by other sciences. This would seem to result from the lack of a practical solution, under normal conditions of limited time and resources, to the problem of macro-regional intensity and detail.

Micro-Regional Sampling Units

The esssential thesis maintained in this paper is that such a solution can be found in a field approach combining microgeographic tech-

---

[1] See J. M. Blaut: "The Economic Geography of a One-Acre Farm in Singapore: A Study in Applied Microgeography," *Malayan Journal of Tropical Geography,* Vol. 1, 1953, pp. 37-48.

niques with formal, i.e., statistically representative, sample design. This involves (1) determining the classes of data needed in a given problem; (2) organizing research procedures, to the greatest extent possible, around the study of micro-regions as field-work units; (3) replicating the micro-regional studies over a small but statistically representative fraction of the macro-region (the "universe"); and (4) supplementing the microgeographic field work with other procedures, such as macro-regional data-collection (marketing routes, climate, etc.), historical analysis, and detailed qualitative study of selected micro-regions.

Microgeographic theory and methods have been dealt with fully by Platt in several pioneering studies.[2] His approach, and that of the present paper, are essentially regional, and might be termed "micro-regional geography" to distinguish them from the large-scale systematic studies of selected features. For our purposes the central concept in the approach is that of the *micro-region*, which may be either a basic, "building-block" unit of area, or an arbitrarily-defined unit of convenient size. In agricultural areas the farm (however defined) is obviously a valid micro-region, viewed from either standpoint.[3] It represents a fundamental unit of resource utilization and organization, material culture, demography, and social organization, and it is a logical starting place for gathering most types of relevant data. The farm, then, is a basic unit of study, and usually of sampling, in the type of work discussed here.

The particular field methods needed for intensive geographic treatment of the individual farm are well known. W.D. Jones, Sauer, Finch, Kniffen, C.M. Davis, and many others have fully explored the methodology of intensive, local study of particular element-complexes, while Platt has dealt with the fusion of these complexes into micro-regions.[4] However, the problem of assembling micro-studies into a full macro-

[2] See, in particular, Robert S. Platt: "Items in the Regional Geography of Panama: with Some Comments on Contemporary Geographic Method," *Annals Assn. of Amer. Geogrs.*, Vol. 28, 1938, pp. 13-36; "Reconnaissance in British Guiana, With Comments on Microgeography," *ibid.*, Vol. 29, 1939, pp. 105-126.

[3] There are, of course, exceptions, where complex tenure and management relations obscure the fundamental land unit.

[4] For example, the following: W. D. Jones and C. O. Sauer: "Outline for Field Work in Geography," *Bull. of Amer. Geogr. Soc.*, Vol. 47, 1915, pp. 520-525; W. D. Jones and V. C. Finch: "Detailed Field Mapping in the Study of the Economic Geography of an Agricultural Area," *Annals Assn. Amer. Geogrs.*, Vol. 15, 1925, pp. 148-157; V. C. Finch: *Montfort: A Study of Landscape Types in Southwestern Wisconsin*, Geographical Society of Chicago, Bulletin 9, 1933; F. B. Kniffen: "Louisiana House Types," *Annals Assn. Amer. Geogrs.*, Vol. 26, 1936, pp. 179-193; H. F. Gregor: "A Sample Study of the California Ranch," *ibid.*, Vol. 41 (1951), pp. 285-306; C. M. Davis: "Field Techniques," in *American Geography: Inventory and Prospects*, Syracuse, 1954, pp. 496-529; and R. S. Platt, *op. cit.*

regional structure appears not to have been dealt with adequately as yet.[5] Ideally, of course, we should seek complete areal coverage by contiguous micro-studies, but rarely would this be possible. It appears, then, that some kind of selection is called for.

Case Studies and Sample Surveys

The same problem, in various forms, is confronted by most social scientists. They find it necessary to derive accurate generalizations about large, heterogeneous populations, yet lack the resources for complete enumeration—corresponding in geography to complete areal coverage. Social psychology, sociology, political science, economics, and agricultural economics have long dealt with this type of problem, and a branch of the last-named, the discipline known as farm management, has had the most experience with, and greatest success in solving, the problem among those fields concerned with rural areas. For this reason, and also because the viewpoint of farm management closely approaches that of agricultural geography, it may be well to consider the methods used in farm management for the selection and replication of unit studies.

During the latter part of the last century, agricultural economists began to perceive the need for careful study of the individual farm's financial structure, in connection with efforts to establish a research base for local extension. Several lines of effort were initiated, and two which proved highly successful became known as the *case study method* and the *survey method*, respectively. Both are essentially comprehensive economic studies of individual farms, although partial studies of particular enterprises are also included. (It might be noted that farm management, concerned almost exclusively with the individual farm as a basic unit in rural economy, bears the same relation to agricultural economics as a whole that microgeography [or micro-regional geography] does to geography.)

The case study method involves detailed investigation of a small number of farms, usually an unrepresentative group. The survey method, on the other hand, sacrifices a certain amount of detail for statistical adequacy: here a probability sample is selected, by orthodox methods, and each farm in the sample is studied. If the sample is truly representative, and field methods are sufficiently precise, norms and variations determined for the sample can be generalized to the statisti-

[5] "There is little or no correlation between the intensive studies of small areas and the more general studies."—Harold H. McCarty, in *American Geography, op. cit.,* p. 268.

cal "universe," the farming area as a whole. The sampling fraction, variability of the area, and various other calculable factors will specify within fairly precise limits the accuracy of generalizations from the sample data. Since, however, the sample survey requires a large number of individual studies, the amount of attention which can be devoted to each is necessarily limited.

The case study method, by contrast, distributes available field time over a much smaller number of farms and allows far greater intensity for each, achieved often through repeated and prolonged visits to those selected. By studying in detail all factors bearing on farm management, and their modes of interaction, it achieves careful understanding of both static characteristics and relationships, structure and function. Many of the features will be somewhat constant throughout a given region, and a degree of generality will thus be achieved; lack of representativeness, conditioned by the limits on time and resources which normally preclude the taking of a fair sample at the case-study level of intensity, make it impossible to judge the actual degree of representativeness of the data, however. By combining both methods in the study of an area, superimposing the one on the other, maximum intensity and maximum generality—micro-regional detail and macro-regional representativeness—can be achieved.[6]

The manner in which farm management has gone about solving the problem of obtaining predictive accuracy without loss of areal scope suggests certain conclusions for geography. Most past efforts in the latter field have been roughly of the case study variety; they have involved the selection of one or at best a few units in a given macro-region, often dealing quite intensively with each unit chosen. By providing the sort of data which are fairly constant, or at least moderately typical, in a cultural or natural region, and determining the characteristics and interrelations of the features studied, they have proven of considerable value. But such micro-regional case studies do not allow generalization for any quantitative variable, and where, as is usually the case, the macro-region is internally diversified, they do not even allow precise generalization for qualitative attributes. At best they dissect, without defining, a norm, and provide little basis for judging intra-regional variation. Further, since their primary purpose usually has been qualitative illustration of regional characteristics as they appear at the microgeographic level, they have tended to underemphasize quantitative variables which would be of significance in planning—income, cultivated acreage, yields, etc. It thus appears that a mod-

[6] These methods, under the same or different names, are used in most behavioral sciences. For a definitive discussion of their use in farm management see J. Norman Efferson, *Principles of Farm Management*, New York, 1953, especially pp. 4-5, 10-12, and 47-67.

erate dilution of over-all intensity, with, however, some increase for relevant quantitative features, is desirable for obtaining a type of micro-study suitable to replication on a representative basis.

While we may argue over the degree of representativeness of sub-jectively-chosen micro-studies, *true* representativeness—of the sort which permits us to state regional norms and variations with confidence and specificity, and also our probable limits of error—can only come with formal probability sampling, or with total-area coverage. Since the latter is prohibitively difficult in most cases, it is suggested here that an adaptation to our own purposes of the survey method, accompanied by statistically-valid sampling, can best reduce the problem to manageable proportions.

Regional Sampling

The choice of a sampling method for any given micro-regional survey will depend on the characteristics of the locality and the type and circumstances of the project. Of the several methods available, each has merits for certain classes of situations and can be fully evaluated only when we have a mass of comparative data from geographic application. Usually the selection of a method for a particular investigation will depend largely on relative cost in relation to the goals of the work, although some methods will often be ruled out as impracticable. A few words on three well-known sampling methods will suffice to illustrate the approach.[7]

The *simple random sample* is obtained by selecting, purely at random, a certain proportion of the farms in a region under study. The farms may be drawn from a list in advance, or may be selected in the field according to some randomizing procedure. Probably the simplest way of using this sampling method is to compile a list of farms, obtaining the list from some reliable and up-to-date source, or by examination of air photos (in areas where photos are available and individual farmsteads or farm houses can be positively identified on them), or, if necessary, by going into the field and counting; then give each farm a number; and, finally, select the farms to be included in the sample by drawing numbers out of a hat or by referring to a table of random numbers.

[7] For general discussions of sampling, including area sampling, see: Margaret Parten: *Surveys, Polls and Samples,* New York, 1950; and M. H. Hansen, W. N. Hurwitz, and W. G. Madow: *Sample Survey Methods and Theory,* 2 vols., New York, 1953. Strahler's "Statistical Analysis in Geomorphic Research" (*op. cit.*) provides an excellent discussion of statistical manipulations with sample-based data. See also a discussion of the analysis of variance with sample-based data in "Design of Experiments for Statistical Analysis of Geological Data," W. C. Krumbein and R. L. Miller, *Journ. of Geol.,* Vol. 61, 1953, pp. 510-532.

The *stratified random sample* is obtained by breaking down the statistical universe—in this case the total set of farms—according to one or more characteristics relevant to the problem, and selecting a random sample from each of the classes or strata. As a result of the breakdown, each of these strata exhibits less variability than the universe as a whole, and lower variability tends to allow a smaller overall sample, or higher accuracy with the same size of sample. A relatively homogeneous population requires a smaller total sample to provide the same level of accuracy, and the division of a population into, say, four parts on the basis of one relevant characteristic will reduce considerably the variability in each stratum associated with that characteristic. Thus the stratified random sample is preferable to the simple random sample, but requires more advance information about the farms: whereas the simple random sample can be drawn if we have a list of identified farms, the stratified sample requires not only this information but also data on a characteristic of the farms which relates to the problem under consideration. Fortunately, if the areal spread is large enough, variations in relief, climate, or major crop can frequently be used for stratification—but only where we know in advance that such features are related to a given problem.

In order to illustrate the problems an investigator may face in trying to obtain a stratified random sample, we may mention an unsuccessful attempt along these lines made by the writer and others in the course of a field study in Jamaica in 1957. The aims of the investigation were to discover the cultural determinants of soil erosion in a badly-eroded portion of the Blue Mountains, and to find a means of altering these factors in order to pave the way for a soil conservation program.[8] The principal procedures employed in this study were interviewing—to discover social and economic attitudes, costs and returns, knowledge of erosion processes and conservation measures, etc.—soil mapping and analysis, observation of farming behavior, and farm mapping. The problem was thus microgeographic in scale and required intensive treatment of each farm. To obtain data which could be generalized to a macro-region (even a small one), it was necessary to employ probability sampling.

Unfortunately, the field team had little prior knowledge concerning the farms in the area and, more important, could not predict with certainty that any of the known characteristics of the farms (approximate acreage, size of family, and a few other items) related directly to erosion-inducing behavior. Thus stratification would have required

[8] The study, as yet unpublished, was sponsored by the Conservation Foundation and the Research and Training Program for the Study of Man in the Tropics (Columbia University). Participants included the writer as director, two anthropologists (Ruth P. Blaut and Michael H. Moerman), and a conservationist (Nan Harman).

either (1) an enumeration of those farms practicing soil conservation, or (2) an index of the degree of erosion present on each farm. To obtain either of these classes of data the team would have had, at the very least, to ask each farmer the boundaries of his farm (usually fragmented into two or more portions), and then observe and map the farm. This would have had to be done at the start to the investigations, before rapport had been established. Questions and behavior of this sort would have branded the team indelibly, in the eyes of the farmers, as agents of the government and therefore suspect, and would have destroyed the much-needed rapport at the start. The goal of obtaining a stratified random sample was, therefore, regretfully abandoned.

This left, as the best alternative, simple random sampling, which was the method finally selected. Farms were located on air photos and numbered; numbers were drawn out of a kettle; and each selected farm was visited. Seventeen out of a total of 51 farms—a one-in-three sample—were studied, and a second sample of seven was drawn for detailed, largely qualitative, analysis.

Even a simple random sample will be unobtainable if circumstances are such that a list of farms cannot be procured beforehand and field selection of farms is impracticable. This problem will arise frequently in underdeveloped areas: official, church, or other agencies which are usually the sources of farm lists may not have them, or the information may be out-dated; and field selection of a simple random sample may be impossible where air photos are either not available or not usable for this purpose. In such cases a third sampling method, *cluster* or *block sampling*, will often prove useful.

The randomized or stratified-random block or cluster sample is a method of sampling area-units rather than farms. In one of its simpler forms it involves dividing a region into a set of equal-sized areal units and sampling these units, each of which includes several farms in most cases, by randomizing procedures. A grid laid over an ordinary topographic map will often suffice for selecting the units. Another form of cluster sampling involves plotting sample points, usually from grid intersections, and selecting a certain area or a certain number of farms around each point.

This sampling method has the incidental, but very useful, advantage of clustering field studies into a relatively small number of localities. However, it suffers from some rather serious limitations, one being the much larger number of farms which will usually be required to attain a given predictive level.[9] and another being the difficulty of locating oneself (or one's assistants) in the field precisely at a given plotted sample point or along the edge of a given sampled grid square. The

9 Cf., Parten, *op. cit.*, p. 118.

first limitation can be overcome somewhat if the areal units can be stratified; the second, if time for checking or surveying field locations is available.

A hypothetical example may be added, in order to demonstrate the theoretical efficiency of the sampling approach. The example deals with a pre-development geographic field study, more or less "regional" in breadth. If it has been determined that a 3 per cent sample will suffice for representativeness and precision in a particular area containing 10,000 farms, 300 micro-studies will be needed. If one field worker can obtain two studies in a day—the writer's experience suggests that this may be a reasonably secure minimum where high intensity is not required and where field time equals or exceeds travel time—the total number of man-days required for the project will be about 150. Although the number of farms in a region under study will normally be much greater than 10,000 where a development program is involved, it may be assumed that available field time and number of workers will be correspondingly greater.

Two supposed shortcomings of the sampling approach in geography should be considered at this point. The notion that sample data must be numerical—intra-unit variables, such as yields, area, income, size of family, proportional importance of each crop, labor time, etc.—is quite incorrect. Qualitative attributes of the unit are equally accessible. Farming type, cultural affinities, language, dominant product, soil type, material-culture complex, and, in fact, any relevant presence-or-absence identification can be determined for each unit. The fact that such features are qualitative does not mean that we can ignore questions concerning their quantitative significance in an area: for our purposes it is not sufficient to say that a given farming type "dominates," or is of "secondary importance" in an area; we must be able to state with confidence the specific proportion of farms falling within the type, since development programs will differ according to type and the allocation of resources for development will depend on this information.

The second objection asserts that accurate maps cannot be prepared from sample-based data. This ignores the existence of a vast number of such maps, dealing especially with climate, demography, and agriculture. Valid statistics concerning each sample point provide a standard for judging the accuracy of interpolated isopleths, as Blumenstock[10] has pointed out in connection with meteorological data, and statistically-firm sample data permit the portrayal of some distributional features with greater confidence and precision than generalized, often superficial and subjective, total-area data. For any macro-region containing a large number of farms the probability is high that sample

[10] David I. Blumenstock, "The Reliability Factor in the Drawing of Isarithms," *Annals. Assn. of Amer. Geogrs.*, Vol. 43, 1953, pp. 289-304.

units will be distributed evenly enough to allow the drawing of isopleths; it will be even higher if stratification is employed. Block sampling, on the other hand, will leave large areas untouched, and some supplementary field work will be necessary for medium- or large-scale maps. Thus, while there are limits to the amount of mapping that can be incorporated in a sample survey, these normally should not pose a serious problem. And, as will be shown later, the amount of detailed region-wide mapping necessary in a survey of this sort should be rather small. The need for maps will be governed rather by the purposes of the research than by the geographer's innate predisposition toward mapping, and thus the project will emphasize highly detailed farm (or village) maps—necessary elements in the survey in any case, since areas will have to be measured in the field—and small-scale, generalized, macro-regional maps showing major subregions, lines of communication, markets, etc., which do not require detailed, total-area field work.

Levels of Intensity

The foregoing discussion has assumed what may be called a single-level approach, with one level of intensity applied to all farms. It will often prove desirable to extend the research to other levels; to seek, on the one hand, further intensification through the use of case studies and, on the other, broader areal coverage combined with lower intensity, by means of selective systematic surveys.

Some farms, of course, will have to be visited more than once, for completion, verification, and correction. However, some classes of data will need further amplification and others will have been left out of the survey entirely for lack of time. Here the case study can be of use, as it was in the Jamaica investigation described earlier. Some features are relatively constant throughout large parts of a natural or cultural region, but at the same time are too complex or obscure for treatment in the initial sample survey. Others, also inaccessible to the sample survey, are significant by virtue of their qualitative characteristics, regardless of quantitative variability. In both instances the highly detailed study of a few selected farms whose representativeness is not known, or cannot be verified statistically, will often prove of considerable value. In some cases it may even by possible to draw these farms as a sub-sample from the original sample. Bases for complex stratification will have been obtained in the initial survey, and the most serious problem in drawing the sub-sample will be that of judging whether the fairly large number of cases required for the sub-sample is justified in relation to the data to be obtained and the cost of obtaining them. If, however, case studies are fitted to a sub-sample, their value will be considerably enhanced: it will be possible to determine the generality of these highly detailed data for the area as a whole. Even greater detail can be obtained from correlations between paired classes of data in the sub-sample where one of the pair is known for the original sample, using a nomograph.

Conversely, higher regional generality on a level which can only be achieved through complete areal coverage may be desired for certain kinds of data. This might hold true for soils information, although the sample survey, by investigating soils, would probably serve in place of a reconnaissance soil survey—and a full soil survey usually follows, rather than precedes, the initial stages of planning in underdeveloped areas. A total-area land-utilization survey might also be useful if the sampling method chosen left large areas uncovered. Under certain circumstances, however, the sample survey combined with a topographic map would allow compilation of a land-utilization map sufficiently detailed for planning purposes. Where up-to-date, large-scale, air photos are available the field work can be used in the preparation of a key, and ground surveys will be unnecessary. In any case, the need for a land-utilization survey to provide data other than those necessary for a map would be eliminated by a sample survey.[11] Data associated with a macro-region as a whole, rather than with the individual farms—climate, relief, over-all settlement patterns, integrating mechanisms such as marketing lines and urban foci, etc.—will, of course, require total-area surveys. But these need only be rapid, inexpensive surveys.

Contributions to Agricultural Development

The chief value of the method of micro-regional sample surveys results from its procedural simplicity, as the easiest means—in most underdeveloped areas the only means—of obtaining primary regional data which are sufficiently precise and detailed to serve as a basis for local agricultural development programs. If such programs are to be more than restricted, unilateral, projects, the research on which they are based must encompass an extraordinary range of phenomena, too broad for any one science except geography. By virtue of his viewpoint and techniques, the regional geographer is in the best position to describe the characteristics and areal patterns of these phenomena, and, equally important, to examine their functional inter-relations. By extension, the task of venturing sound predictions and fashioning realistic planning models is properly his, also. And, since the critical

[11] Wood, *op. cit.*, p. 367.

primary data are, for the most part, found at the level of the individual farm or rural village, the special techniques of microgeographic field investigation, which he has evolved for work at this level,
provide a means of achieving suitable intensity of detail.

But one further element is needed, a methodological tool which will
permit the regional geographer to generalize his data to a macro-
regional planning unit without loss of the required breadth, intensity,
or quantitative reliability. The tool most widely used in other sciences
faced with this type of problem is sampling, by which is meant the
selection of representative fractions by statistically-valid procedures,
and the argument presented here suggests that this tool is accessible
to the regional geographer in his microgeographic investigations of
farming.

In pre-development research of this sort the regional geographer will
serve three functions, each a distinctive geographic contribution, and
each provided with the credentials of dependability which sampling
affords. First of all, by virtue of his special viewpoint and methods,
he will assume responsibility for the investigation of the resource-
utilization complex, seen as a set of related physical and behavioral
processes—clearly as unique and unitary a body of subject matter as is
possessed by any science. Secondly, he will examine the distributional
patterns and areal differentiation of all relevant classes of phenomena.
And, finally, on the theme of the present paper, he will employ the
breadth of perspective of regional geography to secure basic, minimal,
information on essentially all of these classes of phenomena. Ethnol-
ogists, agricultural economists, engineers, and planners can proceed
from there.

16. The Potential Contribution of Cartography in Liberal Education

Arthur H. Robinson

*Maps are a major tool of the geographer. Almost every
article on geography utilizes one or more maps to illustrate
points and to orient the reader. Various ways have been
developed to project the earth's curved surface upon a
flat plane and to depict spatial information on the map.
In this selection, Robinson indicates how cartography
can be taught as a liberal-arts college course. His approach*

*is not only sound but also particularly useful in a time
when every educated person should know something
about the places that are of daily importance in the affairs
of men, whether at the local, state, national, or international levels.*

To begin let me define the significant terms.

By "cartography" I refer in general to the creation of a map for the use and enjoyment of the educated individual. Consequently, the term, as I am using it, involves a broad understanding of the many varied principles of map making; of the more precise elements of a map such as projection and scale; of the wide range of its qualitative aspects, such as symbolism, design, creativity—and even decoration; and with all of them liberally seasoned with an appreciation of the potentialities of the map as a medium for contemplative pleasure involving the communication of significant spatial ideas, facts and interrelationships. In short, what I am referring to is not so much how to make a map, but rather, what maps may be to one who understands them.

By "liberal education" I mean the guiding of the development of the individual with the ultimate objectives of helping him to understand the total world he lives in, to develop an abiding curiosity about all aspects of it, and to heighten his ability to think rationally and to feel emotionally—and, hopefully, to know the difference.

With these introductory statements let me turn immediately to a consideration of the several ways in which I think cartography can contribute directly to the aims of liberal education. In the major portion of the following remarks I wish to enlarge on seven assertions.

The first of these is that the designed graphic expression is a basic form of communication among humans. All evidence points to its existence very early in the development of man, and it is known among most primitive peoples. Writing, when considered as a form of communication, varies from the direct, unemotional, scientific report or tax form, on the one hand, to the subtle characterizations and moods of a novel, on the other. Graphics have as large a range but they are even more complex, for the media used are much more varied, ranging from the hues and values of color to black lines, and from simple or complex geometric organization to pictorial representation. Many of these elements seem to affect the physiologic perceptual processes in complicated ways in addition to their simpler symbolic meanings. The written or spoken word is capable, to some extent, of producing similar responses as a result of such things as alliteration, onomatopoeia, and

SOURCE: Arthur H. Robinson, *Geography in Undergraduate Education*, Association of American Geographers, Commission on College Geography, Washington, D. C. (1965), pp. 34-47. The author is professor of geography at the University of Wisconsin.

other rhetorical devices; but I do not believe these are nearly as complex as the colors, textures, patterns, balance, and so on, of graphic communications.

Unfortunately, in my view, the history, the principles, and the potentialities of graphic communication are not taught in either the depth or the systematic fashion with which we teach these aspects of the written language. What little is learned is only a meager dividend associated with the occasional course in art or design. Even in this, the main emphasis is likely to be focused toward providing an outlet for creative desire, and precious little is devoted to the direct study of graphics as a method of communication. There are no required courses in visual composition or appreciation to compare with English composition or literature; yet there should be. I am not alone in asking for increased attention to the graphic forms of communication. Many individuals involved one way or another with visual perception express similar views, and more than fifty years ago William Morris Davis wrote: "It is well known that there are many geographical matters which are better presented pictorially, cartographically or diagrammatically than verbally. Hence, it is just as important to study the proper and effective use of the various forms of graphic presentation, as it is to study the values of different methods, treatments, grades and forms of verbal presentation." ("The Colorado Front Range," *Annals of the Association of American Geographers*, 1 (1911), 33.)

The modern map, even a relatively simple, straightforward one, is an extraordinarily complex form of graphic expression because it is an artificial thing embodying, in addition to its visual complications, several transformations of reality in scale, shape, and symbolism that are quite beyond the normal experience of most people. To continue essentially to ignore this basic form of communication at higher levels of education is reprehensible in my opinion; it is especially so in American education, when we are now in a period when our immediate environment is no longer the local scene but is the larger region and in many respects the world as a whole, and our basic way of visualizing it must be by way of the map.

My second point involves not only the general desirability of the liberally educated populace to be appreciative of the importance of this method of communication, but also the need for this group actually to be able to read maps.

I firmly believe that we must promote greatly expanded instruction in what I must simply call "map reading and appreciation" while the student is in the "skill" learning phase of his development. Although some people, in later years, do buckle down and develop their abilities in areas that were missed in their education, this is not common. Basic map reading has become a necessary attribute of every educated person. I am not so biased as to equate it fully with the multiplication table or all of English grammar, but for "today's living" I will certainly put it on a par with such things as algebra, laboratory experiment, a portion—at least—of elementary logic, and probably a good share of what actually is done in English composition courses.

As geographers we tend to take as a matter of course the innumerable contacts we have with maps since, one way and another, we have learned to use them at least in a practical way. We do not realize, I think, just how much a mystery a map is to the cartographically uneducated and this includes most college graduates. Yet these people have much to do with maps in a variety of ways: in all sorts of books ranging from novels to foreign policy reports and from encyclopedias to textbooks, in most newspapers and dozens of magazines, on TV, at most public hearings on such things as school building or resource utilization, when driving a car, in flying, in innumerable government reports, and so on, to s ιy nothing of the uses these college graduates will make of maps in almost any business or profession they get into. Furthermore, the atlas on the coffee table has again become a status symbol judging from the hundreds of thousands being sold in this country each year. Yet the average college educated adult hasn't the foggiest notion of what these maps could mean to him, or more important, what they don't tell him, or, even more important, what they seem to say that actually isn't so.

Let me relate an incident. Some time ago I agreed to talk to a conference group made up of a special selection of several dozen outstanding Wisconsin secondary teachers of history and social studies. I chose as my theme "Maps in the Classroom—Hindrance or Help," and to refresh my memory of what these people teach, I asked my daughter, then a senior in high school, to bring home a copy of any history book she had used. She brought one, and in leafing through it I was discouraged, to say the least. It was Zebel and Schwartz, *Past to Present, a World History* (The Macmillan Co., New York, 1960). It was printed with color, and it contained 68 maps, all but a few of which apparently had been especially drawn. There was no grid on any map and only five had scales. Almost no attempt had been made to take advantage of one of the basic potentialities of a map, its ability to show the correlation in place of several distributions, such as, for example, the relation of routes or occupance to terrain or climate. Various selections cut from a Mercator projection were employed, and odd, off-center excerpts from various other projections with considerable deformation had been used. Everything from generalization to linear symbolism was bad. (In the oral presentation slides of four examples were shown and commented upon.)

Now the sophistication necessary to read most history maps is not very great, but imagine the confusions in even the elementary concepts of direction, area, and distance the students receive when they study the maps in that book. It is not unique in having bad maps, as became quickly apparent in the discussion following my talk. My main purpose in referring to this experience here is, however, this: that book was selected and used in an excellent school in a supposedly liberally educated community. It was written by liberally educated historians, it had a liberally educated geographical advisor, and it was presumably taken through the complex editorial and publication process by a considerable number of liberally educated people. Viewed as a whole, the map program of that book is atrocious and is on a par with improper substantive emphasis, ungrammatical writing, and actual misstatement of fact. For educated people to write, publish, and select it as fare for high schools is a reflection, to say the least, on the content of our liberal education curricula.

Education in map reading carries with it the automatic dividend of an increased ability to read and appreciate other kinds of graphics. In teaching an elementary course in physical geography for more than fifteen years I have been impressed by the inability of students to read even elementary graphs and diagrams. They seem to approach them much the same way they do anything involving arithmetic, that is, they call it mathematics, automatically assume it is beyond them, and don't try. In spite of the fact that they go through life seeing things three dimensionally, it appears to be done without conscious thought; and when asked to observe the relation between two or more phenomena presented symbolically in two-dimensional terms, let alone three, they give up without an effort.

In our increasingly complex world the ability to comprehend spatial relationships in several dimensions is becoming more and more necessary to all citizens. It is especially so to the liberally educated who make up the majority of college graduates and upon whom will fall the major responsibility of judging and approving or vetoing the proposals made by administrations at all levels. As the pressure on resources continues to mount we may expect the citizen to be confronted more and more with the necessity to come to a decision regarding policies and operational proposals that concern questions involving spatial factors: the impounding of water and the extension of cropland, the allocation of water rights in a river system, the development policy on the urban fringe, urban renewal, foreign aid, and areal spread of chemical insecticides, to name only a few. To these he must bring an understanding of the interrelation of numerous spatial factors, and the only real way he can develop this sort of thinking is through the study of and the gaining of a familiarity with the methods of graphic and cartographic communication and notation.

Fortunately, cartography may be treated easily in a progressive fashion. One may begin with elementary concepts with which we are all familiar, and then progressively add sophistication in terms of spatial concepts. The facts of amount at place can be transformed to methods symbolizing gradient, such as the isarithmic, and these may range from the familiar, such as slope, to the unfamiliar, such as persons per square mile per mile. They may be pushed to any desired degree of abstraction, such as rates of rates of change over area. The mapping of straightforward spatial correspondence may go so far as the mapping of residuals from regression, or even the variations in the magnitude of spatial correlations. A systematically structured approach to map reading that proceeds beyond the elementary phases (where such a course usually now ends), namely the basic togographic map, will do much to make more elastic the perceptual and analytical abilities of the student in liberal education.

There is a third objective of liberal education to which cartography can contribute directly, and in some respects better than many other disciplines can. This is in the development of a critical eye. Although all methods of communication involve some kinds of restraints, cartography is rather more versatile in this respect. From the pedagogical point of view this is good, for the teaching of the way these constraints operate tends to make the student much more conscious of the problems of intellectual communication. Working with a visual technique puts the map maker under a kind of graphic duress, so to speak, since the results of his doings are so clearly apparent. I have found in my own teaching experience that, after exposing even the ordinary student to the various principles involved in map-making, he experiences little trouble in applying these in specific assignments involving the preparation of a critique. As a matter of fact many of their reviews are so devastating as to be embarrassing to the present state of cartographic art and science. This is not because they judge I will look with favor on destructive criticism; they are able to be constructive and to back up their judgments with chapter and verse.

There are a large number of cartographic elements subject to critical analysis, such as the handling of scale—in several senses, the employment of the various kinds of marks on a map from lines to letters, the manipulation of color, the use of the generalizing processes, and so on. Naturally, I cannot treat them all here; consequently, I shall limit the discussion to an attempt to show how an understanding of the obligatory process of cartographic generalization helps to develop a critical attitude, an attribute I suspect is universally acknowledged as a desirable objective of liberal education.

By its very nature, cartography is intimately involved with the intellectual processes of generalization, since a reduction to scale is implied in all maps. Even in those maps in which there is little variation in scale the processes of generalization require a number of conscious operations of which I select only two as examples: selection and classification.

No map can present everything; therefore, a selection must be made from among the possible components and this selection, perforce, is made in a rational fashion. If the reader is called upon to judge the quality of the map he must include this in his evaluation, and, in order to do so, he must attempt to understand the objectives of the cartographer in order to assay his selection of the various categories of data included. The reader must evaluate the role of significance as it applies to the test of the hydrography, boundaries, settlements, and other factors shown. Are the components chosen the ones relevant to the understanding or the appreciation of the relationships portrayed, or are they extraneous and put there only because some space needed filling or because "it has always been done that way"? I think you can see that even in this one aspect of generalization the critical review of maps is exactly the same as the review of the quality of communication made in other media, such as writing or speaking. From the pedagogical point of view the map has the advantage that the components are visible and, in most cases, bear a direct relationship to the problem at hand. Any desired degree of subtlety, complexity, or intellectual (i.e., cartographic) sophistication can easily be exemplified among the thousands of thematic maps available.

The second element I wish to mention is the necessity of the classification process as an integral part of cartographic generalization. The liberally educated person must be able to evaluate the kinds and qualities of classification which are so necessary in dealing with almost everything in this complex world. Classification as an element of generalization is ideally exemplified in cartography, for example in the selection of class limits as an aid to communicating the characteristics of a continuous distribution whether it be an abstraction, such as population density, or the more concrete concept of mean temperatures. To evaluate and therefore to read properly such maps the student must appreciate the intrinsic characteristics of the distribution and observe what generalization has done by aggregating its variations. The tyranny of class limits in any classification becomes readily apparent when these must be portrayed as definite lines on a rigid cartographic base. I can think of no better way, than by their manifestations on maps, to bring out the necessary and desirable, but at the same time complex and confusing, qualities of the universal intellectual processes of generalization.

There are other aspects of generalization as a logical process, such as the inductive procedures necessary to locate many components of a map in the compilation process, or the deductive, commonly employed when we derive concepts from maps. These are clearly apparent in the carto-graphic context, but there is no point in belaboring the matter. Suffice it to say, that I believe the combination of intellectual and visual com-ponents and processes that characterize cartography are ideally suited to the development of a critical sense in the liberally educated person.

There is a fourth way in which cartography can contribute greatly to liberal education in quite a different fashion from those I have been discussing. Any truly liberally educated person must be able to see the current scene as simply a point in the continuum of time and of man's development. He must have a well developed sense of perspec-tive, and certainly, today, of the rapidity of change. There are few results of man's activities that so closely parallel man's interests and intellectual capabilities as the map. Let me give you a few examples.

The attempts to determine the size and shape of the earth have been intimately coupled with cartography from the beginning. The early Aristotelian guesses, through the relatively sloppy estimates of Eratos-thenes and Poseidonius, their incorrect "correction" in later Greek times, the lack of concern in the medieval mind, the consequences in the period of grand exploration, the contribution of the French geometers in the 17th and 18th centuries and the controversy over the prolate or oblate spheroid, the development of the equipotential concept and geodesy, and the current slight eccentricities of the orbits of satellites make a fascinating story. One cannot help but be impressed by the growth of men's minds, the ups and downs of his interests, the influ-ence of his technical hardware, and so on.

That is but one example. Instead of limiting ourselves to something so seemingly specialized (but basically simple) as the size and shape of the earth we might look at the history of actual map making, that is, the history of cartography itself as opposed to the history of explora-tion, etc. Here we see a similar course of development. In such a sur-vey the critical components become the long period of drawing and calligraphy, the development of engraving and its effect upon style, the development of lithography and the ability to produce shading easily, the development of symbolism, the sudden surge occasioned by photog-raphy and its marriage with the printing processes, the development of color as a standard component of maps, and the period of preprinted materials, scribing, and film manipulation in which we are now. All are reflected in numerous characteristics of the maps produced since the Renaissance.

The elements of cartographic history that parallel the other aspects of man's changing ideas are many: the growth of the topographic map, the changing fashions in map projections, the development of the representative fraction after the introduction of the metric system, the introduction of the thematic map as an outgrowth of the study of the social and physical world, to list but a few. The map is an ideal device around which to build such a study of man's changing interests and abilities because it is visible evidence.

The fifth point I want to make has to do with what I think is one of the more serious problems confronting liberal education. This is the increasing tendency toward specialization in our educational process. As a consequence of the increasing sizes of our institutions, as well as a number of other factors, I suspect that the student in the liberal arts college is tending more and more toward a relatively narrow education in a few fields with comparatively little attention being paid to their interdependence. Cartography is a subject that exposes the student to quite the opposite kind of experience.

The map is truly an interdisciplinary thing: it employs a more or less rigid mathematical framework on which ordinarily are arrayed elements drawn from the subject matter of the political, social, and economic studies as well as from the physical sciences; the design and preparation of it draws upon the fields of psychology and the fine and applied arts; it is an object created largely through logical processes; its lettering commonly requires an appreciation of some aspects of language understanding; and the end product is clearly a form of communication. Not many subjects available for study combine elements from so many fields. One can neither make an effective map nor study and appreciate one intelligently without some understanding of most of these elements.

To try to teach the interdependence of the fields of learning in the abstract is like trying to teach an appreciation of local landscape or ecology without field work, or the theatre without a stage. Furthermore, most maps are eminently practical objects and the student accepts them readily rather than as artificial or inconsequential things dreamed up by some scholar to take the fun out of going to college. Finally, I know of no learning experience that imparts to the student a greater feeling of accomplishment than that which follows the unravelling of the complexities of a map.

As the sixth of the basic assertions I am making I refer briefly to another aspect of liberal education. I assume there is general agreement that one of the most important objectives of liberal education is to instill in the student an appreciation of what he doesn't know. The development of intellectual humility is not easy especially at the age group we are concerned about. The map is an excellent tool with which to do this. Because of its complexity and because of its dependence on so many different fields, it is almost impossible for a student to be fully familiar with all the qualities and content of a given map. Because its components are tangible, that is, directly visible, it is difficult for him to gloss over the elements with which he is not acquainted.

Because it is something that literally can be handled, turned around, measured upon, and pointed at, he likes to work with it. All in all, I do not think map study can be improved upon for this purpose.

The seventh entry in my outline suggests that there are some other aspects of liberal education to which I believe cartography can contribute directly, such as the necessity for students to become aware of the consequences of statistical manipulations. For example, the map can quite properly be considered a statistical device, consisting of a two or three dimensional coordinate system or space in which are displayed a series of elements, each with its particular array of x, y, and perhaps z values. Many of the distributions portrayed on maps are derived parameters, that is generalizations. As is the case when one is working with almost any statistical material he must proceed warily lest he stumble intellectually. What better medium could one use to instill this attitude in order, as Darrel Huff has observed, ". . . to avoid learning a whole lot of things that are not so." Incidentally, elsewhere in Huff's delightful little book *How to Lie with Statistics* (W. W. Norton & Co. Inc., New York, 1954) he observed that "One of the trickiest ways to misrepresent statistical data is by means of a map."

There are other ways less important to be sure, in which cartography can contribute to liberal education, but I shall not try to develop these in what is already becoming a long paper. Instead I will turn to a number of rather lengthy comments which lead toward a conclusion. If there were suddenly complete agreement that a four-year sequence using cartography as the unifying theme would be an ideal component of a liberal education curriculum I would of course, assume I were dreaming. On the other hand, the shock would force me to consider a number of practical realities. There are several, and I would like to touch on them briefly.

The first of these realities is that cartography is classed as a technique—quite properly—and in our present frame of mind has not been generally considered to be of first class stature as a field of specialization by the group that usually houses its teaching, the geography department. It clearly has not carried the aura of intellectual quality we associate with regional geography, economic geography, etc. I do not mean to suggest that geographers have thought cartography to be unimportant; we have long passed that stage. I do mean, however, that geographers have generally classed it as a useful tool, but have not accorded it the respect usually given to English, statistics, foreign languages, speech, and much of mathematics. The fact that these subjects as taught in college, are also essentially techniques and tools, should give the relatively few geographic cartographers comfort, and perhaps it does if they take a long view. But those other educational fields are well established in liberal arts colleges and therefore have a multitude of practitioners; cartography is not and does not.

The second of these realities that I must face has to do with the fact that there is very little doubt that if the student is to learn anything about cartography he will do it in courses taught in geography departments. As a consequence, although it may appear as a lengthy digression, I would like to make some observations about geography in general. My reason for doing so will appear later when I make my concluding observations.

Ever since science began to eclipse the humanities as the dominant element in modern life, its effect has been felt in many ways. Geography has not escaped. There has been, among other things a proliferation of topical courses at the expense of the regional, to mention but one effect. Although in geography this general trend toward the scientific has materially aided the expansion of cartography as a field of learning in recent years, it has also tended to bias its development to some extent. The "science" aspects of geography and the "tool" aspects of cartography are pushing ahead with ingenuity, while the regional aspects of geography and the communicative aspects of cartography seem to be lagging. For example, it is generally not the geographers who are leading the way in their natural field, the "area programs;" it is the political scientists, the historians, and the language people, in short, peculiarly, it is those who discipline is more humanistic. I urge that geographers put more emphasis on these aspects of their subject.

The total environment—by which I mean the array of all "natural" and "cultural" elements including man—is logically indivisible, and the development of the "feel for àrea" is as worthy an objective as the appreciation of any other human creation. After all, the earth in his mind is what man has made and is making of it, and the difficulties of attempting to develop such an appreciation are no more stringent than those within which the writer and the student of history, language, or literature works. Yet the study of literature and communication is considered humanistic; geography is not. Few real attempts, outside literature, have been made in this direction, and very few by geographers, to my knowledge; but many are possible. An interesting example is that contained in Kevin Lynch's little book, *The Image of the City* (Technology Press and Harvard University Press, Cambridge, 1960), wherein an attempt is made to characterizze urban areas as distilled from the various reactions and concepts of their residents.

The region as traditionally conceived by geographers is a human creation, and in a very real sense it is a kind of artistic creation also, because it has a considerable emotional content. The regional mixture of inherited cultural traits and ideas interwoven with attitudes toward "physical" attributes is a sort of ever-changing ecological complex; and as a creation of man, it can be examined and assayed in the same way we punch, poke, squeeze or squint at the other creations of man in our study of his social attitudes, history, philosophy, literature, or art.

I do not wish to belabor this point but, in the broad view, "geography" (of an area) is really "all about" (an area) and embraces every aspect of it. What the student knows and thinks about "area" is extremely important in liberal education, and this kind of geography is more humanistic than it is scientific.

. . . . . .

There is about as much validity in studying maps as human documents as there is in studying the changing attitudes toward romanticism, symbolism, realism, etc., in period literature. This leads me to the third of the realities that I must face.

It is that even geographers themselves, with their proprietary interest in the field of cartography, are generally far less concerned with the more complex communicative and humanistic aspects of cartography than they are with the basic substantive material that appears on maps. It is true that cartographic errors and blatancies such as the improper use of Mercator, no scale or grid on a map, a dot map on a far-from-equivalent projection, and so on, do elicit complaints but the usual editorial review of maps by geographers, even of those in theses they supervise, is rather superficial by comparison with their other editorial attitudes. I suspect that this results from the fact that much of the teaching of cartography, even today, is of a negative sort, more concerned with how to avoid actual mistakes rather than stemming from the positive attitude of reaching for excellence of communication. Even the negative sort is rather thin. For example, I am willing to wager that the majority of geographers in their, no doubt, one course in cartography spent a good deal more time learning to construct and draft a few map projections than they did on the analysis of the consequences to a map reader of the various systems. This is exactly analogous to including spelling lessons and typing in a college course on English composition. What makes it even worse is that they probably took their course in cartography in graduate school.

Too many of us think of a map only as a tool, a more or less precise, factual thing which has no emotional or even much intellectual appeal. We use it, but we rarely appreciate it. We often say "that's a good map," but when we do, it is the same sort of judgment we make of a telephone, or an electric drill.

Occasionally one may hear, "I like that map", but it is not commonly followed by any analysis of its character and qualities.

Acquiring the ability to understand, to some extent, our emotional and intellectual reactions to various stimuli should certainly be one of the goals of a liberal education. This kind of analysis has long been taught in literature and composition courses. There, students and teacher "tear down" a piece of writing in order to find basic ideas—and then note the means employed by the author to bring about a personal involvement in his readers.

Every high school student—every college student—is required to learn the rudiments of English composition. They, themselves, must select a subject, gather data, make an outline, write the rough draft, accept criticism of it, and then turn in a finished piece of writing.

Very few of these students and not many teachers would recognize the parallel procedure in map composition: first, settling upon the objective, then compiling the data, deciding which to use and which to discard, preparing a "rough draft" employing a particular set of techniques, submitting to a critical evaluation, and finally producing a finished piece of cartography.

It is my belief that people who do have some exposure to this process in the making of maps bring to map reading a far greater appreciation of what a map really is.

The liberally educated person should be able to analyze a map—to understand that the colors used affect emotions, perceptibility, and legibility—that the projection employed provides organizational structure—that line width and character convey a variety of meanings—that the curve of a shoreline, the meanders of a stream occur because of conditions inherent in the earth itself—and so on.

I do not advocate advanced cartographic training for everyone such as is suitable for geographers—analogous to advanced literary training, but I do advocate cartographic education for everyone. Maps are used in such a variety of ways in our civilization that it is deplorable to find most of our map readers on a fourth or fifth grade level in comparison with their education in using and appreciating other methods of communication.

I would rather be positive than negative, however, so I would like to close with a serious proposal to this committee. It is that the committee urge the development of a year-length course in "map appreciation" at the undergraduate level. I am not speaking of the usual kind of course in "map reading" with its primary concern for grid, geographic, or magnetic azimuth, advanced topographic map reading, and so on. What I am referring to is a course, without prerequisite, suitable for any liberal arts college undergraduate, that develops to some extent the kinds of things I have been talking about: a course that looks upon the map as one of the oldest methods of communication with a fascinating history; one that makes clear the roles of art, science, and technique in map-making; one that develops a modicum of critical judgment concerning the handling of the graphic elements of a map; in short, a course that, if taught well, will act as a magnet for a large share of liberal arts enrollments, and which incidentally might lead more students to take more work in geography. I think it can be done, and I think most geographers could do it if they wanted to.

17. Generalization in Statistical Mapping
George F. Jenks

One of the most difficult tasks facing the cartographer-geographer is the accurate and effective presentation of statistical data on a map or graph. Analysis of map patterns that depict various kinds of data is vital to geographic study. The layman seldom has any knowledge of the intricacies and skills of map planning and the ways in which statistical data can be symbolized. Jenks offers a guide to these questions, describing, for example, the choroplethic and isometric variations of statistical surfaces. Choropleth is a means of plotting quantities in such areas as states and nations. In order to achieve greater accuracy in registering changes in quantity, the choropleth map can be transformed into an isometric diagram, as Jenks illustrates.

Among cartographers the term generalization usually conveys the concept of selection, or simplification, or evaluation for relative significance, of landscape features which are to be mapped. The processes of generalization, while creative and intellectual, depend upon visual comparisons between large scale source materials and smaller scale compilations. Coast lines are smoothed, settlements are sifted for size or relative importance, patterns of drainage are simplified, etc. In each case, cartographic judgment and scientific integrity influence the cartographer in attempting to achieve a truthful representation of the landscape but his basic generalizations depend upon the fact that he can exploit his own and the map reader's experience in symbolization.

Unlike landscape features, which can be seen by both the map maker and the map reader, abstract statistical distributions have no basis in direct observation. The patterns which are revealed by symbolization

SOURCE: *Annals of the Association of American Geographers*, LIII (March, 1963), 15-26. The author is professor of geography at the University of Kansas.

do not create mental images which allow for critical comparisons and evaluations. In fact, the cartographer himself is often unaware of the nature or the degree of generalization which he incorporates into his presentation. For example, how often does he analyze his representation in regard to the shape of the statistical surface being symbolized, or fully understand the variations involved in selecting different sizes of symbols, different numbers of classes to be shaded, or the results of manipulating and classing his data? Too often, he solves his symbolization problems blindly, following precedents set by others or giving way to his own preconceived ideas and prejudices.

If we make the rather dangerous assumption that statistical cartographers possess a high degree of integrity and therefore desire to present data truthfully, then, why are statistical maps so often unreliable? The answer to this question appears to be, that since it is difficult to visualize abstract forms, the cartographer makes a series of judgments without really understanding what effect these judgments will have upon the reader's interpretation of the distribution. In other words, would he make the same generalization if he could visualize the statistical surface that he is trying to create?

This paper focuses attention upon three interrelated phases of statistical mapping; (1) the concept of the statistical surface, (2) generalizations resulting from the selection of numbers of classes, and (3) generalizations dependent upon the mathematics of classing data. In practice, the cartographer considers all three phases simultaneously, but to simplify exposition each will be treated separately. The reader must be on guard not to lose track of the close interrelationships of all three phases in the map planning process, for if one concept is changed, the planner must automatically consider the effects of this modification upon the other two.

Further, the very nature of the map planning process, in which several cartographic problems are considered and solved simultaneously, complicates analytical presentation of the process. In the preceding paragraph three topics for discussion have been enumerated, but three dimensional statistical surfaces are commonly represented by either choroplethic or isometric symbols and the solutions sought for one type of symbolization need not pertain for the other. Thus, the author has found it advantageous to present this paper in three segments. The statistical surface concept is treated in the first part since it is in this phase of planning that the symbolization method is selected. The second and third sections treat choroplethic and isometric variations of statistical surfaces and in each of these sections problems relating to numbers of classes and to the mathematics of classing are discussed. This duality of organization allows a presentation which, at least to the author, proceeds in logical sequence.

The Statistical Surface Concept

Most maps are two dimensional representations of distributional phenomenon occurring at or near the surface of the earth but, the conception of these phenomenon can be either two or three dimensional. For example, the average dot map can be conceived of only as a two dimensional representation of a two dimensional distribution because the data represented are individual or small groups of individual phenomenon which are located on the map by geographic coordinates. A contour map, on the other hand, must be conceived of as a two dimensional representation of a three dimensional phenomenon, since there is vertical as well as horizontal variation. Thus a contour map represents the surface of a land volume which lies above or below a datum.

A wide variety of statistical data, when mapped, must also be conceived of as volumetric geographical quantities, since they vary in a third dimension over an area. Distributions such as those of precipitation, air pressure, population density, land use ratios, and population potentials are phenomena of this type. Maps of these distributions

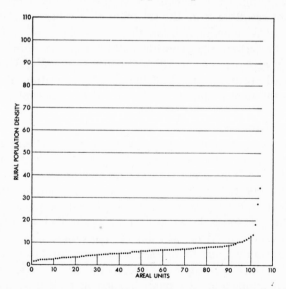

FIGURE 1: Graphic arrays are one of the analytic tools which aid cartographers in understanding the nature of mappable data. In this case, rural population densities for one hundred and five minor civil divisions were ordered and plotted by increasing value. The continuous row of dots which result forms a curve similar to that on a line graph. The curve shown here has a distinctive shape often found in population data and not infrequently in other data series which form the raw materials for statistical maps.

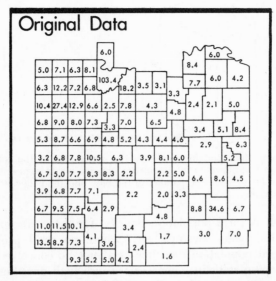

FIGURE 2: Geographic arrays of statistical data are ordinarily prepared as one of the first steps in the map compilation process. The rural population densities are plotted within the boundaries of the collection units—in this case, legal townships. The word, map, has purposely been omitted in the discussion of this illustration because the data are not symbolized in a manner which allows map readers to see areal patterns and thus the intent of mapping has been negated.

must, therefore, be thought of as two dimensional representations of statistical surfaces.[1]

Visualizations of these statistical surfaces are more difficult to grasp than those for land surfaces because they are abstract and because they need not vary in a continuous manner. The land surface is real and experience tells us that we can proceed from one point to another without crossing a void. Some statistical surfaces are directly comparable, e.g., that of air pressure, since the data vary in a continuum and undulations in these surfaces can be thought of as "troughs and ridges." Other statistical surfaces do not fit this concept since there may be two high points separated by a void instead of a valley. Rural population density or value of farm products sold per farm are examples of discontinuous distributions of this type.[2]

Discontinuities in statistical data can occur wherever the phenomena do not exist or wherever there are sharp breaks in the distribution. A

[1] For more complete discussions of statistical surfaces in mapping see:

Arthur H. Robinson, "The Cartographic Representation of the Statistical Surface," *International Yearbook of Cartography*, Vol. 1 (Chicago: Rand McNally & Co., 1961), pp. 53-62, and Calvin F. Schmid and Earle H. MacCannell, "Basic Problems, Techniques, and Theory of Isopleth Mapping," *Journal*, American Statistical Association, Vol. 50 (March, 1955), pp. 220-39.

[2] See Preston E. James and Clarence F. Jones, Eds., *American Geography, Inventory and Prospect* (Syracuse: Syracuse University Press, 1954), pp. 10-11.

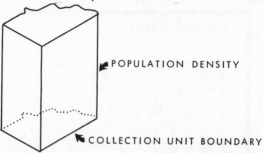

FIGURE 3: Since ratios pertain equally to the entire area of the collection unit a three-dimensional visualization of population density would appear to be a prism. The top of the prism would be parallel to the base and the height would be scaled to the density value.

case in point is rural population density, for there are voids in areas such as cities, parks, swamps, etc., where no rural people live. In addition, rural population densities need not be conceived of as continuously sloping statistical surfaces because high densities may occur in areas (the Nile valley) which are adjacent to very low density areas (the desert). Such distributions can be thought of as stepped statistical

FIGURE 4: The stepped statistical surface is a composite of tangential prisms each of which represents a ratio for a single data collection unit. In this case the sample data are rural population densities and the height of each prism is proportional to these density ratios. When these data are symbolized on isometric block diagrams the cartographer is able to represent each density value exactly to scale and no generalization by classing is necessary.

surfaces with each density value represented by a plane parallel to the datum.

The visual presentation of a statistical surface involves more than the mere classing of distributions into volumetric and nonvolumetric categories. Data are collected by measuring values at points (weather data) and by enumerating for surfaces (census data), and the method of collection influences judgments relating to the representation of the statistical surface. Values measured at points are samples taken from an infinite number of such points, the totality of which form a smooth undulating surface. Enumerated data, however, require a different concept, since they may be thought of either as uniform values over a plane or as sample values for the centroid of the enumeration unit area.[3] The most common rationalization of enumerated data is the former—a stepped surface, although this is changing with the increased utilization of ratio and index values in geographic research.

To focus attention upon different concepts of statistical surfaces and

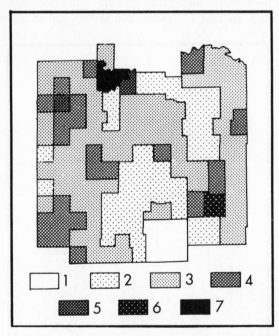

Figure 5: This is one of many different planimetric maps which can be made from the sample data. Choropleths and shading patterns are commonly used to symbolize data of this type and when there is considerable range in ratio values the data are classed into relatively few groups. Generalizing by classing is necessary because the human eye cannot distinguish between gray (or color) tones which have little contrast.

[3] Arthur H. Robinson, *Elements of Cartography* (New York: Wiley & Sons, 2nd Ed., 1960), pp. 182–90.

related cartographic problems, a sample series of data has been processed into a variety of maps and statistical block diagrams. These
data are rural population densities, by minor civil divisions, for eight
central Kansas counties. All of these illustrations present different concepts of the same series of data, and they are presented to call attention
to several variables which are introduced into statistical mapping during data processing. These data are arrayed graphically in Figure 1
and geographically in Figure 2 so that the reader may more easily
follow future manipulations.

If one conceives of population density as a discontinuous volumetric
distribution the population density of each unit area would become
prismatic in form, the base of each prism being contiguous with the
surface of a civil division and the altitude proportional to the density
value.[4] Figure 3. A series of tangential prisms representing population
density for numerous political divisions would form a stepped statistical
surface. Figure 4. This stepped surface can be generalized and represented on a planimetric map using choroplethic symbolization and area
shadings. Figure 5. This representation is but one of a variety of dif-

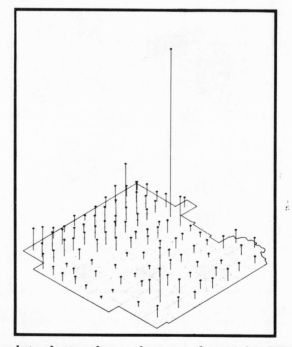

FIGURE 6: Population density values can be conceived as sample values in a smooth
statistical surface. These sample values are visualized as elevated points above a
datum plane. The relative heights of each point above the datum plane are scaled
to the ratio value for the collection unit.

[4] Calvin F. Schmid and Earle H. MacCannell, *op. cit.*, p. 229.

ferent generalizations that could be made of the surface shown in Figure 4. Other variations are discussed in the following sections of this paper.

If population density be conceived of as a smooth statistical surface population density values are arbitrarily assigned to a point on the surface of the unit areas. Theoretically these control points should each be the centroid of the surface of the unit area, but in practice the visual centers of the collection areas are often used. The density values are then visualized as rising vertically above the datum and each becomes a point on the theoretical surface (Fig. 6). This smoothly undulating surface can be represented, on a statistical block diagram, by a series of vertical profiles which are constructed parallel to the X and the Y axes. Figure 7. This surface, when plotted on a planimetric map, is symbolized by isarithmic lines. Figure 8.

The cartographer, like the construction engineer, must make a series of decisions which pyramid into a finished structure. The foundation of the statistical map is the rationalization of the statistical surface as either a stepped or a smooth surface, and this basic judgment in-

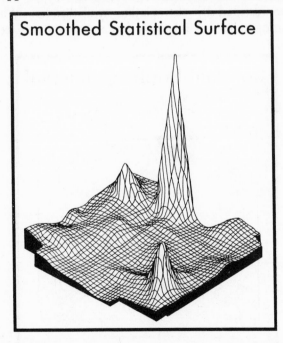

FIGURE 7: Smoothed statistical surfaces are inferred by interpolation between elevated control points. While not ordinarily used for enumerated data, smoothed surfaces are useful and necessary conceptions for statistical correlation. Comparison of this illustration with Figure 4 will enable the reader to see the differences in the two basic types of statistical surface concepts.

fluences all subsequent decisions. But, like the facade of a building, the final appearance or form of the map may be altered considerably by secondary and tertiary decisions. These secondary and tertiary judgments influence map interpretation because they determine those aspects of the map that are immediately visible. Just as the framework shapes the building placed upon the foundation, so the decisions which determine numbers of classes, isarithmic intervals, and class values form the statistical surface. For example, once a stepped statistical surface is decided upon, the choroplethic superstructure can be generalized by a few or many classes. Thus, the map reader may see either a simple or a complex version of the distribution although both maps are representations of a stepped statistical surface.

Variations in Choroplethic Statistical Surfaces

Tabular statistical data collected for unit areas which are political or administrative divisions are often visualized as stepped statistical surfaces and represented by choroplethic symbolization. When this is done, the cartographer has relatively few secondary and tertiary deci-

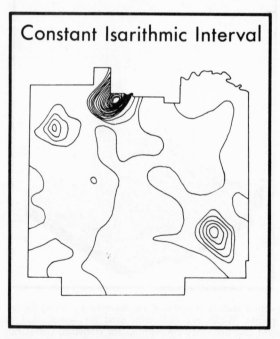

FIGURE 8: Smoothed statistical surfaces, like topographic surfaces, are usually symbolized with isometric or isarithmic lines. This representation was constructed using an isarithmic interval of five persons per square mile.

sions to make, but these decisions influence map reader interpretation to a very high degree. Two important secondary decisions involve the selection of numbers of classes and the choice of limits for these classes. A tertiary decision involves the choice of style, texture, and value (darkness) of the areal shading patterns used. While these patterns modify the visual impact created by the map they are not directly related to data manipulation and thus not discussed in this paper.[5]

The selection of the number of classes and the determination of class

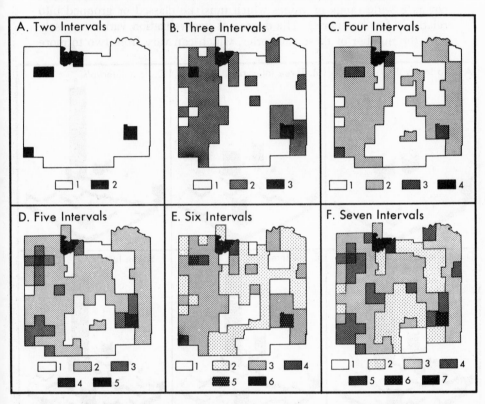

FIGURE 9: Different degrees of generalization can be achieved in mapping statistical data by altering the number of classes. Here the sample data were generalized using geometric progressions and so differences in the maps are essentially due to differences in numbers of classes. The class limits for each of these maps are: A, 1.6, 12.9; B, 1.6, 6.4, 25.8; C, 1.6, 4.5, 12.9, 36.5; D, 1.6, 3.7, 8.5, 19.5, 44.9; E, 1.6, 3.2, 6.4, 12.9, 25.8, 51.6; F, 1.6, 2.9, 5.3, 9.6, 17.3, 31.4, 57.0. For method of calculating these values see caption to Figure 11.

[5] For discussions of these aspects of mapping see:

Arthur H. Robinson, *Elements of Cartography* (New York: Wiley & Sons, 2nd Ed., 1960).

Robert L. Williams, "Map Symbols; Equal Appearing Intervals for Printed Screens," *Annals,* Association of American Geographers, Vol. 48 (1960), pp. 226-53.

George F. Jenks and Duane S. Knos, "The Use of Shading Patterns in Graded Series," *Annals,* Association of American Geographers, Vol. 51 (1961), pp. 316-34.

limits are not two isolated cartographic decisions. Data must be processed for both of these aspects at one time since changes in one will inevitably affect the other. There are, however, an almost infinite number of different combinations which could be determined and utilized, and because of this the author has arbitrarily separated the discussion into two sections and used selected samples to illustrate the concepts of generalization related to each.

The average data series, used as raw material for a statistical map, covers a wide range of values which must be classed or grouped into relatively few categories. The degree of generalization varies inversely with the number of these categories, which can vary from two to more

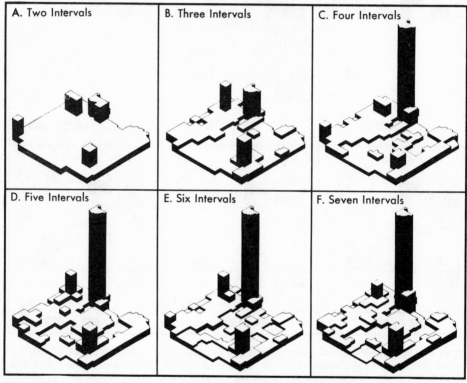

FIGURE 10: A comparison of these isometric blocks with that shown in Figure 4 will show that the degree of generalization varies inversely with an increase in numbers of classes. More accurate generalizations could be achieved if more classes were used, but the reader must remember that the cartographer is limited by the number of shading patterns that he can use. Seven or eight shadings seem to approach the differentiation limit of the average reader. The mean value for each class was used to determine the elevation of that class above the datum. These mean values are: A, 6, 22.8; B, 4.2, 7.8, 34.6; C, 3.2, 6.8, 18.2, 103.4; D, 2.9, 6.4, 10.4, 31.0, 103.4; E, 2.3, 4.8, 7.1, 13.5, 31.0, 103.4; F, 2.1, 4.2, 7.3, 11.5, 22.8, 34.6, 103.4. Since the data are highly skewed only one unit area (103.4) falls into the largest class of maps 10C, D, E, and F. This explains why these four maps have the tall column which is missing on the first two.

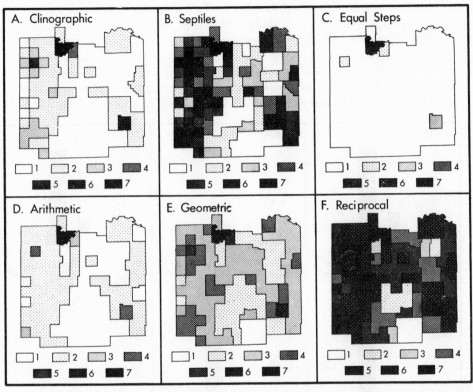

FIGURE 11: Different types of generalization can be achieved by varying the method used in classing data for statistical maps. All of the above maps were constructed with seven classes and the same shadings were used throughout. Therefore, differences can be attributed to the different mathematical systems used in classing. The class breaks and methods of calculating them are as follows: A—1.6, 6.0, 9.0, 14.0, 19.0, 28.0, 35.0. These values are "break points" obtained from a clinograph of the data. B—1.6, 3.2, 4.4, 5.3, 6.7, 7.7, 9.0. The one hundred and five unit areas are divided into seven groups of fifteen unit areas each. The first unit area is 1.6, the sixteenth is 3.2, the thirty-first is 4.4, etc. C—1.6, 16.1, 30.7, 45.2, 59.8, 74.3, 88.8. Obtain range of data, $103.4 - 1.6 = 101.8$; divide this by number of classes desired, $101.8 \div 7 = 14.54$; start with lowest value and add to obtain class limits, $1.6 + 14.54 = 16.14 + 14.54 = 30.68$ etc. D—1.6, 5.2, 12.5, 23.4, 38.0, 56.2, 78.0. Use $A + X + 2X \ldots + NX = B$ where A is the smallest value and B is the largest value and N is the number of classes. Since $A = 1.6$ and $1 + 2 + 3 + 4 + 5 + 6 + 7 = 28$ then $1.6 + 28X = 103.4$, $X = 3.64$, thus $1.6 + 3.64 = 5.24 + 2(3.64) = 12.52 + 3(3.64) = 23.44$ etc. E—1.6, 2.9, 5.3, 9.6, 17.3, 31.4, 57.0. Log $103.4 = 2.01452$, Log $1.6 = 0.20412$. Log difference $1.81040 \div 7 = 0.25863$. Thus $2.01452 - 0.25863 = 1.75589 - 0.25863 = 1.49726$ etc. Anti-log $2.01452 = 103.4$, $1.75589 = 57.0$, $1.49726 = 31.4$ etc. F—1.6, 1.9, 2.2, 2.8, 3.7, 5.4, 10.3. Reciprocal $1.6 = 0.625,000,000$, and $103.4 = 0.009,671,180$, reciprocal difference $= 0.615,328,820 \div 7 = 0.087,904,117$. Thus $0.625,000,000 - 0.087,904,117 = 0.537,095,883 - 0.087,904,117 = 0.449,191,766$ etc. Converting these reciprocals to density values $0.625,000,000 = 1.6$, $0.537,095,883 = 1.86$, $0.449,191,766 = 2.22$ etc.

than ten. It is obvious that the minimum number of classes must be two, since no distribution is shown on a map covered uniformly by a single symbol. The upper limit in class numbers is determined, not only by the nature of the data, but by the fact that the human eye cannot distinguish between very slight differences in the value of shadings. The threshold of differentiation for shadings is not know, either for colors or shades of gray, but it is believed that seven or eight shadings in a spectral sequence approaches the limit for average map readers.[6]

Generalization by numbers of classes is illustrated in Figure 9. The class limits for these maps are all based upon geometric progressions

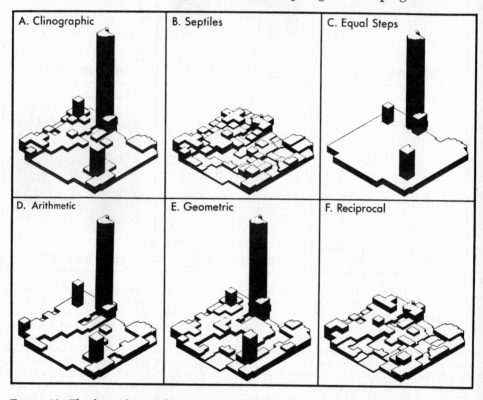

FIGURE 12: The form of generalization achieved in the planimetric maps (Fig. 11) is clearly demonstrated by these isometric blocks. Visual comparison of these blocks with that of the original data (Fig. 4) shows that E is a better generalization of the sample data than the others. However, with other sets of data one of the other methods of classing might give better results than a geometric progression. The mean value for each class was used to determine the elevation of that class above the datum. These mean values are: A, 3.7, 7.2, 10.9, 18.2, 27.4, 34.6, 103.4; B, 2.4, 3.7, 4.9, 6.2, 7.0, 8.2, 20.2; C, 6.1, 22.8, 34.6, 0, 0, 0, 103.4; D, 3.4, 7.6, 14.9, 31.0, 0, 0, 103.4; E, 2.1, 4.2, 7.3, 11.5, 22.8, 34.6, 103.4; F, 1.7, 2.1, 2.3, 3.2, 4.7, 7.4, 24.2. Since there are no unit areas in classes 4, 5, and 6 on Map C, and no unit areas in classes 5 and 6 on Map D, these become four and five step diagrams.

[6] George F. Jenks and Duane S. Knos, *op. cit.*, pp. 316-34.

and the density of shadings was selected according to Williams' curve of the gray spectrum.[7] In addition, scale, pattern texture and drafting specifications were held constant. Thus, since the effects of these variables were minimized, differences are basically due to numbers of classes. The degree of generalization in the statistical surfaces becomes readily apparent when the block diagrams of these maps (Fig. 10) are compared with that of the original data (Fig. 4).

Skilled cartographers usually follow a rational process in classing data, although they often utilize data processing procedures which are unexplained. An analysis of selected maps indicates that three conventional practices are followed and that a wide variety of others are used less frequently. The conventional class intervals are based upon rhythmic or equal steps, arithmetic and geometric progressions. These are indicated by legend values such as: 0–4.9, 5.0–9.9, 10.0–14.9, etc.; 0–4.9, 5.0–14.9, 15.0–29.9, etc.; or 0–4.9, 5.0–14.9, 15.0–34.9, 35.0–74.9, etc. Less common, are intervals determined by frequency graphs, cumulative graphs and clinographs, or those determined from mathematical functions.[8]

Six maps are presented in Figure 11 which give six different generalizations of the sample data. All aspects of these maps were held constant except for changing class intervals and differences between them are solely due to that one factor. The relative degree and form of generalization can be seen in the three dimensional visualizations of these data in Figure 12, and by comparing these block diagrams with that of the original statistical surface (Fig. 4).

The eleven[9] different maps shown in Figures 9 and 11 are but a few of many different visualizations that can be constructed from one data series. All utilize choroplethic symbolization and represent stepped statistical surfaces, and therefore, all are closely related. Each however, represents the data in a substantially different form. They are presented here to focus attention on the fact that the cartographer can control interpretation of a non-continuous distribution by the way in which he manipulates his data.

Variations in Isarithmic Statistical Surfaces

Statistical data which are collected by measurement at specific geographic positions are ordinarily considered to be samples taken in a

[7] Robert L. Williams, *op. cit.*, pp. 226-53.

[8] For a more complete discussion see:

J. Ross MacKay, "An Analysis of Isopleth and Choropleth Class Intervals," *Economic Geography*, Vol. 31 (1955), pp. 71-81 and

George F. Jenks and Michael R. C. Coulson, "Class Intervals for Statistical Maps," accepted for publication in the *Third International Cartographic Yearbook*.

[9] The map with seven classes, 9F, is the same as map 11E.

continuously undulating surface. The total form of the surface is then inferred by interpolating between these sample measurements. Of course, the correlation between the inferred surface and the actual surface will vary with the number, the relative positions, and the degree of accuracy in measurement of these sample data.[10] The correlation of the two surfaces will also vary with the skill and experience of the cartographer making the interpolations.

For purposes of the discussion which follows, let us assume that the sample data are sufficient in number, properly spaced, and accurately measured. Let us further assume that the cartographic skill of the author is consistent throughout the presentation. Having made these assumptions, we can then concentrate on other variables and their re-

FIGURE 13: This isometric block presents a three-dimensional view of the isarithmic map in Figure 8. Compare the areas with lower population densities on this diagram with the diagram of the original data, Figure 4. It is readily apparent that much detail has been lost in these areas and that this generalization is too coarse.

[10] These aspects are covered in detail in:

David I. Blumenstock, "The Reliability Factor in the Drawing of Isarithms," *Annals,* Association of American Geographers, Vol. 43 (1953), pp. 289-304.

John W. Alexander and George A. Zahorchak, "Population-Density Maps of the United States; Techniques and Patterns," *Geographical Review,* American Geographical Society, Vol. 33 (1943), pp. 457-66.

J. Ross MacKay, "The Alternative Choice in Isopleth Interpolation," *The Professional Geographer,* Association of American Geographers, Vol. 4 (1953), pp. 2-4.

Philip W. Porter, "Putting the Isopleth in its Place," *Proceedings,* Minnesota Academy of Science, Vols. 25-26 (1957-1958), pp. 372-84.

lationship to the representation of a continuously undulating surface.

The choice of the isarithmic interval determines the degree of fineness or coarseness of the generalization of a statistical surface. It can, therefore, be compared to the selection of numbers of classes in choroplethic mapping, since a large interval, like few classes, gives a gross generalization. Selecting the isarithmic interval may be done by analyzing the "relative relief" and attempting to visualize the "hills and valleys" of the statistical surface. In the process the cartographer often, consciously or unconsciously, relates these to the contoured land surfaces with which he is so familiar. Thus, little relative relief would be represented by a small, and greater relative relief by a larger, isarithmic interval. Carrying this illusion a step farther, a decision might be reached, if the data suggest it, to use two different isarithmic intervals. This is rationalized in the same way that two contour intervals are sometimes used to represent adjacent level and mountainous topographic areas.[11]

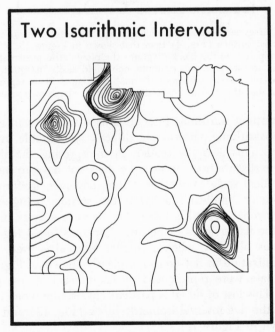

FIGURE 14: An isarithmic interval of two was used for areas with densities of less than ten persons per square mile and an interval of ten was used for the areas with higher densities. When two isarithmic intervals are used the map reader should be forewarned and the lines should be carefully labeled. When this is not done, as in this illustration, the form of the statistical surface can easily by misinterpreted.

[11] For a complete discussion of these aspects of isoline maps see:

Eduard Imhof, "Isolinienkarten," *International Yearbook of Cartography, op. cit.,* pp. 64-98.

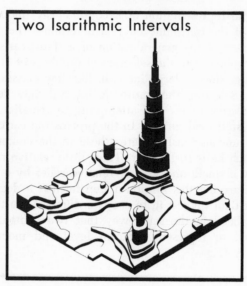

FIGURE 15: This generalization more closely approaches the form of the original stepped statistical surface (Fig. 4) than that shown in Figure 13. While this close correlation is apparent in the block diagrams the planimetric presentation (Fig. 14) is more difficult to interpret. For example, one could easily interpret the isarithmic pattern in the southeastern corner of the map in Figure 14 as representative of a butte-like form, but this feature has quite a different shape on the diagram above.

When a constant isarithmic interval is used to represent a continuous distribution, isarithmic patterns are directly comparable over the total mapped area. This aids the reader, in interpreting the shape of the surface of the distribution, because he does not have to mentally shift from one vertical scale to another. Often, however, uniform isarithmic intervals obscure significant detail if the surface being mapped has great relative relief. Detail is lost either because a large interval over-generalizes the flatter areas or because isarithms bleed together, creating amorphous blotches, when a smaller interval is used. The results of overgeneralization in flat areas are clearly shown in Figure 8 where the sample data were represented by an interval of five persons per square mile. This loss of detail is particularly striking when comparisons are made of the five interval isometric block (Fig. 13) and the smooth surface shown in Figure 7.[12]

[12] The author wishes to point out that the comparisons, between maps and diagrams, made in this paper are based upon the assumption that the cartographer wishes to represent the original statistical surface as closely as possible. I agree with Professor Arthur H. Robinson who pointed out in his critique of this paper that, "There is nothing inherently good or bad about detail or generalization except in relation to objectives." There are often cases where the cartographer purposely eliminates detail to satisfy a need, but here we are dealing with problems of overgeneralization which are neither intended nor desired.

When the sample data are represented by two different isarithmic intervals (two persons per square mile for the lower values and ten persons per square for the larger values) greater detail is shown in the flat areas without significant losses in the peaked areas (Fig. 14). This compromise highlights the problem of interpretation however, since the large peak in the northern section of the map appears to have a steeper slope at its base than it has at higher elevations. Likewise, the peak in the southeast now appears to be almost butte-like in form, while in Figure 8 it appears to be a symmetrical pyramid. These "gains and losses" are apparent when comparisons are made of isometric blocks in Figures 13 and 15.

If the cartographer wishes to employ area shading patterns with isarithms, to accentuate areal differentiation, he must make additional generalizations since he faces the same problems of categorization that were discussed in the choroplethic section of this paper. Thus, if

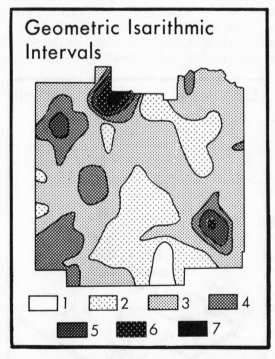

FIGURE 16: When shading is utilized to emphasize areal patterns on isarthmic maps the number of patterns is as limited as those used with choropleths. Here seven tones, ranging from white to black, are used between isarithms selected on a geometric progression. This map has the same class intervals as that shown in the F part of Figure 9 or the E part of Figure 11. Since the number of classes, the method of determining classes, the scale, and the shadings are identical on these maps, differences can be attributed to the different conceptions of the statistical surface.

isarithms 2, 4, 8, 16, 32, and 64 are used to separate shadings on an isarithmic map of the sample data, the resultant map (Fig. 16) corresponds exactly with the choroplethic map shown in Figure 9F. Comparisons of these two planimetric maps and their visualizations in isometric form (Figs. 10F and 17) show this high degree of correspondence, but also demonstrate how the different concepts of the sample data influence the statistical surface.

Conclusions

The map-maker can present to the map-reader for interpretation only one of a multitude of different versions of a statistical distribution. In the creative process of developing this one map, the cartographer makes a series of simultaneous judgments involving his personal concept of the statistical surface, his concept of the most desirable degree of generalization, and his selection of a mathematical process for classing the data. These three judgments control and shape a generalized statistical surface which is then symbolized to represent the abstract data. If the cartographer makes these judgments through rational

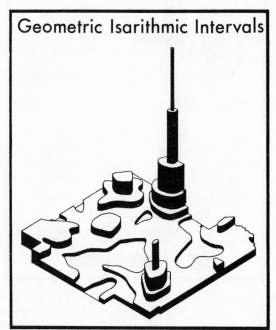

Geometric Isarithmic Intervals

FIGURE 17: This block represents a three-dimensional view of the shaded isarithmic maps in Figure 16. It can, therefore, be directly compared with the block in 10F or 12E to give a clearer understanding of the two different concepts of representing statistical surfaces.

processes he can transmit his concept of the distribution to the reader and the map-reader is obligated to realize that this is a selected generalization.

Map-makers are obligated, however, to create just as realistic representations of statistical data as they do of the earth's surface. Too often we create statistical maps "blindly," failing to recognize how a simple decision can affect interpretation of the final map. Although the decisions are simultaneous and are not separate logical steps, it is hoped that this analysis, and the statistical block diagrams used to illustrate it, has established the need for recognition of the problems involved in mapping statistical surfaces and that more accurate maps may result.

18. A Guide to the Interpretation and Analysis of Aerial Photos

Kirk H. Stone

The interpretation of air photos has become a major analytical tool and an abundant source of information to supplement the map. Stone presents a comprehensive guide to their use.

Recently attention has been refocused on the utility of air photos. Pictures have been taken from fast-moving vehicles at treetop elevations and from vehicles in earth-girdling orbits. Interpretation of them has been dramatized, and their values as an analytical tool have been publicized. Meanwhile, there has been a rapid increase in the use of air photographs in applied and academic geographical work as well as in formal courses on the techniques of interpreting. However, one fundamental need is essentially what it was when the first air photo was taken in 1858: simple listings of methods by which anyone can use aerial photographs as sources of data. Since air photo interpretation is largely locational analysis, geographers can be expected to work with such tools. To facilitate improvement in their use, some basic guides developed during recent decades are presented here to make air photo analysis and interpretation efficient. The guide can be used directly in photo interpretation; and with some qualitative complement and the development of varied indices of specific forms, the guide is a basis for

Source: *Annals of the Association of American Geographers*, LIV (September, 1964), 318-28. The author is research professor of geography at the University of Georgia.

photo analysis. Also, the material is adaptable to an outline of a course on the techniques involved.

The presentation is made with two assumptions. The first assumption is that a specific topic or problem has been delineated for a certain area before application of the technique. Because a photo is a record of everything which reflects light to a camera, the sharp definition of the objective of research is essential. Secondly, we must assume that analysis is most effective when orderly. In geographical air photo interpretation this usually means consideration of all topics; however, sampling areally is as advisable as with any other technique.

General Guides

Five guides provide a logical overall procedure. Generally they are most effective when they are applied carefully, thoroughly, and in the order given.

Use of Source Materials

Air photos are no substitutes for other source materials or for field work on the ground. They are, instead, tools for additional analyses of problems or topics. Before using air photos, an analyst should be thoroughly familiar with all documents: ground photos, maps, statistics pertinent to the general topic, the area of study, and the specific item of investigation. Furthermore, these references should be used constantly during interpretation to prevent the identification of features already known and located.

Use of Multiple Coverage

Rarely is one set of photos sufficient for a research task. Interpretations are likely to be more accurate and complete if more than one set is used. Multiple coverage is available for many areas in the world; and depositories of and agencies holding such coverage are at least generally known. Often small-scale air photos have some advantages over those with large scales, obliques over verticals, color pictures over black-and-white, multiple-lens over single-lens, older photos over newer ones, photos taken in the fall over those taken in summer, and private photography over commercial or military photos. Whenever possible it is advisable to have at least three sets of coverage for an area, and to include coverage with smaller and larger scales.

Determination of the Geographic Characteristics of the Coverage

Before interpreting or analyzing a set of photographs it is expedient to fix the specific location and to compute the scale. Figures in the margins of photographs normally provide general data on scales. In addition, the outlines of selected photos should be plotted on a base map of the area, and the names and locations of specific features should be marked on the photos with grease-type pencils. At the same time, specific scales can be computed for different photos to determine variations resulting from physical changes in the area photographed.

Determination of the Photographic Characteristics of the Coverage

Before interpretation it is also necessary to understand the qualities of the pictures which are the product of the photographic activities: tonal contrasts, the sharpness of images, parallactic characteristics, and the amount of exaggeration of apparent height of features during stereoscopic viewing. The causes of variations in the first three items have been described, and much has been written on the fourth. In any case, an analyst should forewarn himself of the major variations on the photos which do not reflect differences on the ground; this can be done without extensive knowledge of the photographic processes.

Analysis of photographic quality often is especially necessary. Much photography is used for mapping rather than for interpretation. Some commercial photos appear quite distinctive because they were taken with special equipment for a specific purpose. Military cover is sometimes poor because of unusual requirements (e.g., nighttime observation) or because of difficulties resulting from imperfect conditions. Any photos may be of low quality owing to inadequate or lengthy storage.

Analysis by Individual Topics

An air photo often appears to be quite complex because of the great variety of features included; if vertical single-lens photos are used and the view is unfamiliar, there is additional confusion. A recommended solution is to study only one topic in an area at a time. However, specialists on a single topic (e.g., transportation or industry) should also use the general considerations for all other topics given below. This is partly because of probable relationships of the primary subject to other topics and partly because each topical listing is made for the subdivision of that element of the landscape and generally excludes intertopical relationships. Certainly regional geographers need to study most of the topics noted; and everyone will probably find it advantageous to do so in the order given.

This order is founded on two bases: the ease of recognition of features by their shapes, and a progression which is topically logical. It has been found that linear shapes are most easily recognized. Progressively more difficult to recognize are strips, broad areas, and spots.

This is especially applicable when interpretation is begun with small-scale coverage. Thus, the initial topic suggested is transportation; not only are its features generally linear but, also, most interpreters are familiar with several types and transport is basic to most research. The second topic is water bodies, divided as one proceeds upstream from the base levels at coastlines through first-order to third-order drainage features. Both transport and drainage are closely related to surface configuration and work with both should precede the study of natural vegetation. The latter introduces the "domestic" vegetation of agricultural lands which adjoin rural nonagricultural land. Next, military features are listed because they are specialized forms which are widespread, cause much confusion in interpretation, and provide a bridge to urban areas where military installations are also present. The remaining urban features follow, and the last topic is the specialized one of industry. Of course, no order is perfect. But the more effective orders achieve psychological advantages and ease of recognition while noting the variance of photographic scales and the necessities of specific research tasks.

The study of any one topic is efficient when done according to four general rules.

1) *Interpretation should proceed from general patterns to specific features.* Beginning with small-scale or mosaiced photography and the naked eye, the broad patterns of the distribution or shape can be determined for any topic; these patterns may be so subtle or discontinuous that they cannot be observed on medium-scale cover or on single photos. Only after overall characteristics of a feature are determined is it wise to introduce larger-scale photos and magnification, both of which reduce the area seen in one view. In short, time is saved if air photo interpretation is considered to be a deductive, rather than an inductive, process. If only large-scale (larger than 1/10,000) photos are available for an area, an analyst can substitute for the small-scale by making a mosaic of the coverage and by viewing it from a distance or through a reduction projector.

2) *Interpretation should proceed from the known parts of a topic to the unknown.* Comparison is a primary procedure in air photo analysis and interpretation. An analyst saves time and effort by using source materials to identify many parts of a topic and then comparing these with its unknown parts on photo coverage; by this means, the relationships of size and shape are retained and improper identifications are prevented.

3) *Interpretation should be done in the field as well as in the office whenever possible.* Air photo interpretation is not an alternative to field work; it is complementary to direct observation. Interpreters will often find that positive (or sometimes even partial!) identification of a fea-

ture is impossible in the office. The feature may be unrecognizable—it may be obscured permanently or temporarily, it may be newer than the pictures, or the photographs may be inadequate for the interpretation proposed. All analysis should involve study prior to, during, and after field work with both the naked eye and stereoscopic devices. Field observation, however, should not be expected to make certain every interpretation; seasonal variations in appearance may not be the same at the time of field work as at the time of photography, features on old photography may be missing when field observation is undertaken, and there are other possibilities.

4) *Unless recognition of a feature is certain, interpretation should end with several possible identifications.* An interpreter's tendency is to cease deliberation with the first apparently reasonable identification. But cessation should be postponed by the question: What else could it be? This must be asked enough times for the interpreter to recognize several other possibilities and to reduce these to as few as possible.

Under no circumstances may impatience be condoned. Frustration and temporary impossibility of identification are normal. Air photo interpretation requires mental discipline. This discipline in addition to logical procedure and experience in or knowledge of a topic leads to the identifications needed in geographical research.

Topical Guides

Interpretational procedures are presented for eleven topics. These are either major divisions in geographical research, topics on which much interpretation has been done with air photos, or subjects of great potential positive or negative value when air photos are used as source material. The historic and archaeologic aspects of each topic are only partially included because the main objective of this listing is interpretation of present-day occurrences.

The guides apply when work is begun with the smallest-scale photos likely to be used and is continued with increasing scales to the largest likely, that is, from about 1/100,000 to 1/1,000 (although there are smaller and larger). This arrangement leads from the general to the specific, because the procedure is more efficient and because only general knowledge of a topic is essential when analysis or interpretation is started. Of course, an analyst can interpret the details of a topic only if his knowledge of that subject is at least equally detailed.

Transportation

1. Outline provisionally the areas having any kind of elements of transportation present.

2. Circle the major foci of transportation lines, including ports for ships and for aircraft.

3. Mark the more direct lines between, and through, the major foci, and for each:

    a. Determine generally what is at the ends.

    b. Determine whether transport is generally on, above, or below the surface it traverses.

    c. Determine the type of structure where its route crosses a linear physical feature of the landscape.

    d. Determine the characteristics of the route as to width, shape, grade, associated structures, and angle of junction of tributary lines.

    e. Determine the type of vehicle or material moved on it.

4. Reexamine item 1 for possible changes.

5. Circle the minor foci of transportation lines, including ports for ships and for aircraft.

6. Mark the less direct lines between, and through major or minor foci, and for each:

    a. Determine whether the lines are continuous or discontinuous between foci.

    b. Repeat each operation under 3, a. through e., above.

7. Distinguish any lines which appear to be temporarily or permanently unused on any photography.

8. Identify small buildings and structures associated with each line, including those at ports for ships and for aircraft.

9. Determine what else any uncertain transportation line might be (e.g., photographic imperfection, drainage ditch, firebreak, political boundary, coastline, joint on a mosaic, or military feature).

Coastal Configuration

10. Mark the coastlines of large water bodies.

11. Determine the general characteristics of each coastline with respect to:

    a. Shape.

    b. Transportation present (item 1 above).

    c. Depths alongshore.

    d. Distribution of beaches.

    e. Surficial configuration alongshore.

12. Mark the portions of the coast where permanent structures modify the natural shape.

13. For the offshore areas:

    a. Identify provisionally features or disturbances on and in the water.

    b. Determine general variations in depth.

    c. Determine the general configuration of the bottom.

d. Mark parts which are temporarily exposed.

14. For the foreshore areas:

a. Determine the types of transportation present (items 3, 6, and 7).

b. Distinguish subdivisions in shape.

c. Distinguish beach and bedrock areas.

d. Outline areas of active and stationary dunes.

e. Delineate present drainage features.

f. Mark old shorelines.

g. Mark the locations of cultural features other than transportation.

15. For the backshore areas:

a. Repeat each operation under 14. a. through g., above.

16. Reexamine the offshore, foreshore, and backshore areas to complete identification of the physical and cultural characteristics of each.

17. Determine what else any uncertain coastlines might be (e.g., photographic imperfections, edges of large depressions, proposed or new routes of transportation lines, or streams).

Drainage

18. Outline the general areas of permanent and seasonal water bodies.

19. Mark the shorelines of the lakes, trunks of the first-order streams, and areas of distributaries.

20. Compare item 19 with items 1 and 10, above.

21. For the shorelines of the lakes repeat item 11, above.

22. Outline general areas with different patterns of natural surface drainage.

23. Determine the general directions of the flow of water.

24. Circle sharp horizontal and vertical changes in items 19, 22, and 23, above.

25. Outline the areas with artificial surface drainage, including irrigation.

26. Outline provisionally the areas with underground drainage.

27. Identify features on or disturbed surfaces of the lakes and first-order streams.

28. Prepare representative profiles of the bottoms and walls of the valleys of the first-order streams.

29. Mark the second-order streams.

30. Mark the third-order streams.

31. Reexamine item 26 for possible changes.

32. Circle sharp changes in horizontal and vertical directions of flow in items 29 and 30, above.

33. Identify specific features of artificial drainage, item 25, above.

34. Determine what else any uncertain drainage feature might be

(e.g., ridge crest, photographic imperfection, transportation line, coast-line, property ownership line, plowing or harvesting lines, or military feature).

Surficial Configuration

35. Mark the first-order drainage divides.
36. Outline general areas of higher and lower elevations.
37. Outline general areas of mostly slopes, partly slopes, and mostly flat.
38. Compare items 35–37, above, with items 1, 10, and 19, above.
39. Mark the second-order drainage divides.
40. Outline provisionally the unglaciated and glaciated areas.
41. Outline areas subdivided on the basis of length of slopes.
42. Outline areas subdivided by degree of slope.
43. Estimate relative relief.
44. Outline areas of rock outcrop.
45. Outline areas of probable consolidated and probable unconsolidated surface materials.
46. Reexamine item 40 for possible changes.
47. For the unglaciated areas:
    a. Outline subareas of primarily deposition.
    b. Outline subareas of primarily erosion.
48. For the glaciated areas:
    a. Outline subareas of primarily deposition.
    b. Outline subareas of primarily erosion.
49. Identify specific characteristics of individual features on the surface.
50. Determine what else any uncertain feature of the surface might be (e.g., photographic imperfection, drainage feature, results of con-structional or destructional activity by people, or burned or removed vegetational cover).

Surficial Geology and Underlying Structure

51. Outline areas and points of rock outcrop.
52. Outline other areas where the surficial configuration appears to be controlled by bedrock near the surface.
53. Mark continuous and discontinuous lines that appear to be nat-ural features.
54. For areas of thick unconsolidated surface materials (the re-mainder after items 51 and 52, above):
    a. Compare with items 1, 10, 19, and 36, above.
    b. Compare with items 37 and 41–43, above.

c. Mark locations of gravel and sand pits.

d. Outline subareas of probable fluvial landforms, divided into erosional and depositional.

e. Outline subareas of probable marine and lacustrine landforms, divided into erosional and depositional.

f. Outline subareas of probable glacial landforms, divided into erosional and depositional.

g. Outline subareas of probable glacial landforms, divided into erosional and depositional, item 48, above.

55. For areas where the surface configuration is controlled by bedrock (items 51 and 52, above):

a. Repeat each operation under 54, a. through c., above.

b. Mark the locations of quarries, open-pit mines, and mine-head installations.

c. Outline subareas of sedimentary, igneous, and metamorphic rock.

d. Compare item 55 d. with items 22, 24, and 32, above.

e. Within the subareas of sedimentary rock mark the directly observable signs of structural characteristics.

f. Within the subareas of igneous and metamorphic rocks mark the directly observable signs of structural characteristics.

56. Identify the lines in item 53, above.

57. Identify specific landforms in the subareas of:

a. Fluvial landforms.

b. Marine and lacustrine landforms.

c. Aeolian landforms.

d. Glacial landforms.

58. Identify specific structural features in the subareas of:

a. Sedimentary rock.

b. Igneous rock.

c. Metamorphic rock.

59. Determine what else any uncertain geologic feature might be (e.g., photographic imperfection, transportation line, joint on a mosaic, drainage feature, difference in natural vegetation, or the results of an agricultural process).

Natural Vegetation

60. Outline provisionally the areas with natural vegetation.

61. Compare item 60 with items 1, 10, 19, 36–37, 54 c.–g., and 55 c. and d., above.

62. Outline areas of natural vegetation possibly used by people or domestic animals.

63. Outline areas of vegetation which probably have been planted by people.

64. Subdivide provisionally items 60 and 63 into subareas of forest, brush, and grass.

65. For each forest subarea, outline subdivisions according to:

    a. Distributional shapes of stands.

    b. Densities of stands.

    c. Heights of stands.

    d. Recent clearance or selective cutting.

    e. Broadleaf and needle-leaf trees.

    f. Variations in photographic appearance (e.g., tone and texture) which appear to be unrelated to an observable characteristic of the type of vegetation.

66. Reexamine items 60 and 64 for possible changes in the outlines of subareas of brush and grass.

67. For each brush subarea, outline subdivisions according to:

    a. Repeat each operation under 65, a. through d., above.

    b. Variations in photographic appearance (e.g., tone and texture) which appear to be unrelated to an observable characteristic of type of vegetation.

68. For each forest subarea, outline subdivisions according to:

    a. Associations.

    b. Genera.

    c. Species.

    d. Characteristics of the undergrowth.

    e. Probable or possible causes of the differences in item 65 f., above.

69. For each grass subarea, outline subdivisions according to:

    a. Mixtures with trees and/or grass.

    b. Distributional shapes of stands.

    c. Densities of stands.

    d. Recent clearance.

    e. Variations in photographic appearance (e.g., tone and texture) which appear to be unrelated to an observable characteristic of the type of vegetation.

70. Determine probable or possible causes of items 67 b. and 69 e., above.

71. Determine detailed characteristics of individual trees.

72. Subdivide the subareas of brush and grass by species.

73. Determine what else uncertain areas of natural vegetation might be (e.g., military camouflage, unused agricultural areas, photographic imperfections, shadows from clouds or higher surface elevations, or the results of rural nonagricultural activities).

Rural Land Use—Agriculture

74. Outline areas in agricultural use (for the primary production of plants or animals).

75. Outline subareas of item 74 which are cultivated or which are uncultivated but used by animals.

76. Compare item 75 with items 1, 10, 19, 36–37, 54 c.–g., 55 b.–c., and 60, above.

77. Circle the farmsteads.

78. Outline recent changes in the distribution of:
   a. Agricultural areas.
   b. Farmsteads.

79. Outline the subsistence and commercial agricultural subareas.

80. Subdivide item 79 into sections of extensive and intensive agriculture.

81. Outline the field and farm ownership boundaries.

82. Determine the local practices of planting, cultivating, and harvesting of crops or of raising animals.

83. Identify agricultural land uses in areas of extensive agriculture.

84. Identify specific crops.

85. Determine what else an uncertain agricultural feature might be (e.g., rural nonagricultural land use, photographic imperfection, military feature, differences in natural vegetation, a drainage feature, a geologic characteristic, or a shadow).

Rural Land Use—Nonagricultural

86. Replot the major and minor foci of transportation lines, the coastlines and shorelines, the trunks of first-order streams, the areas of higher and lower elevations, and the subareas of natural vegetation types.

87. Outline areas where recreational development is possible.

88. Outline the older and newer built-up areas of villages.

89. Circle the possible locations of older and newer:
   a. Exploitive industry.
   b. Public and semipublic institutions.

90. Refine item 87 to areas of probable recreational development.

91. Circle the possible locations of older and newer:
   a. Hamlets.
   b. Rural public and semipublic buildings outside of the villages.
   c. Rural commercial buildings outside of the villages.
   d. Rural nonfarm residences outside of the villages.

92. Identify recreational areas by type of activity.

93. Outline and identify older and newer subareas of different land use within the villages.

94. Identify the types of features in item 91, above.

95. Identify older and newer specific buildings within the villages.

96. Determine what else an uncertain rural nonagricultural feature might be (e.g., military feature, transportational feature, drainage feature, the results of older or newer agricultural practices, or photographic imperfections).

Military Installations and Effects

97. Make certain that at least items 86 through 96, above, have been completed before proceeding.

98. Compare the date of the photography and the location of the coverage with the times of any known military activity in the area.

99. Outline directly observable evidence of offensive or defensive activity at the time of the photography (e.g., bombs falling or exploding, widespread fires, or shells exploding in the air).

100. Outline and identify areas of general destruction by fire or explosion.

101. Outline the areas of possible military defense or offense by larger fixed installations:

    a. On or in water.

    b. On the ground.

    c. Above the ground.

102. Outline areas of camouflage.

103. Outline areas of major concentrations of military personnel and equipment subdivided into:

    a. Fixed installations.

    b. Temporary installations.

104. Identify the larger fixed installations in item 101.

105. Outline subareas of possible military defense or offense by:

    a. Smaller fixed installations on or in water, on the ground, and above the ground.

    b. Mobile units on or in the water, on the ground, and above the ground.

106. Identify types of camouflage.

107. Distinguish between older and newer military features.

108. Mark the areas of small concentrations of military personnel and equipment.

109. Identify individual fixed installations on or in water and on or above the ground.

110. Identify specific military vehicles of the types:

    a. Naval, including amphibious.

    b. Ground.

    c. Airborne.

111. Determine what else an uncertain military feature might be,

(e.g., photographic imperfection, results of rural agricultural activity, nonmilitary transportation, drainage feature, or results of rural non-agricultural or urban activity).

Urban Features

112. Outline the built-up areas with urban characteristics.

113. Mark the more direct and wider land and water transportation lines going:
    a. Through the city.
    b. Into, but not through the city.

114. Mark the airport.

115. For the built-up area outline subareas of types of:
    a. Water bodies.
    b. Drainage.
    c. Surficial configuration.
    d. Natural vegetation.

116. Divide the built-up area into subareas with differing patterns of streets.

117. Outline the older and newer parts of the city.

118. Identify the more direct and wider transportation lines.

119. Mark and identify the less direct and narrower land and water transportation lines going through the city.

120. Circle the foci and the places where there is a change in the type of transportation in items 118 and 119, above.

121. Outline the primary commercial subareas in the:
    a. Central business district.
    b. Suburbs.

122. Outline the principal industrial subareas, including municipal utilities.

123. Outline subareas of warehouses and open storage.

124. Mark the recreational areas.

125. Mark the cemeteries.

126. Outline sections of the residential subareas by differing char-acteristics of the residences and lots and their relative locations to other functional subareas.

127. Mark the principal administrative buildings.

128. Mark the secondary commercial centers.

129. Mark the isolated industrial plants.

130. Mark the probable locations of light industrial establishments.

131. Mark and identify the lines of internal transportation.

132. Mark and identify individual structures.

133. Determine what else an uncertain urban feature might be (e.g., military feature, specialized industrial feature, photographic imperfection, or joint in a mosaic).

Industry

134. Make certain that at least items 86 through 96 and 112 through 133, above, have been completed before proceeding.

135. On medium-scale photography subdivide each area of industry into its:

    a. Older and newer parts.

    b. Individual factories.

136. For each factory, mark or outline the:

    a. Transportation lines into and out of it.

    b. Subarea of storage of raw materials.

    c. Subarea of generation of power and heat.

    d. Subarea of storage of finished product.

    e. General direction of flow of material through the factory.

    f. General classification as industry for extraction, processing, or fabrication.

137. For each extractive plant:

    a. Locate the source of the material being extracted.

    b. Mark and identify the internal transportation lines.

    c. Identify the heat and power units and the distribution lines from each.

    d. Identify the specific functions in the larger or more significant structures in the plant.

    e. Identify the material being extracted.

138. For each processing plant:

    a. Classify provisionally as to type: thermal, mechanical, or chemical.

    b. Identify the finished product.

    c. Identify the raw materials.

    d. Identify the heat and power units and the distribution lines from each.

    e. Mark and identify the other internal transportation lines.

    f. Identify the specific functions in the larger or more significant structures in the plant.

    g. Reexamine item 138 a., above.

139. For each fabrication plant:

    a. Classify provisionally as to type: heavy or light.

    b. Identify the finished product.

    c. Identify the raw materials.

    d. Identify the heat and power units and the distribution lines from each.

    e. Mark and identify other internal transportation lines.

    f. Mark and identify structures for lifting the semifinished or finished products.

g. Identify the specific functions in the larger or more significant structures in the plant.

h. Reexamine item 139 a., above.

The Future of the Technique

Air photo interpretation is a critical analytical tool of the geographer. The use of the technique is increasing and it probably will continue at an accelerating rate in the next decade. Certainly this will happen as soon as geographers realize that ⸴ arly anyone can interpret and analyze air photos and that these operations do not require knowledge of photographic and photogrammetric processes in detail (although such knowledge sometimes helps).

Every year more ways are found to use air photos as sources of data. These are paralleled by big increases in coverage—from small-scale satellite photos to large-scale commercial pictures. Such can be supplemented easily and cheaply by personal photography from private aircraft. Meanwhile, photographic equipment and materials are constantly being improved. Remote sensing has become a subject of special investigations. It was inevitable that the coupling of several of these changes with techniques of mass data analysis would lead to experiments with the automation of air photo interpretation.

Helpful as all the new materials and equipment may be, the initial phase of air photo interpretation is, and will remain, dependent on a human being. So first we must have an interpreter—analyst who is able to identify features from direct and indirect evidence as single elements of a landscape and in the usual intricate relationships. For him the basic requirements are the simple combination of at least one good eye, a finely divided ruler, a pocket-size stereoscope, the geographical viewpoint, and topical guides.

19. Measurement in Human Geography

J. T. Coppock and J. H. Johnson

While modern data-gathering techniques have provided the geographer with more and more data for analysis, the manpower required to process and evaluate that data has not increased proportionately. As a solution to this problem, Coppock and Johnson suggest that use be made of sampling

*techniques and mechanized data processing. There is no
question that both are becoming increasingly important
tools for the geographer and that the possibilities in
geographic research of using electronic data processing
devices, like the computer, have only begun to be tapped.*

A brief inspection of the geographical writing produced during the past
few decades leaves a firm impression that human geography is becoming increasingly dependent on quantitative data. The dependence may
not always be explicitly recognized, but it is implicit in the wide use
of statistical maps and tables which form an integral part of many
geographical articles.

This current trend is both inevitable and desirable. It is inevitable
because geographers are so few and the facts with which human
geography is concerned are so many that the description and analysis
of areas of any substantial size is only made possible by the use of
statistics collected by others, particularly governments and other official
bodies. The trend is desirable not only because of the precision which
quantitative data add to many of the general statements made by
geographers, but also because mapping and interpreting the various
features of the earth's surface—a process which must involve mensura-
tion of some kind or other—is perhaps the geographer's most valuable
contribution to the work of other disciplines. It is true that in some
aspects of human geography the intuitive approach will remain
supreme; yet dependence on quantitative data is already considerable
and is likely to increase.

In spite of the necessity and potential advantages of using statistical
data there is a very real doubt whether geographers are using this
material as effectively as possible. Thus at present a great *corpus* of
relevant data remains untouched or little exploited; and many geographical investigations are limited to simple factual statements of distribution, neglecting the explanations which more sophisticated analyses
might reveal. Similarly, the correlation among various phenomena is
estimated subjectively by the simple comparison of distribution maps,
largely because statistical techniques are too costly in time and labor,
even though they are more efficient.

Although this situation is regrettable it is surely understandable,
for even if quantitative information is valuable, it is time-consuming to
manipulate and too often requires painstaking doggedness rather than
intellectual perception. Many geographers complain of the vast amount
of detailed information kept hidden in government archives, yet it
is likely that if this material were released its very wealth would be

Source: *Economic Geography*, XXXVIII (April, 1962), 130-37. The authors are
lecturers in the Department of Geography, University College, London.

embarrassing, since it could hardly be exploited by the techniques still commonly used. These methods are so slow and laborious that, by the time a truly comprehensive analysis of any large body of data could be prepared, it would be considerably out of date.

Certainly, this factor is not the only important consideration, but the tardiness with which such analyses can be made diminishes their usefulness to other geographers, to workers in different fields, and, not least, to the general public. Hence common sense demands that geographers should seek to achieve the maximum result with the minimum effort, since only in this way can the relatively small number of geographers tackle the immense amount of material which exists.

This aim could be attained in at least two ways: by the sampling of data and by the mechanization of its processing. These two methods are not exclusive. Ideally they should be combined, and both employ techniques which are already available.

The Possibility of Sampling

Sampling, by reducing both the quantity of data which needs to be collected and the number of subsequent calculations, offers obvious economies of effort. Yet geographers, with some notable exceptions, have paid surprisingly little attention to the possibility of using sample data, although they have long employed illustrative examples. The reasons for this situation are not difficult to discover. One of the clearest lessons demonstrated by geographical field work is the existence of great local variety, and there is a common fear that such variety, the very essence of geography, would be lost if sampling were adopted. Yet, unless geographers are to confine themselves to micro-studies, generalization is necessary, and in the process some variety is inevitably lost. This fact would suggest that many geographical generalizations would be equally valid if based on a sample count. Apart from its greater speed, sampling may have some other advantages, since, as J. M. Blaut has suggested, it combines many of the advantages of detailed survey with those of wide coverage. In addition, certain preliminary steps become essential when sampling is adopted; the source material to be used must be carefully evaluated and the precise aims of the investigation must be clearly thought out, as the scale of the problem and the nature of the data will help to determine the size of the sample. Such a clarification of objectives would be a desirable prelude to any geographical investigation, but they are often neglected in conventional studies.

There are difficulties as well as advantages in sampling and these vary with the purpose of the investigation, its scale, and the nature of the data. Sampling of large areas with the object of obtaining estimates of national or regional totals presents no great problems, provided that the universe being sampled is large and not too diverse. Such estimates are commonly made by government statisticians and those engaged in social surveys. Similarly, no great difficulties are involved in testing the validity of the boundaries of large regions by sampling within them, but where the universes being studied are small and more diverse, larger samples are needed and some stratification of the sample may be required. Thus in experiments with the sampling of British agricultural census data, H. Palca showed that stratification by size of holding produced a marked reduction in sampling errors compared with straight random sampling, the gain being most marked among crop acreages. Satisfactory national estimates are widely made by statisticians on the basis of quite small stratified samples; in the Farm Survey of England and Wales a 14 per cent stratified sample was used to estimate totals from the very varied universe of agricultural holdings, and a 2½ per cent sample was thought adequate for a survey of agricultural earnings because of the relatively low variability of earnings data.

The sampling of small areas to produce a detailed regional picture, comparable with that obtained from a total count, is more difficult. Area sampling has been little explored by statisticians, normally interested in global totals, but it is a theme which might well repay further study. In such work at least two factors must be considered. Many of the items which geographers study, such as fields, farms, or factories, vary greatly in size; and thus variable sampling fractions are desirable so that correct emphasis can be given to the relative importance of units of different size. In addition, geographers are usually concerned with the production of maps, so that the form of sampling adopted will have to include some type of areal control to insure adequate spatial cover. Thus J. W. Birch, in his investigation of types of farming in the Isle of Man, has been able to use sampling as a basis for generalized mapping. For this small area which he knew well, Birch employed a 29 per cent sample of farms, selected systematically at grid intersections, a process which in effect also produced a stratified sample. Similarly, in mapping land use in eastern Wisconsin, W. F. Wood employed a very small sample of 3 per cent, which proved satisfactory for this fairly uniform terrain; but it must also be recorded that Wood was able to relate his work to previous detailed surveys. Clearly, previous knowledge is desirable in planning and evaluating a survey and inspires much greater confidence in the results.

It seems likely, too, that the sample for detailed regional studies will have to be large, especially for the more variable items. Experiments with data from the British Farm Survey have suggested, however, that sampling with smaller fractions and some areal control gives quite acceptable results for the main categories of land use, and that the use of ratios rather than absolute figures may make many of the sampling errors in the more diverse items less serious. Thus, while sampling offers real prospects of saving unnecessary effort, further investigation into the optimum size of sample and the most efficient form of areal control is needed. Even if large samples prove to be necessary, the saving of effort in field work will remain very considerable.

Mechanized Processing of Data

The other approach which will help to speed geographical work is the mechanization of computation and analysis. If worthwhile work is to be done with quantitative data it is necessary to compare, calculate, and sort the information rapidly; and in particular it must be possible to plot it on maps quickly and accurately. While great developments have been taking place along these lines in closely related fields, geographers have generally not taken advantage of the modern methods which could be used for the initial processing of data, for plotting information on maps, and for the conversion of qualitative information into quantitative data.

Apart from the employment of electrical desk calculators, the most obvious application of mechanization is in the use of simple cards with perforated edges, which are punched to facilitate their sorting and abstraction. It is true that the initial punching of cards is time consuming: in a study of land use in Middlesex, in which it was necessary to prepare 50,000 cards, one for each parcel of land, initial labor requirements were increased by 15 per cent. But once prepared, a great variety of statistics could be quickly assembled, and the subsequent savings in manpower were considerable. H. Godwin has used a very similar method in gathering and handling the great body of information summarized in his history of the British flora, and climatological statistics are now being filed using the same system.

This procedure is a simple manual one, but mechanically sorted punched cards can handle much larger amounts of data. Although it is nearly 80 years since Hollerith developed his punched card equipment, and although these methods have long been used for the tabulation and analysis of population censuses, geographers have made little use of them. Yet many geographical investigations, which involves simple calculations and the handing of data relating to a very large number of items, could well be carried out in this way, since between 7,000 and 36,000 cards can be sorted in an hour and tabulations and simple mathematical procedures can be quickly undertaken.

Of particular interest is the use of this technique for the actual production of maps. In the preparation of a floral atlas of the British Isles data were transferred to about 3,000,000 punched cards. A slightly modified 40-column tabulator was used to mark with a dot every ten kilometer square in which a particular plant species occurred. By this method an average map could be made in 15 minutes, and it was estimated that the 2000 maps, which embody the information collected in over five years, could be produced in about six months. On a fairly small scale map of the British Isles this method produced a result adequate for block making, and there seems no reason why the same procedure should not be used to plot information with a greater degree of refinement. It would also be technically possible to record frequency of occurrence as well as the mere location of a particular item.

A further indication of the vast possibilities of punched cards is given by the experiments of workers in Sweden, who have attempted to record the primary census information relating to each individual on a punched card, along with a grid reference giving the location of his dwelling house. By sorting and tabulating these cards in different ways it is possible to calculate various interesting ratios, and the results can be mechanically plotted on a grid, so that isopleth and choropleth maps can be easily prepared. A particular advantage in this technique is that changes in the boundaries of statistical units become irrelevant, with the result that information from a variety of dates can be easily compared. Unfortunately, the expense of preparing individual cards is a major obstacle, and many governments might not be prepared to allow access to census information in this detail.

Where data can be processed electronically, the rate of computation and analysis can be further speeded, particularly where complex numerical operations are involved. The information used by these machines can be prepared on magnetic or punched tape, and data on punched cards can also be fed into them. Thus speeds of more than 1000 additions or subtractions per second can be performed; and in one example a calculation which normally took two to three hours could be done in 30 seconds by computer. Many universities now possess computers of their own; and the data used by geographers and many of the calculations which they need to make are eminently suitable for handling on a digital computer with a large storage capacity, although conventional punched card equipment will generally be preferred where a few simple operations have to be performed on a large body of data. An example of the use of a computer for an investigation comparable to one a geographer might attempt is given by a recent attempt to establish the number of full-time farms in England and Wales. In this project up to 140 items of livestock and crops for each of 75,000 holdings had to be multiplied by a different factor, the results added, and the total compared with standard figures and sorted. Such a project could never have been contemplated by ordinary methods. It is true that programming and the preparation of tape to feed data into the computer is time consuming; but the data can be more adequately checked, and necessary statistical procedures, now generally neglected, can be undertaken. As in sampling, the use of computers has the salutary effect of demanding much preliminary thought about the purpose of the investigation. The saving in man power is, therefore, very considerable, and the range of calculation which it is practicable to undertake is vastly increased.

Even the process of drawing maps can be undertaken by computers. Recent work by meteorologists has shown that synoptic charts can be plotted in a matter of seconds, rather than in a normal time of 10 or 15 minutes for a simple map drawn by hand. These maps can be produced by a line-printer attached to a computer—a method which takes about one minute for the calculation and printing of the map, giving a result which is as good as the data probably justify. A more refined map is produced if the results of the calculation performed by the computer are displayed on a cathode-ray tube, and the map is then recorded on photographic plates. Using this method the delay involved in developing the print is a handicap for meteorological purposes, but this is no hindrance for more humdrum geographical work. Technically, the plotting of results on a cathode-ray tube is of considerable interest, since the mechanical plotting of data is much slower than its computation, so that the computer is idle while its output is being printed. The recording of output electronically solves this difficulty.

Computers can also calculate ratios and densities and plot them by grid references, so that choropleth maps can be quickly prepared. According to O. Hedbom and F. Petrini, agricultural maps of this kind have been made; and W.T. Williams and J.M. Lambert have similarly shown how maps of the association of different plant species can be produced by computer.

By making the production of maps easier in this way a great variety of geographical data could be analyzed quickly. Thus a chance idea occurring to a research worker could be tested by a rough map produced rapidly and accurately, although, at present, shortage of time prevents many interesting and perhaps important byways being followed.

The Measurement of Areas

In the examples so far considered the data have already been in numerical form; but modern techniques can also be used to convert qualitative information into quantitative, either by counting items or by measuring areas. This latter possibility is of great importance to the geographer, for conventional methods of measuring by plainimeter and squared paper are very slow and tedious for the frustrating problem of measuring the areas of highly complex, fragmented distributions.

Several methods go towards solving this difficulty. With the help of colleagues in other disciplines the authors of this paper have conducted experiments in two techniques for measuring black and white distribution maps. One method is to use very sensitive photo-electric cells to measure the amount of light which passes through a map drawn on translucent material, and from this information to calculate the area blacked in. With simple maps this method is very successful, but if the distribution being measured is very fragmented it appeared to be less efficient.

Another approach is to use a flying spot scanner, in which an electronic beam moving across a very fine mesh scans a photograph of the map; in other words it is a very rapid method of counting squares. A series of experiments have shown that neither the distribution of the areas being measured nor their fragmentation affect the results obtained, provided the individual parcels exceed a certain minimum size, related to the fineness of the scanning. Once a photographic negative of the map has been prepared, measurements can be carried out in a few seconds, although several days might have been required using conventional methods of no higher standards of precision. Even with very complex, fragmented distributions an accuracy of at least 95 per cent has been reached using this scanning method. Clearly there is scope here for the rapid conversion of the qualitative data shown on chorochromatic maps (which is exceptionally difficult to handle satisfactorily) into numerical values which can then be processed in the ways already discussed.

Such possibilities are not restricted to the measurement of areas. One method, devised by W. G. Byron, uses a photometer to measure densities from a dot map—a system comparable to one of those described for measuring areas. The photometer is mounted so that it can be made to scan small areas of the map, and it is linked to a recording device to permit the automatic plotting of each traverse. For this method to succeed the dots must be of uniform size, the map must contain no other symbols, and it must be drawn on a homogeneous background. The value of the technique, however, lies in its ability to produce rapid and objective calculations of density. Since the blackness of a dot map is related to the number of symbols upon it, this system can also be used to count the dots. The flying spot scanner can also be adapted to this end.

The techniques so far discussed are merely designed to speed up methods of working which are already part of the general tools of geographical research; but in addition these ways of handling data also open up various new avenues for research. J. P. Latham, for example, has attempted to describe various distributions in a more sophisticated fashion by measuring their occurence along numerous traverses across maps and then manipulating the results statistically. While this work can be carried out manually, the procedure is laborious and its general application to the study of large areas clearly depends on using electronic methods. Indeed Latham has found that equipment can be built to distinguish the various shades of gray on an air photograph, so that even these can be scanned electronically to give quantitative information on particular distributions without the tiresome intermediate stage of plotting on a map.

Similar work has been undertaken at the Massachusetts Institute of Technology, where methods have been devised for representing a band of terrain in numerical or digital form, using information either taken from a contour map or from air photographs. These data are stored on magnetic or punched tape, so that they are suitable for use by computer when required. So far the application of the technique has been in solving engineering problems connected with such tasks as building reservoirs and roads. There is no reason why information on settlement and land use should not be processed in the same way and similarly applied. For example, by collecting data at periodic intervals from air photographs the process of change in the cultural landscape could be quickly and comprehensively analyzed.

Conclusion

It could be argued that many of the limitations of modern geographical writing spring from the fact that geographers exhaust themselves making incomplete analyses by primitive methods, and thus have no energy left for the strenuous effort which good writing and penetrating generalization require. The various methods which have been described in this paper may make it possible for geographers interested in handling quantitative data to free themselves for the vital task of thinking about their results as well as computing their data.

There are doubtless other approaches which might profitably be followed, and some geographers with special aptitudes might well devise new methods for themselves as well as borrowing from other disciplines. But it is not necessary or desirable that all geographers should become statisticians, mathematicians, or engineers; provided they are clear about their aims there is no reason why the skilled

advice of colleagues in other disciplines should not be sought. Whatever their source, the employment of modern labor-saving methods,
which avoid unnecessary drudgery but require careful planning, will
encourage the most appropriate use of academic talents to the en-
richment of the subject as a whole.

20. On Perks and Pokes

Arthur H. Robinson

*Geographers have been preoccupied in recent years with
the place of statistical or quantitative research methods in
their work. The growth of these techniques has resulted
from the attempt by some geographers to make the field
more scientific and theoretical. Others who are concerned
only with empirical research or the "art" side of the
discipline have been disturbed by this development. In this
selection, Robinson takes a middle-of-the-road position,
stressing the value of the quantitative approach of the
"perks", but cautioning them not to get so carried away by
technique that they lose sight of the objective of geography,
which is the understanding of areas. He reminds the
"pokes," the empiricists, that the use of statistics is now as
essential as cartography and that appropriate techniques
often facilitate research. The "pokes" are gradually coming
to see the need for quantitative methods, and the "perks"
are beginning to see these methods as only a part of the
geographer's equipment.*

The recent and remarkable expansion of statistical research methods
has clearly reached geography. Whether its eager adoption by some
stems from an honest desire to get at substantive problems more efficiently, or merely from a desire to appear scientifically more respectable, is an interesting question but one hardly worth investigation.
On the other hand, the fact that there has been such a development
is apparently a matter of considerable moment, judging from the
volume of editorials, reviews, and substantive proposals and papers
that take direct and oblique looks at it. Geography seems currently to
be rather strongly divided regarding the utility of quantitative research

SOURCE: *Economic Geography*, XXXVII (April, 1962), 181-83. The author is professor of geography at the University of Wisconsin.

techniques; in any group to which new ideas are introduced one may observe: the *avant garde* which commits itself rapidly, wholly, and often rather thoughtlessly; the *garde arrière*, which reacts almost instinctively against change; and a larger number that, either through openness of mind or mugwumpism, adopts a watchful wait-and-see attitude.

As one might expect, the differences between the extremists in geography are in matters of degree; the most inspired of the visionaries admit, grudgingly perhaps, that some things can't be counted, and the arch-conservatives are not altogether against arithmetic. Yet the differences appear great enough to make it worthwhile to take yet another look at the causes championed by those one may call the *hyperquantifiers* as opposed to the *hypoquantifiers*, and especially at the former who represent the innovators. We have been led up the garden path before and we ought to be wary; on the other hand one ought not dismiss new ideas without an adequate hearing. In the interest of less redundancy it is appropriate to reduce the designations *hyperquantifier* and *hypoquantifier* by cancelling out their common affixial elements leaving *per* and *po* as categorical stems. These are euphonically wanting, however, and *perks* and *pokes* are far easier terms. Their connotations are a bit "loaded," but not unintentionally; the writer confesses to finding a refreshing "perkiness" among many of the more impassioned supporters of quantification and a rather depressing "pokiness" among their opposites.

Perkiness is not always a corollary of intellectual virtue, however, nor pokiness of its opposite, and it is unfortunate that both the perks and pokes imply that the rest of us ought to get at the business of choosing sides. Such choice will come to pass as a consequence of demonstrations of validity and utility. Nevertheless, in spite of the fact that the most extreme of positions is rarely tenable, it does not seem a waste of time to examine some of the implications and assertions or assumptions of the perks and pokes who seem to be at odds.

To begin with, a few observations on pokiness are in order. The time-honored and demonstrably effective methods on which the pokes would have us rely are no less rigorous and exacting than those of the perks. Denial of this suggests an ignorance of the accomplishments of the discipline. The objectives of the pokes are the same geographical ends claimed by the perks; to dispute this is to verify the ignorance. The indictment of the true poke must rest, rather, on his unwillingness to employ a particular kind of methodology that might illuminate a problem.

The descriptive and analytical usefulness of statistical method is ably recounted in the introductions to most treatises in that field. An understanding of the potentialities of this method, and a competence in using many of its tools, is no more difficult to acquire than are most of the other specialized kind of skills and knowledge traditionally asked of professional geographical training. It is now abundantly clear that there *are* mathematical methods available for dealing with the complexity of things in spatial array for which there are no methodological substitutes. To ignore them on the basis of whim is not a minor intellectual sin of omission; it verges on "know-nothingism" at its worst. But such extremes of pokiness are rarely argued strongly, and it is the pronouncements and activities of the more aggressive and vocal proponents of perkiness that should receive our greatest attention.

If one is to have perks around one must, I suppose, learn to live with hard-to-understand, statistical jargon (although it does make professional life difficult); but one could wish they would come down to earth long enough actually to test, geographically, in simple fashion, the more basic aspects of their techniques in order to make the character of their methods abundantly clear. The majority of geographers need understandable examples and need them in good number. My main concerns with the perks, however, involve three more fundamental matters: (1) they give little consideration to some of the technical problems that are inherent in or arise from the methods they employ; (2) they imply, perhaps unconsciously, that their aims are a cut above those of pokes and others, that their work is more accurate and therefore more scientific, i.e., better, and that through their lofty *search for theory* they will immeasurably advance geographical understanding; and (3) their predilection for quantitative methods may ultimately seriously bias geographical research.

As but one example of the first, let me cite a problem to which the perks have paid little attention, namely, the significance of the inescapable regional bias that must result from the application of mathematical methods to a spatial population the areal limits of which must be arbitrarily defined—unless the whole earth be included in the study. It comes about because any geographical application of a statistical technique requires rigid boundaries around the research area. For example, if one is employing regression analysis, the coefficients obtained must necessarily be affected by the arbitrary definition of the limits of the area being studied. They are thus uniquely biased and, of course, the pattern of any subsequent residual analysis is similarly influenced. To jettison those areas that are inconveniently out-of-line with respect to the general regression is to throw out the baby with the bath water since, as unwanted "atypical" areas are discovered and deleted, the coefficients are changed and new ones will crop up elsewhere until nothing but the tiniest unique is left. "Unique" seems to be an unattractive word to perks, but I suspect that, because of the way it shows up so strongly in arithmetic results, they are going to have to learn to live with it. For them to treat an arbitrary area as a "sample" of a larger (and indeterminate) population is begging the basic question.

Again, the search for theory is a grand thing, providing there is any possibility that there is one. I suspect that the word *theory* as applied by the perks to cultural matters is used simply as a better-sounding synonym for *description*. When one is dealing with physical laws, theories are basic explanations or descriptions of their interaction that, if correct, will apply without regard to time or location. Now man certainly organizes himself in a variety of ways for a variety of complex reasons (and sometimes without reason) but he certainly is not governed by any "natural law" that is independent of himself. Furthermore, man and culture (in the broad sense) evolve continuously in a Lamarckina fashion, that is, the acquired characteristics of culture *are* inherited because society learns and passes on what it learns. Therefore, the only "natural" law of cultural spatial regularity there can be is that change will occur. Consequently, any geographical *theory* can only be a description of current or past operations. One may, of course, adopt the working assumption that "total" man might one day try to organize himself on the whole earth so as to "maximize" his "return" in a sort of materialistic, linear programming fashion, but even then his evaluation of "return" would continually change. There are an infinite number of cultural "orders" and apparent degrees of interrelationships that can be ascertained and described (by either perky or poky methods), but for a geographer to imply that these are independent of unique culture and place is on a par with an historian claiming that "history repeats itself."

Finally, quantitative research methods are useful when a problem calls for them and the data are available. But many important geographical subjects are and *always will be* susceptible of attack only by the methods exclusively employed by the pokes. One who is not used to the often much more difficult poky methods may become fascinated by "having a jolly time with numbers" and find the practice habit forming. Only the research worker who limits his study to technique appropriately may select substantive topics that exemplify the technique being investigated. The suspicion grows, however, that some perks, who are not technical specialists, will undertake a substantive problem *only* if it can be attacked by quantitative methods. In time, as these methods appropriate to geographical research develop, and as the number of research students capable of using them grows, such a practice would inevitably lead to a serious substantive bias in geographical research. Not only would a great number of important subjects begging investigation be ignored but those actually attacked would receive only partial treatment.

I recommend that those who are concerned about these matters should keep in mind the basically simple disciplinary foundations of geography. Geography is still, as always, trying: to understand the manner in which variables exhibit locational interrelationships and functional interconnections through *area* and in *place* at the present or through time; to communicate conclusions about such understandings; and to build a fund of knowledge which will enable future geographers better to undertake the same kinds of tasks. What more could one ask of an honorable science and profession? Nothing, except to keep in mind that *place* and *area* are the passwords for entrance to it, that *all* appropriate methods to achieve its ends must be used, and that either to concentrate almost solely upon or largely to ignore any particularly specialized methodology is unacceptable on any but pedagogical grounds.

21. The Use of Computers in the Processing and Analysis of Geographic Information

Richard C. Kao

High-speed computers are becoming increasingly essential in the processing and analysis of geographic data. They save time, tackle complex problems, and produce accurate results. But the new equipment has outstripped man's ability to use it, so that its potential is still unrealized. Kao discusses the effects of the computer on the present and future of geography.

The purpose of this paper is to assess—at least on a modest scale—the impact of high-speed computers on the collection and use of data in geographic research. Geographic data are customarily classified into two distinct types: locational and areal. By locational data are not necessarily meant only the geodetic coordinates of a small point on earth with respect to some arbitrarily chosen reference system (for example, latitude and longitude), but almost any other form of information which can be associated with that point (for example, its altitude above mean sea level or the normal atmospheric pressure thirty feet

SOURCE: *Geographical Review*, L (1963), 530-47. Dr. Kao is a research economist with the RAND Corporation, Santa Monica, California.

above it along the plumb line). Areal data, on the other hand, are those which characterize a region on the globe (the population of Kenya or the amount of oil deposits off the California coast, for example). Locational data are the values of a "point function," areal data those of a "set function." In either case the domain of definition of the function is the outer shell of the earth—Hettner's *Erdhulle* or Hartshorne's *earth shell*. That this definition includes also points in space is a natural consequence of the kind of reality studied by geographers.[1]

Impact of Computers on Future Geographic Research

It is probably trite to say that any geographic research must have to do with either locational or areal data of some sort. It is equally trite to say that automation in the form of high-speed computers is here to stay. Everyone knows that one of the things these giant brains are supposed to do is to process data on a grand scale and at awe-inspiring speed. A fundamental question then arises: What impact, if any, may they exert on data collection and utilization in future geographic research? This is a large question, to which no neat and simple answer can be given at present. However, two examples may serve to illustrate the manner in which such impact is already, and can be, felt.

The Geographic Ordering of Information

The first example may be called the "geographic ordering of information."[2] All geographers are aware that information in their research must be spatially ordered. However, in the past, owing to certain technologic constraints, such information was often ordered in a nongeographic or quasi-geographic format. Some of these constraints are fast disappearing since the introduction of the computer, but the methodology developed within their context lingers on. A typical case is census data. Traditionally, each census tract is given an arbitrary code designation, and a list of characteristics of the tract is appended. Information so provided can be meaningfully analyzed without any reference whatever to the exact location of the tract. But such analysis is almost by definition nongeographic or, at best, quasi-geographic. The code designation does specify in which state and which county a tract is located, but it is completely random as to location within the county.

[1] See Hans Carol: Geography of the Future, *Professional Geographer*, Vol. 13, No. 1, 1961, pp. 14-18, especially pp. 14-15. From now on I shall avoid using the cumbersome phrase "geographic or spatial data" and shall employ the word "geographic" in its more comprehensive sense..

[2] This example and the discussion of it are based largely on W. R. Tobler: Geographic Ordering of Information, *Univ. of Washington, Dept. of Geogr., Discussion Paper No. 38*, 1960.

A geographic analysis that needs the location of a census tract can therefore be made only by the help of supplementary information. This information is typically in the form of a map showing the exact location of the census tracts. The published tables of information by census tracts can then be spatially ordered and geographically analyzed.

Another familiar method of presenting geographic data is a lexicographic listing of geographic areas with associated information; for example, an alphabetic listing of the states or of counties within a given state. To analyze such information geographically, it is necessary first to extract the information from the listing and transfer it to a map. With the ready availability of computers, it is not difficult to picture the possibility of direct analysis without the transference from tables to maps now required.

Perhaps the most extreme form of the traditionally accepted ordering of geographic data is the metes and bounds system still used in some states for legal description of real property. The description uses bench marks, which may be anything from an oak tree [3] to an abandoned well. This system is as confused and inconvenient as the British coinage system, something to be cherished only by future historians or present-day Englishmen. The township and range system used in the Survey of the Public Lands of the United States, though a considerable improvement over the metes and bounds system for cadastral surveys, still leaves much to be desired. Basically, the township and range system is a combination of an areal (or set, as against point) coordinate system and a lexicographic listing. By an areal coordinate system is meant a coordinate system not for individual points but for unit areas (point sets) on the globe. In the Public Lands Survey the unit areas are the six-mile-square townships. These quadrilateral unit areas are approximately equal in size and are ordered in east–west (range) and north–south (township) directions as points in the plane. Thus, with reference to the San Bernardino Base and Meridian, the unit area with coordinate Township 4 North, Range 9 West, is in the "second quadrant" of the areal coordinate system, and that with coordinate Township 2 South, Range 1 East, is in the "fourth quadrant." Superimposed on this "coarse" areal coordinate system is a lexicographic (in this case, numerical) listing of the thirty-six sections for each unit area arranged in a serpentine fashion beginning with the northeast corner of the unit area.

Two observations are in order. First, to the extent that the township and range system is a partition of areas its units are similar to census or county units. Second, the entire Public Lands Survey system is a collection of different areal coordinate systems with not only limited

[3] "Surveyors Find Witness Trees 131 Years Old," *Surveying and Mapping*, Vol. 21, 1961, p. 84.

but uneven coverage. For example, there is no unit area with coordinate Township 36 South, Range 140 East, Mount Diablo Base and Meridian. For such a unit would be close to Albuquerque, New Mexico, where the reference point is the New Mexico Principal (106° 53' 12" W., 34° 15' 35" N.) rather than Mount Diablo (121° 54' 47" W., 37° 52' 54" N.).[4] That the coverage of different areal coordinate systems is uneven is well known. What may not be generally known is the degree to which unevenness exists. Take, for example, the Humboldt Base and Meridian system and the San Bernardino Base and Meridian system in California. The area covered by the San Bernardino is at least ten times larger than that covered by the Humboldt. These observations serve to point out the highly sectionalized nature of the township and range system, which is clearly a heritage from the pre-automation era—not only chronologically but also conceptually.[5]

The three types of geographic ordering of information mentioned above—census tracts, lexicographic listing, and bench-mark system—are sufficient to prove my first point of contention: that is, as computers are used more widely to process data, geographers will find it more convenient and necessary to order information in an analytic rather than a descriptive form. These are many problems badly in need of research now or soon, before such a transition is possible. For instance, just imagine what geographers would have to do in order to give a workable analytic definition of the seemingly trivial concept of "contiguity."

An excellent illustration of the need to order geographic information in analytic rather than descriptive form is a study by Torsten Hägerstrand.[6] The Swedish census reports information on individual households by street address—a mixture of a lexicographic listing and a bench-mark system. Hägerstrand translated all street addresses into coordinates of the Swedish military grid—an analytic form—and data on each household and the coordinates of that household were punched on Hollerith cards. A listing of this information turns out to be both convenient and sufficient for a wide variety of geographic analyses; for example, analysis of population or income distribution by provinces,

[4] Coordinates from "Manual of Instructions for the Survey of the Public Lands of the United States, 1947" (Bureau of Land Management, U. S. Department of the Interior, 1947).

[5] William D. Pattison: The Original Plan for an American Rectangular Land Survey, Surveying and Mapping, Vol. 21, 1961, pp. 339-345. See also Donald B. Clement: Progress in Cadastral Surveys, ibid., pp. 79-84; Lyle F. Jones: Cadastral Surveys—The Rectangular System Surveys and Protractions, ibid., Vol. 20, 1960, pp. 459-468.

[6] Statistiska primäruppgifter, flygkartering och "Data Processing" -maskiner:Ett kombinerings-projekt, Svensk Geogr. Arsbok, Vol. 31, 1955, pp. 233-255 (with summary in English, pp. 254-255). (Also as separate, Meddelanden fran Lunds Univ. Geogr. Instn. No. 344, 1955.)

or the construction of such useful statistics as the average distance of a household to the nearest neighbor, or the correlation between the distribution of schoolchildren and that of teachers under forty years of age. The objective of Hägerstrand's study is "to investigate if a possibility exists to give to the space-aspect of statistical material the same neutrally objective status as the time-aspect always had." [7]

New Light on Old Problems

The second example is somewhat different. Besides inducing geographers to abandon some old customs, computers may permit new light to be focused on old problems. A concrete illustration may be taken from the field of cartography. Among all available map projections geographers are inclined to use equivalent (or equal-area) maps the most, mathematicians conformal maps the most. Presumably the reason for the difference is a matter both of interest and of emphasis. Geographers are primarily concerned with studying geographic environment, which usually makes reference to area as the variable,[8] only rarely are angles of much significance except for problems connected with navigation. Mathematicians, on the other hand, usually study maps as a special case of the general theory of transformations. When only a system of two functions of two variables, representing two distinct sets of coordinate systems, is concerned, there is available a rather elegant mathematical theory called conformal mapping. However, this theory may or may not have relevance in a particular piece of geographic research.

In a study involving real-time simulation of a great mass of geographic data some years ago,[9] I found geometric (or perspective) maps to be far superior to conformal maps, for the simple reason that the property of conformality, being at best a local isometry, is of relatively little importance to the problem, whereas properties in the large, such as a great-circle path or the property of a point lying inside or outside a region, are far more relevant. As a consequence, metric methods are subordinated to projective or topological methods for both the description and the analysis of the problem.[10] In order that visual esthetics will not be entirely eliminated, sub-routines are prepared that permit

[7] *Ibid.*, p. 254.

[8] The basic units in the township and range system are approximately equal in (areal) size. Hence this system is approximately equal-areal but is not a map projection according to the usually accepted definition.

[9] Richard C. Kao: Geometric Projections in System Studies, in *Quantitative Geography: Proceedings of the NAS-NRC Symposium on Quantitative Methods in Geography*, Chicago, Illinois, May, 1959 (edited by W. L. Garrison). (Forthcoming.)

[10] For an illuminating discussion on the topological, as distinct from the metric, properties of coordinates, see Hans Reichenbach: *The Philosophy of Space and Time* (translated by Maria Reichenbach and John Freund; New York, 1958), p. 244.

instantaneous display of simulated air pictures on a cathode-ray tube in the form of a conformal map. But the real work is carried out in terms of projective coordinates in the computer program because these are found to be particularly suitable for rapid arithmetic manipulation. Here is an instance in which a class of maps generally considered to be uninteresting and antiquated could, because of the computer, compete on equal footing with a class which has hitherto been accepted almost ex cathedra as being the ultimate in cartography. Until computers can perform the function of information storage and retrieval as efficiently as, or even more efficiently than, that of calculation, geometric maps will continue to receive increasing attention both in theory and in practice.

Perspective maps are also becoming more important in another context, that of space exploration, particularly satellite reconnaissance. If we stay sufficiently close to the earth's surface, relatively little distortion is introduced by assuming the surface to be flat. However, as we go to higher altitudes, the curvature of the earth can hardly be ignored. By the very nature of the geometry, the satellite is taking a perspective map if we assume light to travel in a straight line, probably the best approximation if we confine ourselves to the gravitational field around the earth.[11] It is sometimes instructive to stop and think back a little. Perspective maps were first studied because of their intimate connection with certain physical problems; if staying close to the real problem is the criterion, then we can hardly throw away these maps and use others simply because the others may be more appealing from a. mathematical standpoint. Great mathematicians—for example, Hilbert and Poincaré—always insisted on staying close to the real problem even when a most difficult mathematical theory was being developed. They would be the last to abandon the real problem and concentrate on some arbitrary abstraction of it to suit their own convenience. Felix Klein said some fifty years ago: "I should like to emphasize, however, that precisely in geographic practice use is often made of *representations in which angles are not preserved*, so that conformal transforma-

---

[11] It is interesting to speculate here on the extent to which a computer may be substituted for (or complement) an optical device for the correction of the earth's curvature in photogrammetry. In theory, a computer program may be so prepared as to transform photographic inputs from one perspective map into another (or into an analytic map). Such transformation is now facilitated by direct optical devices (camera lens or prism), the design of which requires an increasingly higher marginal cost for further improvement in performance as the limit of technology is approached. One possible trade-off would be a special-purpose computer designed to carry out the necessary transformation on the inputs—preferably in real time—such as the new "space computer" mentioned by P. J. Klass: New Data System Proposed for Space, *Aviation Week and Space Technology*, Vol. 76, No. 21, 1962, pp. 77-79. See also Amrom H. Katz: Observation Satellites: Problems and Prospects (in 6 parts; reprinted from *Astronautics*, 1960), especially pp. 3-5 and 10.

tions should not be regarded, as is often done, as the only important ones" (his italics).[12] If geographic research calls for other maps, there is no scientific rationale to require everybody to use conformal maps exclusively. When we place our emphasis in cartography not so much on the end product of a highly technical process called map making as on the relation between a pair of maps (data processing of geographic information),[13] we may find some old, long-forgotten maps to be handy at times. Hence computers may not only force geographers to abandon old habits; they may also garb geographers in old habits that are no longer considered fashionable, though with good reason.

. . . . .

The desirability of the adoption of a universal mapping system by users of geographic information has been much discussed.[14] But before we decide which particular system to adopt, it is well to ask ourselves what a universal mapping system can accomplish. Such a mapping system is by its very nature only a labeling system. It cannot get to the heart of every conceivable type of problem in which geographic data are being used. What it does provide is a useful and certainly important means of easy communication between users of maps, but easy communication should not always be the overriding criterion when a diversity of problems arise. An analogy may illustrate the point. It cannot be assumed that the adoption of Esperanto, presumably a universal linguistic system, would cause all the peoples in the world to iron out their differences, because it wouldn't. The problems will always exist whether Esperanto exists or not. One thing we may do well to remember is this: by making any system of representation more *general*, we are at the same time also reducing its usefulness for a *particular* application.

It is perhaps instructive to make a general observation here on various maps that have been either proposed or used to process geographic information. If popularity is to be the criterion, most of these tend to

[12] Felix Klein: *Elementary Mathematics from an Advanced Standpoint* (translated from the 3rd German edition by E. R. Hedrick and C. A. Noble; 2 parts; New York, 1932-1940), Part 2 (Geometry), p. 103.

[13] See Richard C. Kao: Geometric Projections of the Sphere and the Spheroid, *Canadian Geographer*, Vol. 5, No. 3, 1961, pp. 12-21.

[14] A universal mapping system is a system of coordinates for storage of spatial data that could be used with equal facility by earth scientists or civil, governmental, and military agencies on a national (or even international) basis. See John A. O'Keefe: The Universal Transverse Mercator Grid and Projection, *Professional Geographer*, Vol. 4, No. 5, 1952, pp. 19-24; and "The Universal Grid Systems," *U. S. Dept. of the Army Tech. Manual 5-241; U. S. Dept. of the Air Force Tech. Order 16-1-233*, Washington, D. C., 1951. I have also benefited from private correspondence with Professor Edward B. Espenshade, Jr., of Northwestern University, Dr. John A. O'Keefe, Theoretical Division, NASA, Goddard Space Flight Center, and Professor Waldo R. Tobler of the University of Michigan.

fall into two types—maps without projections [15] and maps without applications. Maps without projections are generally inventions by users who merely need some sort of geographic representation to plot some data. They either do not care about, or are not fully aware of, the implications of the representation invented or chosen. The information so obtained or represented has no "transfer" value, in the sense that no one else can use it with any degree of assurance as to either the limitations or the probable error. Such maps may be called "unreferenced systems," [16] whose exact relations to the terrestrial reference of geodetic coordinates are not known.

Maps without applications have been invented largely as mathematical curiosities. The best illustration is the class of conformal maps. Apparently, the only basis for the construction of some of these is the fundamental theorem in the theory of a complex variable: every complex analytic function of a complex variable gives rise to a conformal map, and conversely. Since it is also true that composing two analytic functions leads to another analytic function, one may immediately begin a rampage of printing out as many conformal maps as one pleases without any regard whatever as to the utility of most of them. A relevant comment is that in mathematics it is usually the general theory that is of interest and not any particular realization of that theory.

These two extremes may be partly mitigated by the adoption of a universal mapping system. But the choice of such a system can best be made *after,* not before, a careful determination of all requirements that are likely to arise in problems involving geographic information.

Computers and Types of Users of Geographic Data

Let us turn now to the nature of the problems facing users of geographic data. By users of geographic data I mean people in various disciplines who are likely to have need for computers in their work, presumably with reference to geographic information. Typical users would be workers in the earth sciences. We may take the list of component societies of the Division of Earth Sciences, National Academy of Sciences—National Research Council, and ask in each case, "Why and how would an individual in this particular discipline use a computer in his work." The result is a continuum (see figure) that more or less represents a gradation of potential uses of the computer in the various disciplines, ranging from the bookkeeping type to the computation type. Each discipline may be depicted as a distribution over this con-

[15] Richard E. Dahlberg: Maps without Projections, *Journ.·of Geogr.,* Vol. 60, 1961, pp. 213-218.
[16] Waldo R. Tobler: *Coordinates for Geographic Inventories* (draft of unpublished paper, University of Michigan, 1962), pp. 9-10.

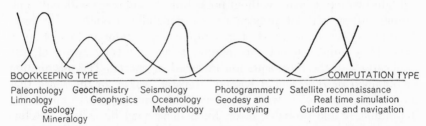

BOOKKEEPING TYPE   COMPUTATION TYPE

Paleontology	Geochemistry	Seismology	Photogrammetry	Satellite reconnaissance
Limnology	Geophysics	Oceanology	Geodesy and	Real time simulation
Geology		Meteorology	surveying	Guidance and navigation
Mineralogy				

tinuum with a mean value situated somewhere within the range indicated. There may, of course, be greater dispersion within disciplines than between them, but our representation is probably accurate when the entire discipline is considered. Geography does not appear on the continuum since this subject seems too encompassing or dispersed to fit into any one place. Indeed, one needs only to recall the various kinds of geography studied to appreciate the dilemma. To put the matter differently, it may be necessary to draw a multi-modal distribution to represent geography on this continuum. However, it is likely that the highest of the modes would fall within the one-quarter interval at the left end of the continuum. There is, of course, no necessary implication in the continuum of a one-to-one correspondence between disciplines and the peak values of distributions on it. Geography is one example, many others might be given. One that might be mentioned— just to illustrate the range of the problems we must be prepared to face before we can choose this or that particular universal mapping system as best for our purpose—is civil defense. The reason for using this example is twofold: the problem is becoming one of the central issues in the discussion of national security policy, and very little is known or done about it.

Problems in civil defense are generally of three types, belonging to the preattack, during-attack, or postattack phase.[17] In the preattack period the primary interest is in stockpile or inventory statistics of transportation, production, and the like. We want to know what types of survival articles to store and how much of them, where to store them, and according to what priorities they are to be stored. Food, fuel, and medical supplies undoubtedly head the list, then perhaps come spare parts for machinery, implements for restoring power and communication, fertilizers, and so on.[18] The basic problem is to pro-

[17] See B. F. Massell and S. G. Winter, Jr.: *Postattack Damage Assessment: A Conceptual Analysis* (The RAND Corporation, RM-2844-PR, November, 1961).
[18] See, for example, two papers by Donald V. T. Bear and Paul G. Clark, "Industrial Survival in Nuclear War," *Quart. Rev. of Economics and Business*, Vol. 1, No. 3, 1961, pp. 39-51, and "The Importance of Individual Industries for Defense Planning," *Amer. Econ. Rev.*, Vol. 51, No. 2, 1961, pp. 460-464; and Harold Mitchell: *Ecological Problems and Postwar Recuperation: A Preliminary Survey from the Civil Defense Viewpoint* (The RAND Corporation, RM-2801, August, 1961).

duce a cartogram of inventory statistics that will provide a basis for rational planning.

When attack has been initiated and is continuing, we are faced with new and radically different problems that require solution in real time to provide a useful basis for immediate action. Warning and bomb-alarm systems certainly will be of no value if information updating has not been possible or is too slow. Problems of action such as civilian evacuation and dispersal and determination of fallout coverage and direction will be likely to have time as the limiting factor. Hence the problem of updating information in real time has been added on top of the stockpiling problem of the preattack stage.

The postattack period has two types of problems: those related to immediate survival and those related to long-term recovery. For immediate survival new estimates of supplies and personnel are needed, which must be correlated with the estimates made in the preattack phase for proper adjustment and execution of the preattack plan, since stockpiles and personnel included in the original plan were themselves possible targets and may have been destroyed during the attack. Real-time determination of these types of information is an absolute requirement. On the other hand, types of information for long-term recovery are directed toward possible economic reorganization and political reorientation, and may evolve slowly with time. It is not crucial that such information be forthcoming in a day or so. Reliable and carefully determined information would be preferable to rough and perhaps highly unreliable information, which could, however, be generated very quickly.

It would seem, then, that there are basically two distinct types of problems in civil-defense planning, each requiring its own kind of attention. It would be a mistake not to carry out a thorough study but to pick some arbitrary universal mapping system to store all the needed stockpiling and personnel statistics. Perhaps it might even be desirable to have these statistics stored in different forms to meet the different requirements described above.

A less sanguinary but somewhat related problem is poll prediction. Basically, this problem is of the bookkeeping type, though large and complicated. However, computers can now carry out this bookkeeping job so efficiently that results in early election returns could be made available to "influence" later returns. Consideration of the possibility and its political implications was voiced in Congress in regard to the future role of the various mass media and communication systems. What it means is that a job previously assumed to be time-consuming and hence politically "neutral" can now be performed with such efficiency as to provide a basis for shaping an instrument of policy. This example clearly shows the dynamic character of a problem that results from increased efficiency in processing and communicating information that is basically of a geopolitical character. It comes down to this, then. Although a universal mapping system is highly desirable as a common frame of reference for all geographic data, its users should be as willing to abandon it as they are to adopt it. Only by doing so can we keep up with the progress of time.

VI. TRENDS IN THE SCIENCE OF GEOGRAPHY

For years scholars have asked themselves if geography is an art or a science, a social science or a physical science. The answer in many cases is not clear cut as geography includes phenomena that are classified individually as social or physical. It is the complex of factors in a given area that are the concern of the geographer.

As the discussions continue, researchers have been looking for ways of making geography less empirical and more theoretical and predictive, that is to say, more scientific. For a long time, the lack of sophisticated and precise techniques made the search difficult. The application after World War II of higher mathematics and statistical methods facilitated the task and also stimulated greater rigor in those aspects of the discipline that did not lend themselves to quantification. Ways are now being found, and continually sought, of dealing scientifically with the unique character of phenomena on the earth's surface. The scientific advance has been impressive, but it has not eliminated the need for empirical research and accurate description of the landscape.

The following articles illuminate some of the "growing edges" of geography. The writers point out the opportunities for the development of theory and indicate the place of the map and cartography in understanding the earth's complexities.

22. The Way Lies Open
J. Russell Whitaker

Presidential addresses at the annual meetings of the Association of American Geographers have been traditional places for review of past accomplishments and recommendations for the future. Whitaker summarizes the accomplishments and problems of the first half-century of professional geography in the United States. The 1950s

was a turning point in the development of the discipline.
The young men trained just after World War II were
beginning to have an impact in government, business, and
particularly higher education. The quantity and quality
of research increased and the caliber of students rose.
New methods, particularly of the quantitative type,
were rapidly gaining adherents. The way was indeed open
for the more abundant harvest prophesied by Whitaker.

This meeting marks the close of the fiftieth anniversary of the Association of American Geographers. The high quality of papers and discussions at this conference is eloquent testimony to the substantial growth of our field and of our society since its initial meeting, which took place in this city in 1904. Much has been said regarding that first meeting and the developments since that time. I am sure we all feel the satisfaction that comes from seeing a task well done. We can say to ourselves, "This much has been accomplished. Here are landmarks to indicate the distance that we have traveled."

But the concern of the founders of this society was with the future of geography rather than with its past. They were confident that association around a common purpose would be rewarding, both for the development of the field and for the personal satisfactions that every scholar deserves—such as the pleasure of association with persons of like purposes, the thrill from mental tussle with worthy opponents, and the sense that one does not work alone.

There are men and women in this audience who can testify to the personal satisfactions that have come to them through this Association, not only during this week, but through ten, twenty, thirty, forty, and even fifty years; and all can read in the printed record the evidence of the role of this Association in the field of scholarship. Achievements have been substantial, and we rejoice in them and honor the men and women who have made them.

There are suitable times for pausing to take stock and to assess the need for reorientation of one's efforts. Such times come to all of us, provoked perhaps by changes within us, by external circumstances, or by both. This particular stock-taking is set by the calendar and by the habit men have of pausing at fifty-year intervals to check on the course they have taken. If the stock-taking so prompted coincides with a genuine rhythm in the life of the person or persons so much the better. I believe that this occasion does come at such a time for us, a time when North American geographers should take stock of the past and plan for the future.

SOURCE: *Annals of the Association of American Geographers*, LXIV (September, 1954), 231-44. The author is professor of geography at Peabody College.

The principal questions I would have you consider with me, then, are these three: What gains have been made in the fifty years since this society was founded? What are the principal needs for the future? What are the changes required to meet those needs?

I

These fifty years have expanded our endeavor until now geographers occupy a wide range of useful positions. Little needs to be said here about that. Also impressive, as one assesses achievements to date, is the well-balanced, useful understanding that geographers now have of the scope of their work, as a result of long and sincere searching by a great number of scholars, both here and abroad.

One of the achievements of which geographers of this organization may rightly be proud has been this slow, sometimes painful, and even boresome identification and elaboration of the various facets of their endeavor. Thanks to a succession of philosophical papers, and to several volumes prepared in part or whole by members of this organization, an apprentice geographer can now quickly discover the main outlines of his field.

As a result of the labors of our predecessors and associates, a broad, matured, and sharply effective system of thought guides our work. Never before has the range of operations been so wide and so challenging and the theoretical groundwork so well thought out.

To say, however, that a broad frame of reference for our field has been adequately delineated is to risk being misunderstood. Certainly one should keep an open mind for new ideas. There are still large aspects of the field that have not received adequate examination, gaps which others of this society will surely do their best to fill in the years ahead. My thesis is not that our philosophy may now be considered a closed system, but rather that it now has sufficient balance and direction to give each of us the comforting assurance, particularly as we set out as young geographers, that our own task fits into an evolving whole, that what we are doing will contribute to the work of men operating at different points throughout our field. I make this statement with confidence in part because of the publication of the volume, *American Geography, Inventory and Prospect*, the recent presidential address on population geography, and the maturity of the philosophical papers read at this meeting.

However, I would like to sound a warning prompted by a weakness long evident in the thinking of American geographers. Having arrived at a broad, challenging view of the scope of our field, we should resist most sturdily any effort to shrink it and impoverish it. Those of you who are familiar with the history of the efforts in North American to delimit our field realize that too commonly individual geographers have tried to force this broad field into the narrow frame set by their special aptitudes and interests. It has been difficult for some to define the field save as outlined in their own mental image. If leaders have avoided this pitfall, some of their followers have not succeeded in doing so, hence the succession of dogmas and shibboleths that has plagued us.

In the summer of 1921, a visiting geographer from England was distressed by the reception of his philosophy. Said he, "When I talk about man-earth relationships, my colleagues and students are enthusiastic, but I find no support for my interest in the distribution of things over the earth." Had he returned twenty years later, he would have found the reverse to be true in many quarters. Similarly, in the late 1920's one of America's most distinguished geographers visited a university where he spread consternation among members of the geography staff because he talked about topical geography and practical problems instead of regional geography and purely scientific work; but later that same university conferred on this man an honorary doctorate, citing as the basis for it his achievements in topical and applied geography!

The limited grasp of geographers and the haste to discard recently adopted ideas remind me of an incident told by a missionary who had just returned from Northern Rhodesia. In describing the changes that had resulted there from the introduction of maize, he told of a ripening cornfield that had been ravaged by wild animals. One morning it was found that ears of corn had been plucked and thrown on the ground all along between two of the rows. The next morning two more rows had been treated in the same way. The third night a watcher saw an old baboon come waddling out of one edge of the forest clearing, break off an ear of corn and tuck it under one arm, and then another and put it under the other arm. Then he broke off a third ear and in raising an arm to receive it, dropped the ear being held there and put the more recently plucked one in its place. In this fashion he ambled across the field, breaking off ear after ear, dropping one every time he raised his arm to tuck a fresh one in place. He disappeared into the woods with only two ears of corn.

If one has studied and digested the thinking of geographers for a half century, one surely has sufficient wisdom to see that both "distributions" and "relationships" matter; that changing conditions of the physical earth do "influence" man; that man does make "adjustments" to earth conditions; that the "content of area" does present a challenge to geographers; that, however much geographers are interested in the whole earth, they find it convenient to divide it into parts; that, however carefully they center their efforts on a subdivision of the earth, they fall short of their goal if they ignore its spatial relations with the rest of the earth; that geographers should have room in their thinking for both the uniqueness of every place and the oneness of the world. And so I might go on to identify values in many other ideas about which geographers have debated during the last fifty years.

A troubled hope entertained some thirty years or so ago was this, "Surely there must be more to geography than what we now have, something deeper, richer, more worthy of a scholar's wholehearted devotion." That vision of richness of thought is now a reality and need trouble one no longer. The challenge for the near future is not so much to expand our view of our common endeavor as to conserve it and to use it as a guide in substantive work. We shall want to revise its major parts and, as a consequence, refine the whole structure from time to time. We should encourage disagreements, but not discard ideas indiscriminantly. Rather, we should keep what we have gained from home and abroad, steadfastly resisting any effort to narrow, impoverish, or distort it.

II

And so we move from a consideration of the scope of the field of geography to its substance, particularly to the printed record of our work. I anticipate a *major* change in this regard. The years immediately ahead should see, not necessarily more devoted scholarship, but more concentrated, mature, productive scholarship.

Once upon a time a college geography professor called an undergraduate into his office. "What is your major?" he asked. "Why don't you concentrate on geography? One of the delights in geography is that you are never far from the unknown. There is an abundance of opportunity for research." And he might have added, "a necessity for research, if a geographer is to function with a scholar's conscience." Whether one be a geographer in a university position, a government employee, a teacher in a small college, a high school or elementary teacher, or even that rare person, a geographer in business, he is under obligation to be a consistently inquiring person. Few other disciplines confront a worker with so many unknowns, from his very doorstep to the farthest parts of the earth. Albert Perry Brigham's remark before this Association that a great deal of fragmentary research goes into the preparation of a geography textbook applies to practically every professional endeavor in which a geographer engages.

It seems appropriate at this point to review some of the major phases of geographic research, noting the special character of each in our day.

In the first place, as we all recognize, the number of geographers has been so few and the opportunities so abundant that there is need for the services of everyone of us to find answers to all of the questions which seem worth answering. As William Morris Davis once put it, "We have scarcely begun to describe this earth of ours."

Knowing the life-long devotion of William Morris Davis to the study of landforms and climate, we may be sure that studies of such relatively permanent phenomena would loom large in his thinking were he speaking to you now. The vigorous studies now being pursued in climatology, from localities to the world as a whole, are an index to the need and to the response. There are signs, too, that the study of landforms is undergoing a revival and a reorientation that will lead to a description of landforms as they actually are. Certainly large numbers of geographers could find satisfying research careers in these fields, and nearly all could do some local work along the same line.

There is an obvious urgency in the need for geographic research, for part of what is here today may be gone some years from now. This applies especially to human geography. A first responsibility of every generation of geographers might well be to make and preserve essential records of the geography of their time, to get the concrete data that may soon be beyond reconstruction.

Not only do geographers have a special obligation to study contemporary conditions, and not only do they find that to be an unending job because of ceaseless change, but they also have a large responsibility, one not so commonly accepted, for revising and expanding the knowledge of the geography of the past. Too commonly we have rolled up our record and laid it away to lie untouched. A new day is dawning for the historical geographer, in part because his studies can soon be based on the records prepared by trained geographers of bygone days. That is not only a cause for satisfaction, but it may well give some of us pause, for later generations of historical geographers will subject our own studies to rigorous examination. They will have more time for sifting and weighing evidence than has one who is preoccupied with contemporary geography.

Looked at in historical perspective, the geographer's job as a scholar is vast because of the constant unrolling of new scenes to study and the yearly addition of old ones to keep in mind, to learn more about, to revise. But there is still another view, one of spatial perspective, from which the individual geographer's responsibility looms large and the necessity for research correspondingly great.

Most of us would surely agree that the geographer is peculiarly responsible, or at least has a peculiar opportunity, for study of his home locality and regions. We are burdened by the cost in time and money required to study areas at a distance, we may be blocked by language barriers or the hostility of the inhabitants, and we may not know the special channels of information. In all these ways the geographer at home has an advantage. While I would not for one minute argue that the home geographer has no business to study elsewhere, or, on the other hand, that he has a monopoly of local study, I have long thought that he is the proper person to do most of the work on his home area.

Opportunities are great, too, in the home country as a whole. We are reminded of the statement by the French geographer, Albert Demangeon, that geography has taken on nationality. This aspect of geography has grown in part out of the role of geography in war. And if geography has taken on nationality, it has to a similar degree taken on policy implications. One who is a national is in the best position to grasp these and, indeed, to work toward their development.

Even more important, however, is the facility with which a geographer studies his home country. Expense is generally less, library collections are more accessible before and after field study, and field work and correspondence meet with more ready cooperation from those who are in a position to help. Perhaps the best way to appreciate our limitations when working in a foreign country is to consider the difficulties that a foreigner encounters in our own. We are amused, if not irritated, when a visitor from another land appears to believe that he has delved to the bottom of things in brief visits here. So also must our observations in other countries be shallow and sketchy unless based on long and exhaustive study.

Many geographers have done original work on American geography that has led to publication, and all American geographers have made original observations, vast in total extent, which have not appeared in print. The United States has provided a rich area in which to practice. But to a regrettable, even to a distressing, degree geographic study of the United States has remained at apprentice levels. The usual studies have been those that could be rounded out in a year or two with a minimum investment of time and money, of observation and reflection. Badly needed to supplement our knowledge of this country are more comprehensive, exhaustive works.

The special opportunity for the geographer in the study of locality, region, and nation is matched by an obligation to avoid a narrow provincialism and nationalism; and to see, however dimly, the whole of which his area of study is but a part. John Wesley, founder of Methodism, could say, "The world is my parish"; and David Fairchild, plant explorer, entitled one of his books, *The World Is My Garden.* Surely geographers have the obligation to recognize that the total area being investigated is the entire earth surface. As it becomes possible for geographers to travel with less expenditure of time to all parts of the world, as geographers multiply in numbers over the earth, and as they accept more wholeheartedly the obligation to make use of productive scholarship in other languages, they will work more effectively toward a comparative regional geography of the world and a rounding out of world patterns of particular geographic features, associations, and spatial relations.

This leads to a more general question which might well call for consideration and reflection: what, in sum, are the end products of geographic scholarship? Daring a provisional answer, I would suggest, to begin with, that we are engaged in preparing a record of the changing life layer of the earth. As time passes, we add to that record, and we not only try to get at the meaning of what we are seeing and recording, but we also have the opportunity, with the passage of time, to correct the record of the past and to revise interpretations of past geography, both in terms of how it came about and of consequences that flow from it. When we think of an end product of geographic study as a record, descriptive and interpretative, of the nature and changes in the face of the whole earth, much of the distinction between historical and contemporary geography disappears, and we concern ourselves with the total geographic record, its extensions and its revisions through time. Not until geographers accept some such conception of their work will they produce many great books of enduring worth.

Perhaps you agree that the geographic record is the principal end product of geographic scholarship to date. Some of you might wish to point out, however, that this record is, in part, made up of generalizations on facts of first or primary order. In neglecting dissimilarities and recognizing likenesses, a regional delimitation, for example, is a form of generalization. The generalizations involved in summarizing and simplifying the geographic record are, however, functions of specific times and places.

But many geographers are tantalized by fragments of a different type of generalization less sharply tied to place and time. What they perceive, and want more of, is something akin to generalizations in physical sciences, the recognition of recurrent phenomena, of recurrent sequences which are not so closely tied to specific places and which are applicable to the earth at different times.

One of the more promising lines of generalization is in the study of the location of specific phenomena. Surely geographers, of all persons, should be exploring the theory of location of various cultural features. One who moves into this area will find systematic social scientists already working there, and must either retreat or join hands with them in this endeavor.

Another type of generalization that interests some has to do with man-earth relations. Currently some American geographers are shying away from "relations" because, they say, all things are related, and relations are too complex to be treated in a rewarding way. Neither basis is solid ground, in my opinion, for avoiding this kind of study. Whether generalizations dealing with such relations will be so closely tied to time and place as to be unique and, therefore, of limited use outside of their context, or so elementary as to be useless, are questions we are not in a position to answer now.

A third type of generalization deals with sequences. Some have experimented with this in the field of resource depletion and conservation, for example. Such generalizations have value in providing insights and in organizing one's understanding of geographic change, and they have predictive value, although some might say, "Yes, of the obvious." But one could reply, "Perhaps, but not obvious to the persons actually involved in the situations on which the generalizations have been based."

Whether one believes it worthwhile to develop a large body of generalizations which, though derived of necessity from particular time-place situations, are applicable to other places and times, the fact remains that work of that kind is being done. Whether geographers writing at the end of the next fifty years will list sound generalizations of this type as one of the "end products" of geographic scholarship remains shrouded in the mists of the future.

As American geographers get a firmer grasp of the various aspects of geographic scholarship summed up in such end products as the geographical record and geographic generalizations, they may well be aware of the need for a renewed zeal in self-examination, not so much in terms of what ought to be done as in terms of what geographers have done, in terms of the history of geographic thought. Thus I identify a third end product of geographic scholarship, one which some students would consider as including the two already identified.

We need a history of geographic thought that shows the time setting of each major essay in geographic philosophy and methodology. What a man writes from his heart today is not what he would have said twenty years ago or what he would feel compelled to say ten or twenty years hence. We utterly misjudge the view of geography as "human ecology," for example, unless we see it in its nearness to "geographic influence" and "content of area." We fail to understand a critique of regional geography published in 1937 unless we see how far the pendulum had swung toward regional description in the years immediately preceding, for the Second World War has since carried us far toward an appreciation of the topical approach.

I am wondering too if it is not high time that more attention be given to the ideas of our forefathers regarding the problems and findings of substantive research. Is it not possible that hidden in their writings are germs of thought we need? What questions should be addressed to Matthew Fontaïne Maury, to John Wesley Powell, to others on whom our discipline rests? What were they seeking, how did they go about their work, what gaps did they fill for their time, what contributions did they make on which we can build?

We also need a dispassionate study of our forebears as individuals. Indeed, we must have that if we are properly to interpret the remembrances and records of their work. It might be an embarrassing occasion if each member of this group were asked what William Morris Davis stands for in the development of our field, or Rollin D. Salisbury, or Ellen Churchill Semple. Do we know of the long years of service of Ray Hughes Whitbeck, of Almon E. Parkins, and of Richard Elwood Dodge? Has anybody ever called our attention to the felicity of expression of Albert Perry Brigham? Such questions reveal the need for biographical studies of North American geographers.

I dare say that we geographers have never learned to make truly effective use of our great men. We have ignored them perhaps, as we certainly have Matthew Fontaine Maury, Nathaniel Shaler, and John Wesley Powell. If we have not ignored them, we have worshiped them uncritically, or have allowed them to hamper and to bind us. Great men can actually cost more than they are worth if we follow as blind copyists or if we allow the examples they have set to dampen our ardor for further investigation and writing or to make us belittle our own efforts.

Here, then, are identified three of the end products of geographic scholarship: the geographic record, geographic generalizations somewhat divorced from time and place; and, paralleling the preparation of these products, the record of geographic thought, including the history of geographers themselves. The next few years will see notable progress along these three lines, as well as along others of major importance. But if these studies are to be rich and of enduring worth, we must move on from the fragmentary research that so commonly expresses itself orally and passes away with the fading of our memory. North American geographers have the obligation to record a larger part of their observations in more permanent and more widely distributable form. The major challenge for the next twenty-five to fifty years is to reach a higher level of productive scholarship.

The total geographical library resulting from the work of North American geographers is relatively meager. There are many reasons for this, but lack of industry on the part of our geographers is not one of them. On the contrary, if you examine the personal history of any geographer who has been active in the United States over the last twenty or thirty or forty years, you are likely to be impressed with the large number of things he has done. He has initiated many college courses. He has written textbooks. He has spent an enormous amount of time working on college and university problems. He has tackled and successfully elaborated the scope and methodology of his field. He has done, in short, all of these things which added together have given geography a substantial position in the world of learning, all except one thing—the development of a broad and rich professional library, particularly a library of mature monographs and books that are neither dissertations nor textbooks. Have you ever tried to prepare a reading list of American books for economic geography, or historical geography, or North America? If a non-geographer should ask you for a list of top-notch books in geography, what would you give him? You could scarcely turn over to him a list of textbooks, no matter how satisfied you might be with them; nor would it be suitable to hand such a person books on geographic philosophy and methodology.

One is tempted to pause here to comment on the kinds of books that are needed, but I suppose that an adequate though brief statement would be to say, "all kinds." Books on neglected areas, such as a recent, excellent book on the Philippines. Books in which each of the older members of the Association brings together in one place his various theoretical or philosophical ideas. Books that are largely devoted to the more interpretative aspects of areas and of topical phases of geography. And so on. Fifty years from now the librarian of any large university will not be able truthfully to say, as one did recently, that his library has numerous geographical magazines and many geography texts, but that there is a marked gap where he would expect to find books not specifically designed for classroom use.

Thus far in this paper I have developed two propositions: first, that American geographers now have a reasonably adequate grasp of the breadth and depth of their field as a scholarly discipline, but that they must take care to preserve it against shrinkage, impoverishment, and distortion; and, second, that the next fifty years will see an unprecedented expansion of and revision of the geographic record, substantial expansion of geographic generalizations, and much attention given to the history of geographic thought—all set down to an increasing degree in monographs and books.

III

How will the need for a greater output of mature, scholarly writing be met? It can hardly come from greater industry or devotion on the part of geographers. When one recalls the zeal and earnestness of W. W. Atwood, R. H. Whitbeck, Isaiah Bowman, A. P. Brigham, and Ellsworth Huntington, to name only a few, one is not unhappy about the industry, the devotion, or the intellectual powers of our leaders during these five decades. What then can be done? This is a question I would lay on your hearts, to ponder and to answer in your own way, just as I hope you will think about each of the other questions I have raised. But here again, I would like to identify some of the elements of what seem to me to be the answer.

In the first place, there are reasons to believe that, thanks in part to the work of the first five decades, geographers in academic posts will now have more time to devote to sustained scholarship: field work, library study, reflection, and writing. It will not be necessary to devote so much time to organizing and presenting new courses, in part because there are more of us and in part because so much of this work has already been done, and the results made available in handbooks, probably the best textbooks produced anywhere in the world. Some of you may have heard J. Paul Goode say that he had initiated a new course every year or so, and you may also remember the large amount of work evident in the syllabi of his courses. When Professor R. H. Whitbeck was teaching South America in the early twenties, there was not a single textbook on that continent available. The authors of currently used texts on Latin America were still graduate students or were just beginning their postgraduate study.

Closely related to the saving in organizing new courses is that made possible by the reduced need for additional texts. Relatively few geographers now need to devote a large share of their time to that kind of writing, or to channel into texts their creative efforts and their original ideas and findings. Doubtless some of you remember the occasion when one of our number, who has spent much of his professional lifetime preparing textbooks rich in ideas, read a paper before this society and was warmly praised for it. He wryly replied, "All this and more is in my textbook." Not that we want less creative, less original texts, but we do want the products of scholarship so presented that they are not discarded with outdated texts. Moreover, it is good to have a man's creative writing sufficiently isolated so that he himself is known as its source.

There is reason for confidence in increased productivity of geographers because there are increasing numbers in positions which permit and encourage productive scholarship. To see this one has only to recall the large number of geography departments recently established in various parts of Canada and the United States. I am confident, too, that greater opportunity for mature productive scholarship will appear as less energy of the average university professor goes into training of young professional geographers. So long as university departments were few, a large percentage of university men gave so much time to the training of apprentices in our field that they had little time or energy for pursuing their own scholarly interests.

One can hope, too, that the next fifty years will not be so demanding of time of geographers for war efforts and related activities. Many of our older geographers took time out twice for this kind of work; and, however much it added to their own geographical knowledge, it must surely be considered a net drain on geographic productivity. In the late 1930's the number and quality of young geographers coming into the field made it seem that our human resources would at last prove adequate to the task we envisaged. Then came the war, and their efforts were diverted. The post-war period has been less fruitful than some had expected. Perhaps the fruit is taking longer to ripen, though most of us have had ample proof that young men require many months, perhaps even a decade, in which to recover their normal stride following active military service.

But all was not lost in the last war and its aftermath. To an unprecedented degree, young North American geographers studied in other lands. This changed their view of their home land and provided for the first time a large body of geographers who have a sound grounding in field study of foreign areas. The results are beginning to appear in book-length works, as for Japan and southeast Asia.

Doubtless every profession could recruit its numbers with greater care. One recalls the identification made by a keen French social scientist of the two essentials in the personality of productive scholars: the zeal to solve problems, and the zeal to collect. Such essential qualities should be possessed by a high percentage of the young people entering our field. A successful college president once confided, "In recruiting a faculty you need to bring in only persons of distinct promise, for, sure as fate, half of them will have failed of that promise by the time they reach mature years, and quite possibly through no fault of their own." I have often wondered if Jesus just hit by chance on a similar ratio when He told of the ten virgins, half of whom had no reserves of oil for their lamps, and so could not go into the feast. In the long run, the future of geographic scholarship lies in the hands of the persons most actively recruiting new workers for the field.

All the factors I have mentioned have a bearing on the basic need: greater productivity in geographic scholarship. To these each of you will add still other factors. In addition to these, I, too, would call attention to what I believe to be the major way in which we are now moving toward higher levels of productive scholarship—that is, by a degree of personal concentration that will go far beyond that commonly reached by the older members of this association.

The continuance of the practice of most geographers as generalists is a remarkable case of cultural lag in an age that demands specialism. And now that specialism has been carried so far in many quarters that it is often decried, it may seem strange for one to advocate further movement in that direction. It is possible to go too far, of course, and the time will doubtless come when a president will urge on you a broader approach to your work, but geographers as a group have far to go before they reach diminishing returns from specialization.

It would not be fair to ourselves to pass on without recognizing some of the reasons for tardy specialization. We have had the problem faced by all pioneers, who need to do many things and, therefore, can scarcely become experts at any of them. Many have doubtless followed uncritically the example and pronouncements of men of earlier generations, whose needs were different from ours. Thomas Jefferson was a well-rounded scientist, and something of a geographer; Nathaniel Shaler was a geologist, a geographer, and a man of letters; William Morris Davis, you may remember, recommended both a continent-wide concentration and, at the same time, emphasis on a world-wide topic. It is possible that Davis' advice is suitable for some of us, who haven't moved even that far, but there are others who should drive a salient along one direction into the great unknown. Some men have felt shut off from profitable specialization because of the intellectual fashions of the day. And most of us have had the limitations that a teacher's life imposes. We have faced the difficulty of combining the broad coverage required for teaching with the depth essential to specialization. We have too commonly developed a mental hardpan, resulting from shallow plowing of the same ground over and over for our elementary students.

But these difficulties, while real and large, need not deter us longer. We need a new mind set in teaching, one that recognizes that scholarship is required of the teacher too. We need a larger measure of co-operation—we need to rely on fellow scholars for the findings in their special fields, as we range ahead along special lines. Our dependence on the work of other scholars increases as we become more specialized in our own area. Fuller use of the results of the labors of others is an essential trait of this era of more intense and sustained concentration into which we are clearly moving.

How should one specialize? The course one takes involves one's bent, preparation, and opportunities. Preparation and opportunity I pass over to give special attention to bent or talent. Each man, declared Ralph Waldo Emerson, has a calling indicated by his talent, and, so Emerson insisted, no other calling but that. A young geographer may well subject himself to some soul-searching to discover his bent, for only in pursuing lines for which he has special aptitudes is he likely to be original or very productive. And here we have reason to rejoice because of the range of geography and of the various kinds of work now called for in this field.

In this big camp of diverse tasks there is room for a wide variety of interests and capacities: for the academic mind, and the practical; for the person who must visualize, and for the person who likes to deal in abstractions; for the historical mind, and the mathematical; for one who must analyze a situation down to its minutest elements and for the person who is gifted at seeing wholes; for the writer adept at description, and for the man who loves exposition but who has not the gift of visualization. There is room here for geographers who delight in taking pictures, and for those who prefer to draw maps; for the worker who is unhappy unless he is outdoors, and his fellow worker who is never so near heaven as when he is buried in a document room; for the person who is satisfied only with the actual concrete details of earth location, and for the one who quickly forgets details, but is constantly searching for generalizations; for the geographer who prefers to study in the home of his boyhood and youth, and the one who is most happy when studying in foreign lands; for the person who is most attracted by unknowns in contemporary geography, and for the student who is happy to reconstruct the past. There is a place, too, for the man who is limited to the use of his native language, and for the scholar who is gifted at serving as an intermediary between those of his own language and those whose thoughts require transla-tion. We have need for the geographer of expansive range and prodi-gous memory, who writes voluminous definitive works, as well as for the one of limited energy, but critical bent, who is a sharpshooter, looking for gaps and errors in the structure of geographic thought; for the man who is on the lookout for repeating associations and sequences, and for the worker who is most impressed with the unique, the non-repetitive, in his study of geography.

As you think about the men you know with these various talents and interests, you are supporting my next observation: that in reality specialization by North American geographers is already well under way. The early years of the 1950's have seen one after another of our younger geographers declare their special interests, and back their declaration with published work for all to criticize and judge. A few years ago it was hoped that somehow each university would specialize in a few fields, but that then seemed a forlorn hope. During the past two years a number of the leading university departments have made clear in official statements the fields in which their faculty members are most competent. At the annual meetings of the Association in very recent years small groups have met to consider specialized topics, a sure index to the increase in the number of specializing persons, and one of the rewards of the specialist, who like other folk, does not enjoy always walking alone.

And so we come to a new phase in the life of this Association. Draw-ing apart, we shall find it all the more important that we come together occasionally. Treading the lonely paths of specialists, we shall welcome even more the opportunity to get together in small groups under the aegis of this Association. Working in areas beyond the range of useful criticism by the generalist, we shall need the caustic comment of men specializing in the same areas. Concentrating on relatively small aspects of a large, overall endeavor, we shall need more and more to join up with others, in order that the pieces may fit together. Distracted from the whole endeavor by the demands of our specialty, we shall need all the more to sit in plenary sessions to listen to men discuss other phases of our work. Moving in the direction of greater specialization, we do so that we may become more mature, productive scholars in a large field of learning. As we move in that direction, we shall find this Association of greater value than ever before, as it fosters and sustains concentration, as it supplies antidotes to the less desirable results of specialization, and as it provides each with the friendly association in face-to-face groups that every human being craves.

IV

Some of you have children who will attend the one-hundredth anniversary of the Association of American Geographers. Perhaps they will then look back to this occasion, wondering just how we saw ourselves in 1954, whether we were truly aware of the richness of our heritage and of the opportunities and responsibilities ahead of us. We do not know all that they will read in the one hundred-year record of the Association, but we can be reasonably sure of some things and hopeful of others.

We can be sure that they will see the first fifty years of this organization as a period during which our field of endeavor was blocked out, our place in the sun established.

We hope they will see that, having blocked out our field of endeavor, we had the good sense in the second fifty years not continually to elaborate its outlines and structure, but to accept more fully the obligation to fill in the frame with mature, substantial scholarship, scholarship in every activity, from teaching to business, but especially in productive scholarship leading to substantial professional papers, monographs, and books.

To one who reviews the years since 1904, when this Association first met, the opportunities for a fruitful, adventurous, satisfying life as a geographer in North America appear never to have been so promising as now. Many limitations to the range and depth of our thinking have been removed, new positions for geographers are opening, and intriguing problems lie at every hand. The way lies open. The first fifty years of this Association have seen the pioneering tasks completed, the land taken up, the clearing done, the seed planted. Our task is to produce more abundant harvests as the years go by.

23. Geomorphology and General Systems Theory

Richard J. Chorley

General systems theory is providing an effective framework for study and research in many aspects of geography. Model building is becoming an important part of research design. In Chorley's words: "An appreciation of the value of operating within an appropriate systematic model has emerged from the recognition that the interpretation of a given body of information depends as much upon the character of the model adopted as upon the inherent quality of the data itself." He indicates the advantages and disadvantages of closed and open systems and gives simple analogies.

Chorley cites the following advantages of the open system framework in the study of landforms: (1) It focuses attention upon the possible relationship between forms and processes. (2) It takes into account the multivariate character of most geomorphic phenomena. (3) It permits more freedom in aims, methods, and thought than the "structure, process, and stage of landforms" approach of William Morris Davis does. (4) It allows for consideration of the entire landscape. (5) It introduces into geography, via geomorphology, the open systems model which may have significance in the study of human geography. This last point should be emphasized; it is becoming evident that geographic literature can now treat both the physical and cultural environment as a whole or in part with much more rigor than previously. Thus, Chorley's article bears on the future of all of geography, not only geomorphology.

SOURCE: *Theoretical Papers in the Hydrologic and Geomorphic Sciences*, Geological Survey Professional Paper 500-B (Washington, D.C.: Government Printing Office, 1962). The author is a member of the Department of Geography, Downing Place, Cambridge, England.

During the past decade several valuable attempts have been made, notably by Strahler, by Culling, and by Hack, to apply general systems theory to the study of geomorphology, with a view to examining in detail the fundamental basis of the subject, its aims and its methods. They come at a time when the conventional approach is in danger, of subsiding into an uncritical series of conditioned reflexes, and when the more imaginative modern work in geomorphology often seems to be sacrificing breadth of vision for focus on details. In both approaches it is a common trend for workers to be increasingly critical of operating within general frameworks of thought, particularly with the examples of the Davis and Penck geomorphic systems before them, and "classical" geomorphologists have retreated into restricted historical studies of regional form elements, whereas, similarly, quantitative workers have often withdrawn into restricted empirical and theoretical studies based on process.

It is wrong, however, to confuse the restrictions which are rightly associated with preconceived notions in geomorphology with the advantages of operating within an appropriate general systematic framework. The first lead to the closing of vistas and the decrease of opportunity; the second, however, may increase the scope of the study, make possible correlations and associations which would otherwise be impossible, generally liberalize the whole approach to the subject and, in addition, allow an integration into a wider general conceptual framework. Essentially, it is not possible to enter into a study of the physical world without such a fundamental basis for the investigation, and even the most qualitative approaches to the subject show very strong evidence of operations of thought within a logical general framework, albeit a framework of thought which is in a sense unconscious. Hack, for example, has pointed to the essential difference between the approaches to geomorphology of Gilbert and Davis, and in this respect the fundamental value of the adoption of a suitable general framework of investigation based on general systems theory becomes readily apparent.

Following the terminology used by Von Bertalanffy, it is possible to recognize in general two separate systematic frameworks wherein one may view the natural occurrence of physical phenomena; the closed system and the open system. Hall and Fagan have defined a system as ". . . a set of objects together with relationships between the objects and between their attributes." In the light of this definition, it is very significant that one of the fundamental purposes of Davis' approach to landforms was to study them as an assemblage, in which the various parts might be related in an areal and a time sense, such that different systems might be compared, and the same system followed through its sequence of time changes. Closed systems are those which possess clearly defined closed boundaries, across which no import or export of materials or energy occurs. This view of systems immediately precludes a large number, perhaps all, of the systems with which natural scientists are concerned; and certainly most geographical systems are excluded on this basis, for boundary problems and the problems of the association between areal units and their interrelationships lie very close to the core of geographical investigations.

Another characteristic of closed systems is that, with a given amount of initial free, or potential, energy within the system, they develop toward states with maximum "entropy." Entropy is an expression for the degree to which energy has become unable to perform work. The increase of entropy implies a trend toward minimum free energy. Hence, in a closed system there is a tendency for leveling down of existing differentiation within the system; or, according to Lord Kelvin's expression, for progressive degradation of energy into its lowest form, i.e., heat as undirected molecular movement. This is expressed by the second law of thermodynamics which, in its classic form, is formulated for closed systems. In such systems, therefore, the change of entropy is always positive, associated with a decrease in the amount of free energy, or, to state this another way, with a tendency toward progressive destruction of existing order or differentiation.

Thus, one can see that Davis' view of landscape development contains certain elements of closed system thinking—including, for example, the idea that uplift provides initially a given amount of potential energy and that, as degradation proceeds, the energy of the system decreases until at the stage of peneplanation there is a minimum amount of free energy as a result of the leveling down of topographic differences. The Davisian peneplain, therefore, may be considered as logically homologous to the condition of maximum entropy, general energy properties being more or less uniformly distributed throughout the system and with a potential energy approaching zero. The positive change of entropy, and connected negative change of free energy, implies the irreversibility of events within closed systems. This again bears striking similarities to the general operation of the geomorphic cycle of Davis. The belief in the sequential development of landforms, involving the progressive and irreversible evolution of almost every facet of landscape geometry, in sympathy with the reduction of relief, including valley-side slopes and drainage systems, is in accord with closed system thinking. Although "complications of the geographical cycle" can, in a sense, put the clock back, nothing was considered by Davis as capable of reversing the clock. The putting back of the clock by uplift, therefore, came to be associated with a release, or an absorption into the new closed system, of an increment of free energy, subsequently to be progressively dissipated through degradation.

Also, in closed systems there is the inherent characteristic that the initial system conditions, particularly the energy conditions, are sufficient to determine its ultimate equilibrium condition. This inevitability of closed-system thinking is very much associated with the view of geomorphic change held by Davis. Not only this, but the condition of a closed system at any particular time can be considered largely as a function of the initial system conditions and the amount of time which has subsequently elapsed. Thus closed systems are eminently susceptible to study on a time, or historical, basis. This again enables one to draw striking analogies between closed-system thinking and the historical approach to landform study which was proposed by Davis.

Finally, it is recognized that closed systems can reach a state of equilibrium. Generally speaking, however, this equilibrium state is associated with the condition of maximum entropy which cannot occur until the system has run through its sequential development. In addition, it is impossible to introduce the concept of equilibrium into a closed-system framework of thought without the implication that it is associated with stationary conditions. The only feature of the cyclic system of Davis which employed the general concept of equilibrium was that of the "graded" condition of stream channels and slopes which, significantly, Davis borrowed from the work of Gilbert, who had an entirely noncyclic view of landform development. Characteristically, the concept of grade was the one feature of Davis' synthesis which seems least well at home in the cyclic framework, for it has always proved difficult to imagine how, within a closed system context, a graded or equilibrium state could exist and yet the associated forms be susceptible to continued change—namely, downcutting or reduction.

The foregoing is not meant to imply that it is unprofitable to consider any assemblage of phenomena within a closed system framework, or, as Davis did, to overstress those aspects or phases which seem to achieve most significance with reference to the closed system model. It is important, however, to recognize the sources of partiality which result, not from any inherent quality of the data itself, but from the general systematic theory under which one is operating. In reality, no systematic model can encompass the whole of a natural complex without ceasing to be a model, and the phenomena of geomorphology present problems both when they are viewed within closed and open systematic frameworks. In the former, the useful concept of dynamic equilibrium or grade rests most uncomfortably; in the latter, as will be seen, the progressive loss of a component of potential energy due to relief reduction imposes an unwelcome historical parameter.

A simple, classic example of a closed system is represented by a mass of gas within a completely sealed and insulated container. If, initially, the gas at one end of the container is at a higher temperature than that at the other, this can be viewed as a condition of maximum segregation, maximum free energy, and, consequently, of maximum ability to perform work, should this thermal gradient be harnessed within a larger closed system. This is the state of minimum entropy. It is obvious, however, that this state of affairs is of a most transient character and that immediately an irreversible heat flow will begin toward the cooler end of the container. This will progressively decrease the segregation of mass and energy within the system, together with the available free energy and the ability of this energy to perform work, bringing about a similarly progressive increase of entropy. While the system remains closed nothing can check or hinder this inevitable leveling down of differences, which is so predictable that, knowing the initial energy conditions, the thermal conductivity of the gas and the lapse of time, one could accurately calculate the thermal state of the system at any required stage. Thus the distribution of heat energy and the heat flow within the system have a progressive and sequential history, the one becoming less segregated and the other ever-decreasing. Nor is it possible to imagine any form of equilibrium until all the gas has attained the same temperature, when the motion of the gas molecules is quite random and the static condition of maximum entropy obtains.

Open systems contrast quite strikingly with closed systems. An open system needs an energy supply for its maintenance and preservation, and is in effect maintained by a constant supply and removal of material and energy. Thus, direct analogies exist between the classic open systems and drainage basins, slope elements, stream segments and all the other form-assemblages of a landscape. The concept of the open system includes closed systems, however, because the latter can be considered a special case of the former when transport of matter and energy into and from the system becomes zero. An open system manifests one important property which is denied to the closed system. It may attain a "steady state" wherein the import and export of energy and material are equated by means of an adjustment of the form, or geomeary, of the system itself. It is more difficult to present a simple mechanical analog to illustrate completely the character and operations of an open system but it may be helpful to visualize one such system as represented by the moving body of water contained is a bowl which is being constantly filled from an overhead inflow and drained by an outflow in the bottom. If the inflow is stopped, the bowl drains and the system ceases to exist; whereas, if the inflow is stopped and the outflow is blocked, the system partakes of many of the features of a closed system. In such an arrangement, changes in the supply of mass and energy from outside lead to a self-adjustment of the system to accommodate these changes. Thus, if the inflow is increased, the water level in the basin rises, the head of water above the outflow increases, and the outflow discharge will increase until it balances the increased inflow. At this time the level of water in the bowl will again become steady.

Long ago, Gilbert recognized the importance of the application of this principle of self-adjustment to landform development:

The tendency to equilibrium of action, or to the establishment of a dynamic equilibrium, has already been pointed out in the discussion of the principles of erosion and of sculpture, but one of its most important results has not been noticed.

Of the main conditions which determine the rate of erosion, namely, the quantity of running water, vegetation, texture of rock, and declivity, only the last is reciprocally determined by rate of erosion. Declivity originates in upheaval, or in the displacement of the earths crust by which mountains and continents are formed: but it receives its distribution in detail in accordance with the laws of erosion. Wherever by reason of change in any of the conditions the erosive agents come to have locally exceptional power, that power is steadily diminished by the reaction of the rate of erosion upon declivity. Every slope is a member of a series, receiving the water and the waste of the slope above it, and discharging its own water and waste upon the slope below. If one member of the series is eroded with exceptional rapidity, two things immediately result: first, the member above has its own level of discharge lowered, and its rate of erosion is thereby increased; and second, the member below, being clogged by an exceptional load of detritus, has its rate of erosion diminished. The acceleration above and the retardation below diminish the declivity of the member in which the disturbance originated: and as the declivity is reduced, the rate of erosion is likewise reduced.

But the effect does not stop here. The disturbance that has been transferred from one member of the series to the two which adjoin it, is by then transmitted to others, and does not cease until it has reached the confines of the drainage basin. For in each basin all lines of drainage unite in a main line, and a disturbance upon any line is communicated through it to the main line and thence to every tributary. And as a member of the system may influence all the others, so each member is influenced by every other. There is an interdependence throughout the system.

This form-adjustment is brought about by the ability of an open system for self-regulation. Le Châtelier's Principle (originally stated for equilibrium in closed systems) can be expanded also to include the so-called "Dynamic Equilibrium" or steady states in open systems:

Any system in . . . equilibrium undergoes, as a result of a variation in one of the factors governing the equilibrium, a compensating change in a direction such that, had this change occurred alone it would have produced a variation of the factor considered in the opposite direction.

A geomorphic statement of this principle has been given by Mackin:

A graded stream is one in which, over a period of years, slope is delicately adjusted to provide, with available discharge and with prevailing channel characteristics, just the velocity required for the transportation of the load supplied from the drainage basin. The graded stream is a system in equilibrium; its diagnostic characteristic is that any change in any of the controlling factors will cause a displacement of the equilibrium in a direction that will tend to absorb the effect of the change.

The cyclic adaptation of the concept of grade did not give sufficient importance to the factors, other than channel slope, which a stream system can control for itself, and in this respect Davis' ignorance of the significance of the practical experiments of Gilbert is most evident. A stream system cannot greatly control its discharge, which represents the energy and mass which is externally supplied into the open system. Neither can it completely control the amount and character of the debris supplied to it, except by its action of abrasion and sorting or as the result of the rapport which seems to exist regionally between stream-channel slope and valley-side slope. However, besides adjusting the general slope of its channel by erosion and deposition, a stream can very effectively and almost instantaneously control its transverse channel characteristics, together with its efficiency for the transport of water and load, by changes in depth and width of the channel. As Wolman put it:

The downstream curves on Brandywine Creek . . . suggest that the adjustment of channel shape may be as significant as the adjustment of the longitudinal profile. There is no way in which one could predict that the effect of a change in the independent controls would be better absorbed by a change in slope rather than by a change in the form of the cross section.

It may be, therefore, that a stream or reach may be virtually always adjusted, in the sense of being graded or in a steady state, without necessarily presenting the smooth longitudinal profile considered by the advocates of the geomorphic cycle as the hallmark of the "mature graded condition." The state of grade is thus analogous to the tendency for steady-state adjustment, it is perhaps always present and, therefore, this presence cannot be employed necessarily as an historical, or stage, characteristic. It is interesting that the concept of the vegetational "climax," which has often been compared to that of grade, has passed through a somewhat similar metamorphosis. The original idea of a progressive approach to a static equilibrium of the ecological assemblage has been challenged by the open system interpretation of Whitaker, with an historical link being provided by the "individualistic concept" of Gleason, much in the same way as Mackin's concept of grade links those of Davis and Wolman.

The forms developed, together with the mutual adjustment of internal form elements and of related systems, are dependent on the flow of material and energy in the steady state. The laws of morphometry express one aspect of this relationship in geomorphology. In addition, adjustment of form elements implies a law of optimum size of a system and of elements within a system. This is mirrored by Gilbert's symmetrical migration of divides and by Schumm's constant of channel maintenance, and is illustrated by Schumm's contrast between basin areas of differing order.

Although a steady state is in many respects a time-independent condition, it differs from the equilibrium of closed systems. A steady state means that the aspects of form are not static and unchanging, but that they are maintained in the flow of matter and energy traversing the system. An open system will, certain conditions presupposed, develop toward a steady state and therefore undergo changes in this process. Such changes imply changes in energy conditions and, connected with these, changes in the structures during the process. The trend toward, and the development of, a steady state demands not an equation of force and resistance over the landscape, but that the forms within the landscape are so regulated that the resistance presented by the surface at any point is proportionate to the stress applied to it.

Erosion on a slope of homogeneous material with uniform vegetative cover will be most rapid where the erosional power of the runoff is greatest. This nonuniform erosional process will in time result in a more stable slope profile which would offer a uniform resistance to erosion.

In this way the transport of mass and energy (i.e., water and debris) is carried on in the most economical manner. With time, landscape mass is therefore being removed and progressive changes in at least some of the absolute geometrical properties of landscape, particularly relief, are inevitable. It is wrong, however, to assume, as Davis did, that all these properties are involved necessarily in this progressive, sequential change. To return briefly to the analogy of the bowl. If the rush of water through the outflow is capable of progressively enlarging the orifice, the increasing discharge at the outflow, uncompensated at the inflow, will cause the head of water in the bowl to decrease. This loss of head will itself, however, constantly tend to compensate the increasing outflow, but, if the enlargement of the outflow orifice proceeds, this is a losing battle and an important feature of the system will be the progressive and sequential loss of head. However, not all features of this system will reflect this progressive change of head, and, for example, the structure of the flow within the bowl will remain much the same while any head of water at all remains there. The dimensionless ratios between landscape forms, similarly, seem to express the steady state condition of adjusted forms from which mass is constantly being removed. The geometrical ratios which form the basis of the laws of morphometry, and the height-area ratios involved in the dimensionless, equilibrium hypsometric integral are examples of this adjustment:

In late mature and old stages of topography, despite the attainment of low relief, the hypsometric curve shows no significant variations from the mature form, and a low integral results only where monadnocks remain. . . . After monadnock masses are removed, the hypsometric curve may be expected to revert to a midde position with integrals in the general range of 40 to 60 percent.

In a drainage basin composed of homogeneous material, in which no monadnocks would tend to form, it seems possible, therefore, that the dimensionless percentage volume of unconsumed mass (represented by the hypsometric integral) may achieve a time-independent value. It has been suggested, however, that the construction of the hyposometric curve may be so inherently restricted as to make the hypsometric integral insensitive to variations of an order which would be necessary to recognize such an equilibrium state. This steady state principle has been tentatively extended by Schumm to certain other aspects of drainage basin form:

. . . the form of the typical basin at Perth Amboy changes most rapidly in the earliest stage of development. Relief and stream gradient increase rapidly to a point at which about 25 percent of the mass of the basin has been removed, then remains essentially constant. Because relief ratio [the ratio between total relief of a basin and the longest dimension of the basin parallel to the principal drainage] elsewhere has shown a close positive correlation with stream gradient, drainage density, and ground-slope angles, stage of development might be expected to have little effect on any of these values once the relief ratio has become constant.

In the steady state of landscape development, therefore, force and resistance are not equated (which would imply no absolute form change), but balanced in an areal sense, such that force may still exceed resistance and cause mass to be removed. Now, as has been pointed out, removal of mass under steady-state conditions must imply some progressive changes in certain absolute geometrical properties of a landscape, notably a decrease in average relief, but by no means all such properties need respond in this simple manner to the progressive removal of mass. The existence, for example, of the optimum magnitude principle for individual systems, or subsystems, implies that if the available energy within the system is sufficient to impose the optimum magnitude on that system, this magnitude will be maintained throughout a period of time and will not always be susceptible to a progressive, sequential change. Thus, Strahler has indicated that erosional slopes which are being forced to their maximum angle of repose by aggressive basal stream action will, of necessity, retain this maximum angle despite the progressive removal of mass with time.

Total energy is made up of interchangeable potential energy and flux, or kinetic, energy and even if the potential energy component decreases within an open system due to its general reduction, in other words along with a continual change in one aspect of form (i.e., relief), the residual flux energy may be of such overriding importance as to effectively maintain a steady state of operation. In practice the steady state is seldom, if ever, characterized by exact equilibrium, but simply by a tendency to attain it. This is partly due to the constant energy changes which are themselves characteristic of many open system operations, but the steady state condition of tendency toward attainment of equilibrium is a necessary prerequisite, according to Von Bertalanffy, for the system to perform work at all. Now, once a steady state has been established, the influence of the initial system conditions vanishes and, with it, the evidence for a previous history of the system (i.e., was our bowl full or empty at the start?). Indeed, in terms of analyzing the causes of phenomena which exhibit a marked steady-state tendency, considerations regarding previous history become not only hypothetical, but largely irrelevant. This concept contrasts strikingly with the historical view of development which is fostered by closed-system thinking. Wooldridge and Linton have gone so far as to say that:

Any such close comprehension of the terrain can be obtained in one way only, by tracing its evolution.

An even more extreme statement of the same philosophy has been made by Wooldridge and Goldring:

The physical landscape, including the vegetation cover, is the record of *processes* and the whole of the evidence for its evolution is contained in the landscape itself.

The whole matter hinges on the rapidity with which landscape features become adjusted to energy flow, which may itself be susceptible to rapid changes, particularly during the rather abnormal latest geologic period of earth history. Obviously, most existing features are the product of both past and reasonably contemporary energy conditions, and the degree to which these latter conditions have gained ascendancy over the former is largely a function of the ratio between the amount of present energy application and the strength (whatever this may mean) of the landscape materials. Thus, the geometry of stream channels and the morphometry of weak clay badlands show remarkable adjustments to contemporary processes—on whatever time level the action of these processes may be defined—whereas, at the other end of the energy/resistance scale, erosion surfaces cut in resistant rock and exposed to the low present energy levels associated with the erosional processes of certain areas of tropical Africa can only be understood on the basis of past conditions. Between these two extremes lies the major part of the subject matter of geomorphology including considerations of slope development, and it is here where the apparent dichotomy between the two systematic approaches to the same phenomena, termed by Bucher "timebound" and "timeless," is most acute. In a related context, the problem of timebound-versus-timeless phenomena becomes especially obvious when rates of change and the ability to adjust are underestimated, as when vegetational assemblages have been correlated with the assumed stages of geomorphic history in the folded Appalachians by Braun and in Brazil by Cole.

One can appreciate that in areas where good evidence for a previous landscape history still remains, the historical approach may be extremely productive, as exemplified by the work of Wooldridge and Linton on southeastern England. However, in many (if not most) areas the condition is one of massive removal of past evidence and of tendency toward adjustment with progressively contemporaneous conditions. It is an impossibly restricted view, therefore, to imagine a universal approach to landform study being based only upon considerations of historical development.

Another characteristic of the open system is that negative entropy, or free energy, can be imported into it—because of its very nature. Therefore, the open system is not defined by the trend toward maximum entropy. Open systems thus may maintain their organization and regularity of form, in a continual exchange of their component materials. They may even develop toward higher order, heterogeneity, hierarchical differentiation and organization. This is mirrored in geomorphology by the characteristic development of interrelated drainage forms, and goes along with a concept of progressive segregation. This, to a minor extent, militates against the general view of adjustment previously discussed, insofar, as, with time, rates of interactions between form elements in an open system may tend to decrease. Therefore, it is quite reasonable to assume that mutual adjustments of form within geomorphic systems might be more difficult of accomplishment and delayed where the relief, through its influences over the potential energy of the system, is low rather than where there is a higher potential energy in the system.

Steady-state conditions can be interrupted by a disturbance in the energy flow or in the resistance, leading to form adjustments allowing a new steady state to be approached. These adjustments, however, do imply a consumption of energy and there is a "cost of transition" from one steady state to another. A particular geomorphic instance of this dissipation might be presented by the phenomenon of "overshooting" where active, but sporadic, processes are operating on weak materials, as instanced when the failure of steep slopes reduces them to inclinations very much below their repose angles, and by the excessive cutting and subsequent filling of alluvial channels associated with flash floods.

The dynamic equilibrium of the steady state manifests itself in a tendency toward a mean condition of unit forms, recognizable statistically, about which variations may take place over periods of time with fluctuations in the energy flow. These periods of time may in some instances be of very short duration, and the fluctuations of transverse stream profiles are measurable in the days, or even minutes, during which changes of discharge occur. These constant adjustments to new steady-state conditions may be superimposed on a general tendency for change possibly associated with the reduction of average relief through time. This general relief change, however, does not imply a sympathetic change of all the other features of landscape geometry. As has been demonstrated by Strahler and Melton, for example, drainage density is controlled by a number of factors of which relief is only one, Recent work seems to be indicating that relief (naturally including considerations of average land slope) probably has only a relatively small influence over drainage density, which may be masked or negated altogether by the other more important factors (for example, rainfall intensity and surface resistance) which are not so obviously susceptible to changes with time. Denbigh, Hicks and Page have pointed out that:

Quite large changes of environment may take place, without the need for more than a small internal readjustment.

Horton did not believe, as did Glock, that drainage density could be employed as a measure of landscape "age," and, indeed, it is not difficult to entertain the possibility that certain features of landscape geometry may be relatively unchanging, in actual dimensional magnitude as well as in dimensionless ratio, throughout long periods of erosional history.

For many landscape units, changes on either level are slow, or in some instances nonexistent. Under steady state conditions, therefore, corresponding local morphometric units will, as regards their form and magnitude, tend to crowd around a very significant mean value, imparting to a geomorphic region its aspects of uniformity. Strahler's "law of constancy of slopes" is an expression of one phase of this adjustment. It is interesting that the general principle of the operation of a steady state condition was intuitively recognized long ago by Playfair:

> The geological system of Dr. Hutton, resembles, in many respects, that which appears to preside over the heavenly motions. In both, we perceive continual vicissitude and change, but confined within certain limits, and never departing far from a certain mean condition, which is such that in the lapse of time, the deviations from it on one side, must become just equal to the deviations from it on the other.

Often the achievement of exact equilibrium in nature occurs only momentarily as variations about the mean take place, and in these instances the existence of the steady state can only be recognized statistically. In the study of landscape, the steady state condition indicated by discrete, close and recognizable statistical groupings of similar units, is characteristic of regions of uniform ratios between process and surface resistance.

Davis' view of landscape evolution was that the passage of time, of necessity, imprinted recognizable, significant and progressive changes, on every facet of landscape geometry. The recognition, however, that landscape forms represent a steady-state adjustment with respect to a multiplicity of controlling factors obliges one to take a less rigid view of the evolutionary aspects of geomorphology. When a geometrical form is controlled by a number of factors, any change of form with the passage of time is entirely dependent upon the net result of the effect of time upon those factors. Some factors are profoundly affected by the passage of time, others are not; some factors act directly (using the term in the mathematical sense) upon the form, others inversely; some factors exercise an important control over form aspects, others a less important one. Thus, if a particular geometrical feature of landscape is primarily controlled by a factor the action of which does not change greatly with time, or if the changes of factors having direct and inverse controls tend to cancel out the net effect of the changes, then the resulting variation in geometry may itself be small—perhaps insignificant.

A last important characteristic of open systems is that they are capable of behaving "equifinally"—in other words, different initial conditions can lead to similar end results. Davisian (closed system) thinking is instinctively opposed to this view, and the immediate and facile assumption, for example, that most breaks of stream slope are only referable to a polycyclic mechanism is an illustration of the one cause—one effect mentality. The concept of equifinality accentuates the multivariate nature of most geomorphic processes and militates against the unidirectional inevitability of the closed system cyclic approach of Davis. The approach contrasts strikingly with that of Gilbert:

> Phenomena are arranged in chains of necessary sequence. In such a chain each link is the necessary consequent of that which precedes, and the necessary antecedent of that which follows . . . If we examine any link of the chain, we find it has more than one antecedent and more than one consequent . . . Antecedent and consequent relations are therefore not merely linear, but constitute a plexus; and this plexus pervades nature.

To sum up, the real value of the open system approach to geomorphology is:

Firstly, that it throws the emphasis on the recognition of the adjustment, or the universal tendency toward adjustment, between form and process. Both form and process are studied, therefore, in equal measure, so avoiding the pitfall of Davis and his more recent associates of the complete ignoring of process in geomorphology:

> In a graded drainage system the steady state manifests itself in the development of certain topographic form characteristics which achieve a time-independent condition . . . Erosional and transportational processes meanwhile produce a steady flow (averaged over a period of years or tens of years) of water and waste from and through the landform system . . . Over the long span of the erosion cycle continual adjustment of the components in the steady state is required as relief lowers and available energy diminishes. The forms will likewise show a slow evolution.
>
> Applied to erosion processes and forms, the concept of the steady state in an open system focuses attention upon the relationship between dynamics and morphology.

The relation between process and form lies close to the heart of geomorphology and, in practice, the two are often so intimately linked that the problem of cause and effect may present the features of the "hen and the egg." Approach from either direction is valuable, however, for knowledge of form aids in the understanding of process, and studies of process help in the clearer perception of the significant aspects of form.

The study of form may be descriptive merely, or it may become analytical. We begin by describing the shape of an object in the simple words of common speech: we end by defining it in the precise language of mathematics; and the one method tends to follow the other in strict scientific order and historical continuity . . . The mathematical definition of a "form" has a quality of precision which was quite lacking in our earlier stage of mere description . . . [employing means which] are so pregnant with meaning that thought itself is economized; . . .

We are apt to think of mathematical definitions as too strict and rigid for common use, but their rigour is combined with all but endless freedom . . . we reach through mathematical analysis to mathematical synthesis. We discover homologies or identities which were not obvious before, and which our description obscured rather than revealed: . . .

Once more, and this is the greatest gain of all, we pass quickly and easily from the mathematical concept of form in its statical aspect to form in its dynamical relations: we rise from the conception of form to an understanding of the forces which gave rise to it; and in the representation of form and in the comparison of kindred forms, we see in the one case a diagram of forces in equilibrium, and in the other case we discern the magnitude and the direction of the forces which have sufficed to convert the one form into the other. . . .

. . . Every natural phenomenon, however simple, is really composite, and every visible action and effect is a summation of countless subordinate actions. Here mathematics shows her peculiar power, to combine and generalize. . . .

A large part of the neglect and suspicion of mathematical methods in . . . morphology is due . . . to an ingrained and deep-seated belief that even when we seem to discern a regular mathematical figure in an organism . . . [the form] which we so recognise merely resembles, but is never entirely explained by, its mathematical analogue; in short, that the details in which the figure differs from its mathematical prototype are more important and more interesting than the features in which it agrees; and even that the peculiar aesthetic pleasure with which we regard a living thing is somehow bound up with the departure from mathematical regularity which it manifests as a peculiar attribute of life. . . .We may be dismayed too easily my contingencies which are nothing short of irrelevant compared to the main issue; there is a *principle of negligibility.* . . .

If no chain hangs in a perfect catenary and no raindrop is a perfect sphere, this is for the reason that forces and resistances other than the main one are inevitably at work . . . , but it is for the mathematician to unravel the conflicting forces which are at work together. And this process of investigation may lead us on step by step to new phenomena, as it has done in physics, where sometimes a knowledge of form leads us to the interpretation of forces, and at other times a knowledge of the forces at work guides us towards a better insight into form.

Secondly, open-system thinking directs the investigation toward the essentially multivariate character of geomorphic phenomena. It is of interest to note that the physical, and the resulting psycholgical, inability of geographers to handle successfully the simultaneous operation of a number of causes contributing to a given effect has been one of the greatest impediments to the advancement of their discipline. This inability has prompted, at worst, a unicausal determinism and, at best an unrealistic concentration upon one or two contributing factors at the expense of others. Davis' preoccupation with "stage" in geomorphology has been paralleled, for example, by an undue emphasis on the part of some economic geographers upon the factor of "distance" in many analyses of economic location.

Thirdly, it allows a more liberal view of changes of form with time, so as to include the possibility of nonsignificant or nonprogressive changes of certain aspects of landscape form through time.

Fourthly, while not denying the value of the historical approach to landform development in those areas to which the application of this framework of study is appropriate, open-system thinking fosters a less rigid view regarding the aims and methods of geomorphology than that which appears to be held by proponents of the historical approach. It embraces naturally within its general framework the forms possessing relict facets, those indeed which form the basis for the present studies of denudation chronology, under the general category of the "inequilibrium" forms of Strahler. There is no uniquely correct method of treatment for a given body of information, and Postan has been at pains to demonstrate the purely subjective distinction which exists between alternative explanations of phenomena on an immediately causal or generic basis, as against an historical or biographical one:

For the frontier they draw separates not the different compartments of the universe but merely the different mental attitudes to the universe as a whole. What makes the material fact a fit object for scientific study is that men are prepared to treat it as an instance of a generic series. What makes a social phenomenon an historical event is that men ask about it individual or, so to speak, biographical questions. But there is no reason why the process should not be reversed; why we should not ask generic questions about historical events or should not write individual biographies of physical objects. Here Spinoza's argument still holds. The fall of a brick can be treated as a mere instance of the general study of falling bricks, in which case it is a material fact, and part and parcel of a scientific enquiry. But it is equally possible to conceive a special interest in a particular brick and ask why that individual brick behaved as it did at the unique moment of its fall. And the brick will then become an historical event. Newton must have been confronted with something of the same choice on the famous day when he sat under the fabulous apple tree. Had he asked himself the obvious question, why did that particular apple choose that unrepeatable instant to fall on that unique head, he might have written the history of an apple. Instead of which he asked himself why apples fell and produced the theory of gravitation. The decision was not the apple's but Newton's.

Davis was metaphorically struck by landscape and chose to write a history of it.

Fifthly, the open-system mentality directs the study of geomorphology to the whole landscape assemblage, rather than simply to the often minute elements of landscape having supposed evolutionary significance.

Sixthly, the open-system approach encourages rigorous geomorphic studies to be carried out in those regions—and perhaps these are in the majority—where the evidence for a previous protracted erosional history is blurred, or has been removed altogether.

Lastly, open-system thinking, when applied to geomorphology, has application within the general framework of geography; for geomorphology has always influenced geographical thinking to a great, and possibly excessive, degree. Open-system thinking is characteristically less rigidly deterministic in a causative and time sense than the closed-system approach. The application of this closed-system approach to problems of human geography is extremely dangerous because, of its nature, it directs the emphasis toward a narrow determinism, and encourages a concentration upon closed boundary conditions, upon the tendency toward homogeneity and upon the leveling down of differences. Open-system thinking, however, directs attention to the heterogeneity of spatial organization, to the creation of segregation, and to the increasingly hierarchical differentiation which often takes place with time. These latter features are, after all, hallmarks of social, as well as biological, evolution.

24. The Changing Relationships of Economics and Economic Geography

Robert B. McNee

*As boundary lines between disciplines become less distinct,
it is essential to constantly reevaluate relationships
between relevant complementary disciplines. The core of
a field of knowledge should remain solid, but the peripheries must be flexible enough so that they can be entered
to advantage by any scholar from a neighboring discipline.
This is certainly true in the case of economics and economic geography. McNee explains the differences between
the two fields and their changing relationship. In a world
seeking more and more room for its economic activities,
an understanding of the spatial factor—geography's
realm—becomes crucial.*

The vigorous growth of economic geography will be stimulated and
enhanced by clarification of its relationships with a sister discipline,
economics. These relationships are not self-evident, despite the avowed
common interest in economic phenomena. This fact has been noted
by many geographers, including Wooldridge and East,[1] Stamp,[2] Finch,[3]
Murphy,[4] and Fisher.[5] Some geographers have discussed not only existing relationships but also what they believe these relationships *ought
to become.* Ballabon[6] wants a more "economic" economic geography

[1] S. W. Wooldridge and W. G. East: *The Spirit and Purpose of Geography,* London,
1951, pp. 103-120.
[2] J. C. Stamp: "Geography and Economic Theory," *Geography,* Vol. 22, 1937, pp.
1-13.
[3] V. C. Finch: "Training for Research in Economic Geography," *Annals Assn. of
Amer. Geogrs.,* Vol. 24, 1944, pp. 207-215.
[4] Raymond E. Murphy: "The Fields of Economic Geography," *American Geography:
Inventory and Prospect* (James and Jones, Edits.), Syracuse, 1954, pp. 240-245.
[5] C. A. Fisher: "Economic Geography in a Changing World," *Trans. and Papers of
the Inst. of Brit. Geogrs.,* 1948, pp. 69-85.
[6] M. B. Ballabon: "Putting the 'Economic' into Economic Geography," *Econ. Geogr.,*
Vol. 33, 1957, pp. 217-223.
Source: *Economic Geography,* XXXV (July, 1959), 189-98. The author is professor of geography at the University of Cincinnati.

while Lukermann[7] urges a more "geographic" economic geography. What sort of relationships *should* geographers try to develop with economics? Or, to put the matter differently, how much economics can economic geographers use? The purpose of this paper is to throw light on these questions by examining the historically changing relationships of the two fields in terms of disciplinary central problems and their changing social setting.

This article is concerned with *central problems* rather than with disciplinary definitions. Central problems have been described as disciplinary cores,[8] core topics, and target centers.[9] These are the questions that geographers or economists seek to unravel and to answer. They have a clarity and precision normally lacking in definitions. To be inclusive, definitions must be so broad and so generalized that they often conceal more than they reveal. At best, definitions are static descriptions, while central problems reveal the *direction* of disciplinary growth. The starting point for any discipline is the clear perception of a problem; the field grows as a methodology is developed which is relevant to the problem and as awareness of the ramifications of the problem leads to the examination of related problems.

Central problems must be examined in terms of their social setting. They are essentially meaningless except in terms of the societies which have given them birth and nourished them. Like most social scientists, economists and geographers are likely to cultivate those central problems most pertinent to the society of which they are members. Therefore, historical changes in the circumstances, structure, and problems of society are important in understanding the evolution of the two disciplines and the changing relationships between them. These changes may be summarized briefly in terms of two time periods: (1) The Age of European Commercial Expansion, during which economic geography and classical economics developed as isolated but complementary disciplines, and (2) the present Urban-Industrial Age, during which the two fields have broadened and have moved from complementary toward cooperation.

European Commercial Expansion

The remarkable commercial transformation of Europe and the world after the 15th Century created new social, economic, and political prob-

[7] F. Lukermann: "Toward a More Geographic Economic Geography," *Prof. Geogr.*, Vol. 10, 1958, pp. 2-10.

[8] Nevin Fenneman: "The Circumference of Geography," *Annals. Assn. Amer. Geogrs.*, Vol. 9, 1919, pp. 3-11.

[9] Edward L. Ullman: "Human Geography and Area Research," *Annals Assn. Amer. Geogrs.*, Vol. 43, 1953, pp. 54 and 56.

lems. These problems were not easily resolved in terms of the pre-Columbian thought patterns of Europeans. Many new branches and divisions of thought gradually evolved in the attempt to understand and cope with these problems, economics and economic geography among them.

Two dominant characteristics of the Occidental system were the growth of markets and the global expansion of the commercial powers of Europe. The opening of the world in the 15th Century began a 400-year boom, perhaps not yet ended. The so-called "Commercial Revolution" reshaped Europe from within. Old centers of production and consumption withered away: new trade centers flourished where isolated farming and fishing villages had been. The geographic reshuffling which occurred in the British Isles created, in a sense, a new country. The expansion of the system over the earth created a new world, a universe of exchange. The struggles between political states were primarily struggles for control of this exchange world, struggles for trading and resource space on the surface of the earth. Economics developed as the study of one aspect of the system, the market mechanism, while economic geography developed as the study of another aspect of the system, the consequent complexity of economic similarities and differences among areas within the global system.

The Interpretation of Classical Economics

Economics as we know it grew out of a great social need, the need to harmonize the Medieval logic of the "schoolmen" with the changed conditions of the market-dominated Age of Trade. Economists (originally political economists) sought to solve two closely related social problems. They sought a value basis for the formulation of social policy, and they sought the most efficient economic means to carry out social policy. They were both social philosophers and efficiency experts. As a part of the classical system of economic logic, they developed an elaborate Benthamite "economics of welfare." This welfare concern has been primarily with people as consumers rather than as producers. As Robert Solo has pointed out, Communists and Capitalists alike have taken consumer interest as the . . . "full and sufficient standard for the ultimate evaluation of alternative economic systems." [10] Thus, although economists from Adam Smith onwards have been interested in production, consumption has been emphasized more than production. As efficiency experts, economists have been concerned broadly with the economizing problem, the proper allocation of scarce means (resources) to social ends. In analyzing this problem, the economists developed the familiar concepts of land, labor, and capital.

Economics developed as a deductive system of logic. It was strongly

[10] Robert Solo: "A New Direction for Economic Inquiry," *Social Sci.*, Vol. 29, 1954, p. 135.

influenced by the "rational thinking" of the 18th Century, especially in England and America. It has tended to be more abstract and less empirical and descriptive than other social sciences such as economic geography or sociology which were more influenced by the "Darwinian thinking" of the 19th Century. Economics has attained great intellectual heights in the building of abstract models, though these models have not always been tested in the real world. Perhaps many of them are not testable. Nevertheless, these models are of great value in interpreting, if not predicting, economic behavior in the real world. As guiding hypotheses, they are superior to anything else thus far developed in the social sciences.

Most economic models are tools for analyzing the market. This emphasis on the market has been quite appropriate, since historically the market has been the principal mechanism for resource allocation in the Occidental world. With the commercial expansion of Europe, it soon became apparent that markets were not only the central mechanism of the Occidental system, they were also a key to understanding and controlling it. Since the economic theorist was interested in the market *qua* the market, entirely apart from the extremely complex web of historical and geographical circumstances in which a particular market might be embedded, both temporal and spatial variables could be assumed as constants in order to concentrate on such variables as demand, supply, and price. This reduction of variables may seem a gross oversimplification to geographers, but it permitted the growth of an organized system of economic theory appropriate to the understanding of many market problems. After successful static models were developed, many economists turned to the making of dynamic models. Few have shown similar interest in reintroducing the spatial variable, a tendency described by Isard as the Anglo-Saxon bias.[11]

The elimination of the spatial variable from serious consideration in economic theory decisively separated economics from geography. Although early economists such as Adam Smith filled their works with geographic or spatial suggestion and inference, the gradual refinement of theory created a highly abstract, spaceless, world. According to the concept of perfect competition, innumerable, rational, well-informed buyers met innumerable, rational, well-informed sellers in a single (spaceless) market to exchange goods and services, thus establishing prices, incomes, and the allocation of resources. Classical trade theory, as exemplified by the so-called "law of comparative advantage," assumes several production and consumption points, but spatial characteristics remain irrelevant to the theory. Various economists, such as Loesch, Weber, Ohlin, and Myrdal,[12] have shown the weaknesses of

[11] Walter Isard: *Location and the Space Economy*, New York, 1956, p. 24ff.
[12] Gunnar Myrdal: *Rich Lands and Poor: The Road to World Prosperity*, New York, 1958.

spaceless trade theory but without developing a spatial trade theory fully acceptable to general economics.

The elimination of the spatial variable from theoretical economics also left a serious void in economic interpretations of economic growth. Was it not the "conquest of space" by the use of the new technology (sailing ships) that shifted England and the Low Countries from positions on the economic margin of Europe, from the edge of the world, to the economic center of the world? Was it not English awareness of the importance of spatial mobility (sea power) that led England to world dominion? In short, it would appear that the spaceless nature of English economic theory did not stop the empirical English from "blundering through" to the establishment of a spatial system of international trade linking those parts of the world readily accessible to salt water ports. Perhaps it was the very ease of transport on the broad and limitless oceans which led English economists to consider accessibility almost entirely in terms of political "interferences" with trade (tariffs, etc.) and to ignore the limitations of distance and natural barriers. At any rate, it is significant that more interest has been shown in location theory in the more self-contained, land-based, economies such as those of Germany, the Soviet Union, and the United States. Alternatively, one might assume the economist's lack of concern for spatial variability to be caused by ethnocentrism. It might appear eminently reasonable to think in terms of *a market* rather than many markets when England was unquestionably the industrial and market center of the world, when cotton prices were determined almost exclusively in Liverpool and Manchester. Further, Britain was such a small country that spatial variation within it might appear unimportant in comparison with the total volume of sea-borne trade. However, Myrdal considers the problem to be more basic, a moral problem. He suggests that behind the neat abstractions of classical trade theory lay the desire to avoid consideration of the morally embarrassing economic inequalities among the (spatially differentiated) countries of the world. In any case, the growth of economic geography has been, at least in part, an attempt, conscious or unconscious, to fill the vacuum created by the elimination of the spatial variable from economic theory.

The Interpretations of Economic Geography

The beginnings of economic geography were quite different than those of economics. While economics grew from the social philosophy of the Middle Ages, economic geography developed from Medieval cosmography and from the intellectual reaction of the Europeans to a suddenly expanded world. The Ancient and Medieval Worlds were small worlds. Although there was considerable spatial variation, this variability was very minor in relation to the immensely varied and seemingly limitless world which opened out before the adventurous Europeans of the 16th Century. Greek and Arab geographers had begun the analysis of earth space, but this analysis was largely cartographic and descriptive rather than abstract and theoretical. Consequently there were relatively few theoretical foundations on which to build spatial understanding in the post-Columbian era, while the need to develop such understanding was immediate and pressing. Thus perhaps it is not surprising that the classical economists developed abstract models without including an important abstraction, spatial variability, whereas geographers began empirical study of the newly important spatial variability.

The great outpouring of maps, atlases, and geographies or cosmographies witnessed to the need of the Europeans to understand the areal differentiation of the world they were exploring and organizing for world-wide trade. Most of this geography was general, not confining itself solely to economic spatial variation. Though Alexander von Humboldt is best known for his studies of biological geography, he also studied the "economic geography" of the Spanish Colonial Empire. The great surveys of western North America had a partially economic orientation. Many geographic studies of the habitable world and of the limits of the agricultural frontier revealed a strong interest in the geography of Occidental economic expansion.

The great expansion of world-wide trade, the gradual erosion of isolation, and the rise of the commercial vocational school [13] have led toward a more specifically "economic" type of geography. J. C. Stamp has suggested that the real parentage of modern American economic geography is in ". . . the Eighteenth Century masses of unrelated [i.e., conceptually unrelated] facts . . . everything useful for the merchant to know." [14] This early commercial geography was undeniably useful but had little coherence and few organizing principles. Thus when Götz called for the development of *economic geography* in 1882, he was most careful to distinguish it from practical but unsystematic "commercial geography." However, the commercial geography despised by Götz became closely identified with the new economic geography, at least in England and America. But commercial geography did not remain without principles and organization. Perhaps it is not wholly accidental that a more scholarly commercial geography developed in Great Britain, the chief trading nation. This geography flourished at the turn of the century under the leadership of Chisholm in Great Britain and Whitbeck and Smith in the United States. It stressed the study of trade routes, the production and movement of commodities, and the character of economically specialized production areas, espe-

[13] Sidney Rosen: "A Short History of High School Geography," *Journ. of Geogr.*, Vol. 56, 1957, pp. 406-413.
[14] J. C. Stamp, *op. cit.*, p. 3.

cially agricultural regions. Production, rather than consumption, was emphasized. According to Sapper,[15] the geography of consumption was not clearly defined until 1929, by Schmidt. Primary production was treated in some detail, but secondary and tertiary production received little attention. The natural environment was fully treated, not only because of the pervasive environmental determinism (really a form of Social Darwinism) of the period, but also because the natural environment is highly pertinent to most forms of primary production. Thus the American economic geography of the early 20th Century was primarily a naturalistic geography of primary production, especially production important to trade.

Few theories and few generally acceptable verbal generalizations were produced. As a pioneering field, geography was concerned primarily with bringing order out of chaos by careful classification and mapping of economic phenomena. However, geographers developed the map as a highly effective form of visual generalization. They learned to state economic problems in cartographic form; as H. H. McCarty has pointed out, an adequately annotated and properly documented map may constitute the statement of a research problem in economic geography. Further, the many studies of small areas produced generalizations which could then become hypotheses for the study of other areas, a process which could eventually lead to the development of generalizations and principles applicable to large areas of the earth.[16]

Economics and Economic Geography Compared

The economics and economic geography which had developed by the early decades of the 20th Century were very different. They were complementary though not highly cooperative. Geographers took the market as a research perimeter while economists took areal differentiation as a research perimeter. Thus geographers discussed the production and flow of primary materials without market analysis while the economists analyzed markets without regard for their spatial variability. Similarly, geographers stressed primary production while the economists stressed consumption. Economists were generally more sensitive to social values, though some geographers were pioneers in the study of conservation. Economic geography was largely empirical; economics was highly abstract. The differences between the two fields were too great to be satisfactorily bridged at the level of theory. Yet the central problems of the two fields were interrelated parts of a larger social problem. Both fields sought to understand the same basic phe-

[15] Karl Sapper: "Economic Geography," *Encyclopedia of the Social Sciences,* Vol. 6, pp. 626-628.
[16] H. H. McCarty: "An Approach to a Theory of Economic Geography," *Econ. Geogr.,* Vol. 30, 1954, pp. 95-101.

nomenon, the world market economy created by European expansion. The vacuums in knowledge created by the disciplinary structure of one field were filled, at least in part, by the efforts of the other. Thus, although the two fields developed in isolation from each other and although little cooperation of a formal nature emerged, economics and economic geography were complementary disciplines.

The Urban-Industrial World and the Broadening of Inquiry

The related processes of the new industrialization and urbanization gradually have transformed the relatively simple agro-commercial world of western expansion into a new and much more complex world. This new urban-industrial world differs from its predecessor almost as much as the age of Occidental expansion differed from the fragmented and isolated Medieval World. The new age of industrial chemistry, electricity, and the internal combustion engine has brought new social problems and a new relevancy and urgency to old social problems. The importance of trade between developed and underdeveloped regions has declined, while the importance of trade within and among developed regions has increased. Energy sources and their location have new meaning for industrial location with each passing day. Economic localism and atomization have given way to giant corporate industrial combines, agencies of the state in totalitarian countries and semi-independent corporations in the rest of the world. The old, compact city and the old urban-rural dichotomy are giving way to something new, something as yet so dimly understood that it is without a generally accepted name (suburbia-exurbia, urban region, urban agglomeration, conurbation, megalopolis, and so on). In short, society is struggling with the new meaning of space and with the creation of a social order appropriate to this new meaning.

The attempt to probe the new problems of society has already influenced economic geography and economics profoundly. Both disciplines have broadened the field of inquiry, adding many new branches and specialties. Yet the central interests of the past remain. Economics is still concerned with resource allocation and hence with the functioning of the market mechanism, economic geography with *production geography*.[17] However, while the cores remain distinct, the broadening of inquiry has led to much overlapping of interest. Historic distinctions have become hazy in many areas peripheral to both fields.

[17] Howard F. Gregor: "German vs. American Economic Geography," *Prof. Geogr.*, Vol. 9, 1957, pp. 12-13.

The Broadening of Economics

Some of the very evident broadening of economics can be traced rather directly to the great economic crises of the day, in an era of increasing economic complexity with the consequent need for planning in business, labor, and government. The great economic crises of the 20th Century include the endemic agricultural crisis, the Great Depression, and the two World Wars. The first has fostered a great expansion of both theoretical and applied studies in agricultural economics. Some of these studies have been market-oriented, closely related to the traditional central theme of economics. Others have been production-oriented, and consequently related not only to economics but also to traditional agricultural geography.

The Great Depression fostered the rise of Keynesian economics and its statistics, the analysis of National Income. The Occidental world was faced with an unparalleled problem in unemployment, a crisis presumably due to the malfunctioning of one aspect of the historic market system, savings and investment. Keynesian economics and the analysis of national income were the tools for understanding and solving this newly relevant social problem. Unfortunately, this great forward step in economics had little immediate relevance for geography. At this time geographers were preoccupied with studies of small areas rather than with gross national aggregates. The geographic emphasis on small-area studies may have been prompted primarily as a reaction to the earlier environmental determinism in geography, as Warntz[18] suggests. However, geographers were responding also to the depression-born need for active social intervention in the economy. The change in geography from environmental determinism to resource inventory and analysis was related to the change from laissez-faire economics to Keynesian analysis. Both fields were influenced by the crisis, though in different ways.

The two World Wars involved many economists in the war mobilization of resources and in regional international economic planning. The activity of economists in such international programs as the Marshall Plan, the Colombo Plan, the World Bank, and the Technical Assistance programs generated interest in regional economics. The Cold War magnified the problem of great international discrepancies in levels and rates of economic development and encouraged economists to search widely for explanations. All of these developments have very direct bearing on economic geography.

The emphasis on planning may partially account for the renewed

[18] William Warntz: "The Unity of Knowledge, Social Science, and the Role of Geography," address at the geography session, National Council for the Social Studies, Pittsburgh, 1957.

interest in the economics of location by a few economists. Walter Isard seeks to harmonize the various location theories, especially those developed by German economists. Although his first volume is the best summary of the literature on location and although Isard contributes many ideas of his own, it is important to stress that this is not yet a truly general theory of location. It is an exceedingly important step in the development of a *market* theory of location. That is, Isard successfully relates location theory to established equilibrium theory and to the concept of monopolistic competition. Thus the economics of location is market-oriented and remains in the economic tradition of emphasis on the market mechanism. Perhaps the growth of a more general theory must await the further development of economic explanations of production and productivity. Furthermore, Isard's space is largely abstract; it is not the real earth-space of the geographer. Nevertheless, the re-introduction of the spatial variable removes one of the major obstacles to cooperation between economics and economic geography.

The emphasis on planning may also account for the increasing interest in the economics of production. Economists have always been interested in production but interest in production and productivity *per se*, apart from any market connection, has been increasing. Perhaps this change has been encouraged by the growing social awareness that productivity is the key to plenty in the 20th Century just as trade was the key in centuries past. Erich Zimmermann described his resource studies as a "probing downward" from a "limited section of the cultural superstructure" of society "toward the physical foundation." [19] However, his efforts can also be viewed as an attempt to develop an economics of production broader than that previously developed. However, this classic work is more descriptive than theoretical. More specifically, Leontief introduced a new method of analyzing the many linkages in the productive process, input-output analysis. Isard and others have applied this approach to *areas* as well as industries. Western Europeans, struggling for survival in a bi-polar economic world, have produced many studies of productivity. This increased concern for production and productivity has many implications for traditional economic thinking. Recently, Robert Solo has called for a "new direction for economic inquiry," a "true economics of production analyzing the utilization of resources and probing the mysteries of productivity." [20]

The Broadening of Economic Geography

Economic geography also has broadened, from the narrow mercantile

[19] Erich W. Zimmermann: *World Resources and Industries*, rev. ed., New York, 1951, p. xi.
[20] Robert Solo, *op. cit.*, p. 136.

geography of the 19th Century to the complex clustering of related specialties described by Murphy as the "fields of economic geography." As with economics, the increasing complexity of the urban-industrial world has encouraged this transformation. Economic geography has continued to stress primary production, but more broadly conceived and balanced by studies of manufacturing, transportation, marketing, ports and hinterlands, urban geography, and even recreation. Recent geographic studies of the journey-to-work[21] and of employment may herald a new geography of labor. A recent paper combines the study of primary production, manufacturing, marketing, and transportation through the geographic study of industrial corporate structure, introducing the spatial dimension into the analysis of the firms.[22] Several geographers have shown interest in the development of a geography of capital and investment, analogous to economic studies of banking, capital formation, and money flows. Concurrently with these changes, economic geography has become less oriented toward the natural world and more oriented toward the social world. Preoccupation with the mutual relationships between economic phenomena and the natural environment has declined, a fact much lamented by some geographers. Similarly, economic geographers today are expressing more concern for the social values involved in conservation, regional economic development, and industrial relocation.

Broadening of the field of inquiry has led also to increasing contacts with other social sciences, especially economics. Such contacts have been fostered not only by the increasing overlapping of subject matter with economics but also by the growing interest in developing a unified theoretical structure for economic geography. An important effect of the broadening of the field has been the dramatization of the need for such unifying theory. As Murphy points out, "general economic geography" (has) "ceased to exist as a research specialty, if, indeed, it could ever have been so regarded." [23] Some geographers have turned to economic theory, hoping that the abstract models developed to solve the problems of the economist can be adapted to the problems of the geographer. Waibel,[24] Melamid,[25] Hartshorne, and others, have examined the Thünen model and applied it to various historical and geographical situations. Conclusions on the utility of the

[21] Robert E. Dickinson: "The Geography of Commuting: The Netherlands and Belgium," *Geogr. Rev.*, Vol. 47, 1957, pp. 521-538.
[22] Robert B. McNee: "Functional Geography of the Firm, with an Illustrative Case Study from the Petroleum Industry," *Econ. Geogr.*, Vol. 34, 1958, pp. 321-337.
[23] Murphy, *op. cit.*, p. 242.
[24] Leo Waibel: *Probleme der Landwirtschafts-geographie*, Breslau, 1933, pp. 47-78.
[25] Alexander Melamid: "Some Applications of Thünen's Model in Regional Analysis of Economic Growth," paper delivered at American Economic Association Meeting, December 27, 1954.

model have been rather mixed. Recently Kraus[26] stressed the value of economic location theory in the analysis of regional organization and the concept of economic costs in the analysis of man-land relations.

Awareness of the potential value of location theory to economic geography is spreading widely among American geographers, as indicated by the recent article by Ballabon.[27] However, acceptance of the utility of economic location theory in economic geography does not imply that economic geography can be, or should be, fully integrated with economics. On the contrary, Hartshorne has indicated aptly the narrowly specialized viewpoint which the economist brings to geography. As he says, the economist ". . . is apt to think almost exclusively in terms of relative location, considered purely geometrically, and to ignore other variants of areas . . . ."[28] Furthermore, there are many stated and unstated assumptions underlying standard economic theory which limit the direct applicability of such models in geographic research.

Economic geographers seeking a unifying theory have turned also in other directions. Warntz[29] is working from a frame of reference much broader than that of classical economics. He believes geographers should emulate social physics, through reducing geographic problems to basic dimensions expressed mathematically, the most important dimension being distance.

Alternatively, economic geographers continue to seek theoretical principles from a more traditional source in geography, empirical research. For example, the "principles of spatial interchange" developed by Ullman from his specialized studies of commodity flow[30] and Philbrick's "principles of areal organization"[31] are steps toward the development of empirically-derived unifying theory in economic geography.

Summary and Conclusions

Historically, economic geography and economics have been quite distinct because their central problems have been different. Both fields have their roots in the Age of Trade. Economics became the science of the market place while economic geography became the science of

[26] Theodore Kraus: "Wirtschaftgeographie als Geographie und als Wirtschaftswissenschaft," *Die Erde*, Jahrgang 88, Heft 2, 1957, pp. 110-119.

[27] Ballabon, *op. cit.*

[28] Richard Hartshorne: "The Nature of Geography," *Assn. of Amer. Geogrs.*, Lancaster, Pa., 1949, p. 421.

[29] William Warntz: "Transportation, Social Physics, and the Law of Refraction," *Prof. Geogr.*, Vol. 9, 1957, pp. 2-7.

[30] Edward L. Ullman: *American Commodity Flow*, Seattle, 1957.

[31] Allen K. Philbrick: "Principles of Areal Functional Organization in Regional Human Geography," *Econ. Geogr.*, Vol. 33, 1957, pp. 299-336.

areal differentiation of the production important to trade. This was essentially a complementary relationship. However, industrialization and urbanization brought new social problems. Economic crises and the complexities of the new society have encouraged economists and economic geographers alike to broaden the field of inquiry.

Economics is balancing its spaceless models with others including the spatial variable, its historic market and consumer emphasis with an expanding interest in productivity, its social competence with more technological competence, and its verbal and mathematical abstractions with more empirical observations. Meanwhile, economic geography is balancing its production geography with studies of consumption, marketing, transportation, and many other economic phenomena. A new concern for social values is being added to the historic knowledge of technological and naturalistic conditions. And economic geographers, no longer satisfied with cartographic generalization alone, are reaching out more vigorously than before to develop verbal and mathematical generalizations and principles. Economics and economic geography are drawing together, in spite of their histories of isolation. This is occurring at all levels, in theoretical studies as well as in applied studies. Thus the newly emerging relationship of the two fields is more than merely complementary; it is truly cooperative. Neither the duration nor the depth of this new cooperation can be predicted, but the benefits to both fields will surely be substantial and lasting.

In the unpredictable future, cooperation could lead to an integration of economics and economic geography, perhaps as parts of that elusive larger whole, an integrated and cohesive social science. But for the present, one may conclude that economics is of only limited *direct* utility in solving the central problems of economic geography while it is of great *indirect* value in helping to understand these problems in their broader social setting. Therefore, geographers should not attempt to recast their subject in the mold of economics; neither should they insist on "splendid isolation" within a narrowly conceived "geographic" economic geography. Rather, they should seek to solve the central problems of economic geography in every way the mind can devise, including, for those with the requisite training and interest, economic location models, national income statistics, productivity analyses, or other advances in the field of economics.

25. Recent Developments of Central Place Theory

Brian J. L. Berry and William L. Garrison

Quantitative methods have enhanced the rigor of certain kinds of geographic research in the post-World War II period. A major prewar stimulus to the development of these methods was Walter Christaller's central place theory, which stated that urban places were so arranged that a larger central place was equidistant from smaller places and so arranged that a hexagonal pattern resulted. The theory provided the framework for considerable economic and urban geographic study. In the following article, Garrison and Berry, major contributors to such research in America, summarize the status, consequences, and potentialities of central place theory. They discuss the possibility of reformulating it in the light of new findings and indicate the kinds of research that could grow out of a modified theoretical framework.

In central place theory the term "central place" has meant "urban center." In the past the theory sought to account for these urban centers. It consisted of a series of assertions and definitions, logical consequences of which were a hierarchical ranking of urban centers according to functions (*e.g.*, hamlets, villages, towns, and cities) and associated market areas and transportation networks.

Concern with the full array of urban centers and associated market areas and transportation routes remains basic to central place theory. Important recent work, however, has shown the usefulness of the theory in understanding the spatial structure of retail and service business (whether this business be located in alternate urban centers or in shopping districts within cities) and the content of the theory thereby has been increased. These changes have resulted in an increased generality of the application of the theory (*i.e.*, the theory may be more widely used; it serves as a theory of tertiary activity) and a more pow-

SOURCE: Regional Science Association, *Papers and Proceedings*, IV (1958), 107-20. Reprinted by permission of the authors and the Association. Dr. Berry is associate professor of geography at the University of Chicago, and Dr. Garrison is professor of geography at Northwestern University.

erful theory (*i.e.*, its assertions are more plausible; its logical consequences are more explicit). Elaboration of these results is the purpose
of the ensuing discussion.

Three topics are treated. First, the development of the theory is
reviewed, especially in order to identify some important recent contributions. Second, some consequences of the theory are treated, especially in terms of results of recent empirical work and implications
from this work for the reformulation of the theory. It is noted here
how several concepts from economics serve to enrich work with central
places. More important, it is noted that the theory may be formulated
in terms of a simple concept of *threshold*. This frees the theory from
complicating assumptions about the shape and homogeneous character
of city trade areas. Finally, strategic research problems are identified
from the standpoint of the present status of the theory and related
theories.

Notes on the Formulation of Central Place Theory

Schemes explaining urban growth and arrangement are many in number. Most of these likely stem from common origins. It seems likely,
thus, that generic roots of central place theory extend in many directions and are joint with those of competing schemes. That these things
may be true is taken for granted in the present discussion. The present
discussion begins with the pragmatically taken position that central
place theory began with Walter Christaller in 1933. To begin with
Christaller and outline chief contributions of subsequent workers is a
sufficient statement of the theory for present purposes. The complete
statement of the growth of the theory awaits the never-to-be written
definitive work on the development of ideas about urbanism.

Following the review of Christaller's work, contributions to the
theory by August Lösch are reviewed. Following the discussion of
Lösch's work the recent reformulation of central place theory is
presented.

Initial Formulation of the Theory

Central place theory as formulated by Walter Christaller in his *Die
zentralen Orte in Süddeutschland*[1] and presented elsewhere by Edward Ullman[2] is relatively well-known. The content of the theory may
be stated in a summary way with an outline of its definitions, relationships, and consequences.

[1] Christaller, *Die zentralen Orte in Süddeutschland,* Jena: Gustav Fischer, 1933.
[2] E. L. Ullman, "A Theory of Location for Cities," *American Journal of Sociology,*
vol. 46, 1941, pp. 853-864.

A. Terms defined included:
   (1) A central place.
   (2) A central good.
   (3) A complementary region.
B. Relationships specified included:
   (1) Variations in prices of central goods as distance from point of supply changes.
   (2) Explicit extremization behavior in the distribution and consumption of goods (*e.g.*, goods are purchased from the closest place).
   (3) Inner and outer limits for the range of distances over which central goods may be sold.
   (4) Relationships between the number of goods sold from a central place and the population of that place.
C. A statement which used the terms defined and relationships specified (within the simplifying assumption of homogeneous distribution of purchasing power in all areas) and described the arrangement of central places and complementary regions was made.

Essential features of this statement were:

(1) Hexagonal market areas for any set of central goods.
(2) Overlapping sets of hexagons. The hexagons overlap in such a way that larger hexagonal market areas (resulting from a set of central goods) are divided into smaller hexagons when supplied by other central goods. The smaller hexagons nest into the larger according to a rule of threes (this is the K-3 network described by Lösch).
(3) Transportation routes serving the system of cities.

Generalization by August Lösch

A good portion of August Lösch's now classic *Die raumliche Ordnung der Wirtschaft*[3] was given to an evaluation and extension of notions of the arrangement of central places. Lösch's additions to the notions fall into three major divisions.

A. The explicit statement of two aspects of the system:
   (1) The derivation of demand cores over areas for goods.
   (2) Verification of the hexagonal-shaped complementary region as the "best" shape where purchasing power was uniformly distributed.

[3] Lösch, *Die raumliche Ordnung der Wirtschaft*, translated by Woglom and Stolper as *The Economics of Location*, New Haven: Yale Univ. Press, 1954.

B. Clear linking of that arrangement of transportation routes among cities to central place notions.

C. The extension of the special case of a K-3 network to a more general description of a system containing all possible relationships of evenly-spaced central places and nests of hexagonal shapes of complementary regions. In the system he develops he maintains:

(1) That consumer movement must be minimized.

(2) That no excess profits can be earned by any firm.

Lösch further asserts, but does not demonstrate, that one outcome of his system is a hierarchical class-system of central places both as sources of central goods and as intersections upon the transport network.

Recent Developments

As developed, central place theory related only to alternate urban centers and the transport network linking urban centers. The statement was in terms of homogeneously distributed purchasing power (hence, the hexagonal trade areas) and, thus, restricted in applicability in more realistic situations. Too, such assumptions as the absence of excess profits in the system were troublesome. Recent work tends to show however:

A. That central place theory may be considered more readily, is more understandable, and definitely more viable, when reformulated in terms of a series of simple concepts.

B. That reformulation in terms of these concepts enables a hierarchical structure to be developed without the uniformity assumptions concerning purchasing power basic to the arrangement of hexagonal trade areas. One consequence of this is that the theory is applicable to areas within cities as well as areas without.

C. That the notion of no excess profits can be relaxed.

Empirical work associated with the developments listed above has shown how they simplify the problem of the empirical verification of the theory. The empirical work is also a good example of the value of such references in the refining of theory and better comprehension of the character of the hierarchical system of central place foci in the space-economy.[4]

THE CONCEPT OF THE RANGE OF A GOOD / A concept with an important

[4] See Brian J. L. Berry and William L. Garrison, "The Functional Bases of the Central Place Hierarchy," forthcoming in *Economic Geography; idem,* "Central Place Theory and the Range of a Good," forthcoming in *Economic Geography;* Brian J. L. Berry, *Geographic Aspects of the Size and Arrangement of Urban Centers,* unpublished M.A. thesis, University of Washington, 1956.

role in present central place theory is that of the range of a central good. This range delineates the market area of a central place for the good. It has a lower limit which incorporated the *threshold* purchasing power for the supply of the good (see below) and an upper limit beyond which the central place is no longer able to sell the good. Each good will have different limits to its range because of competition between central places supplying the good (in the case of the upper limit) and differing internal economic characteristics of the supplying firms which determine threshold (in the case of the lower limit).

THE CONCEPT OF THRESHOLD / Later in the present discussion it will be illustrated with a scale that there is some minimum size of market below which a place will be unable to supply a central good. On this scale this is the point where sales are large enough only for the firm to earn normal profits. This minimum scale, the lower limit of the range of a central place, is the minimum amount of purchasing power necessary to support the supply of a central good from a central place, and is here termed the *threshold* sales level for the provision of that good from the center.

THE HIERARCHICAL SPATIAL STRUCTURE / It can be argued that *whatever* the distribution of purchasing power (and whether in open countryside or within a large metropolis) a hierarchical spatial structure of central places supplying central goods will emerge. This argument requires only the concepts of range and threshold just given.

For the sake of exposition assume an area to be supplied with n types of central goods. Let these be ranked from 1 to n in ascending order of threshold sales requirements. The central place supplying good n will require the largest market area (in terms of amount of purchasing power) to support it. Let a central place supplying good n be called an A center.

As many A centers will exist in the area as there are threshold sales levels to support firms supplying good n. These firms compete spatially, hence are distributed so as to supply their own threshold most efficiently. If total sales levels are an exact multiple of thresholds for good n, market areas will be bounded by lower limits to the range of A centers. Firms will earn only normal profits, and these *only if* they minimize costs by: (a) locating to minimize distribution costs if the product is delivered, or (b) locating to minimize consumer movement if the consumer comes to purchase the products.

If sales in the whole area are slightly greater than an exact multiple of threshold, but not great enough to justify another A center, then excess profits may be earned. Ranges reach a more competitive upper limit.

The question arises as to how good n–1 will be provided. Presumably, it will be supplied from the A centers, which have sought out the most efficient points of supply. Too, there will be advantages from association with other establishments providing central goods. The threshold of good n–1 is less than that of good n and hence, spatial competition determines market areas (these are delimited by upper limit ranges) and excess profits may be earned. This argument will be the case for goods n–2 and down to good 1 as well.

But there may be one or more goods, say good n–1, in which case the interstitial purchasing power located between threshold market areas of A centers supplying good n–1 will themselves reach threshold size. In this case greater efficiency is reached if a second set of centers, which may be termed B centers, supply the good. These B centers again locate most efficiently relative to their threshold market area. If the market area is just at threshold only normal profits are earned by firms supplying good n–1. If part-multiples of threshold are present some excess profits are earned. Good n–1 may be termed a *hierarchical marginal good*. B centers will also provide lower threshold goods, n–(i+1) through good 1.

Let us assume that good n–j (j>i) is also a hierarchical marginal good, supporting a third set of central places designated as C places. These are a lower order of central places and provide only goods n–j through good 1.

The pattern of provision of goods by centers in this hierarchical system may be displayed in an array (Table I). The table displays how sets of goods build up hierarchies of types of central places. For example, the set of C places and places in the tributary areas of C places rely upon either B or A places for goods n–i to n–(j–1) and upon A places for goods n to n–(i–1). B places rely upon A places for goods n to n–(i–1). All places will be located at the point from which they most efficiently serve tributary areas with central goods.

TABLE I.   How n Goods are Supplied by M Centers

Centers	Goods				
	$n^*, n-1, \ldots$	$n-i^*, n-(i+1), \ldots$	$n-j^*, n-(j+1), \ldots$	$\ldots$	$k^*, (k-1), \ldots 1$
A	X	X	X	$\ldots$	X
B		X	X	$\ldots$	X
C			X	$\ldots$	X
.				.	.
.				.	.
.				.	.
M					X

* Indicates hierarchical marginal good. X indicates the set of goods supplied by the center.

Yet at the same time excess profits may be earned in the system. Where n goods are provided it is likely that the hierarchical marginal firm will tend to earn only normal profits. This is the firm which satisfies Lösch's condition that excess profits shall be at a minimum. However, all supramarginal firms in the hierarchy will have the opportunity to earn excess profits to the extent that they are able to compete spatially with other firms for the sub-threshold purchasing power which exists between threshold market areas in the spatial system.

The question may quite properly be raised, why argue a step hierarchy of functions and one with excess profits (profits over and above normal profits) when a system without excess profits can be argued (Lösch) using notions of nested hexagonal trade areas? The argument used was presented because recent empirical work indicates it is more like reality than the alternate argument. A discussion of this empirical work follows.

Consequences of Recent Empirical Work and Links with Other Theory

Formulation of central place theory using only simple concepts and readily comprehendable terms and with attention directed toward the arrangement in hierarchies in retail and service business rather than the hierarchical system of central places itself, was motivated by results of empirical work and has enabled empirical tests of theory to be formulated. Critical results from empirical work were the identification of hierarchies of central place functions and identification of threshold marginal goods.

EXISTENCE OF A HIERARCHY / The existence of a hierarchical spatial structure has been asserted many times and many "tests" utilizing intuitive "indicators" of centrality, or assumed class-systems, have been utilized.[5] Given the notion of a basic hierarchical system of business, however, tests were designed to determine whether, indeed, a natural class system of types of business in alternate urban centers exists, and whether a hierarchy of urban centers was related to the classes of business. These tests have been reported elsewhere and will not be described here.[6] Suffice it to say that they were executed successfully and that a hierarchical system was proved to exist. The functional bases of the hierarchy and associated characteristics in the study area are discussed at length in the published reports of these empirical tests.

[5] See the references in Berry and Garrison, "The Functional Bases . . . ," *op. cit.*, and the more complete bibliography in Berry, *op. cit.*
[6] Berry and Garrison, *op. cit.*

EXCESS PROFITS / Likewise, the existence of a possibility to earn excess profits was demonstrated. Marginal hierarchical firms were identified and the nature and amounts of possible sub-threshold excess profits which could be earned by supramarginal firms in the hierarchy estimated.[7]

A NOTE ON THE ASSOCIATED TRANSPORT NETWORK / The spatial pattern of central places and market areas is obviously indissolubly linked to a transport network. Problems of optimal design and utilization of such communication networks have been studied elsewhere.[8] What implications does central place theory provide for the understanding of such problems? Obviously, an hierarchical pattern of central places and an hierarchical pattern of business implies an hierarchical pattern of consumer movement. This in turn implies a like pattern for an optimal transport network to support such a system. Feeder roads to low order centers are supplemented by trunk lines between higher order centers. As many ranks of trunk lines occur as there are ranks of higher order centers. The higher the order of the center, the greater the convergence of routes. The denser the distribution of purchasing power, the denser the transport network.

Lösch maintained an associated characteristic would be an hierarchical pattern or route intersections. In his system of networks each

TABLE II.   Railway Intersections at the 100 Largest Cities in the U.S., 1955

Number of Rays at the Intersection	Number of Cities that had the Number of Rays
12 and more	10
11	2
10	6
9	3
8	2
7	10
6	22
5	19
4	19
3	6
2	0
1	1

[7] Berry and Garrison, "Central Place Theory . . . ," op. cit.
[8] One such study is R. E. Kalaba and M. L. Juncosa, "Optimal Design and Utilization of Communication Networks," Management Science, vol. 3, 1956, pp. 33-44. This work contains further references. See also W. L. Garrison and Duane F. Marble, "The Analysis of Highway Networks: A Linear Programming Formulation," 38th Annual Meetings of the Highway Research Board, Washington, D.C., 1958.

metropolis would have twelve or more intersections and within its sphere of influence would be two centers with six intersections and three with four intersections.

This assertion was subjected to an empirical test by Wallace.[9] The 100 largest cities in the United States were taken and a count of all separate rail lines entering each of these cities within a radius of 25 miles made (Table II). Some general validity for the Lösch assertion is seen. Wallace reported that few intersection centers increased as more smaller centers were included in the sample. Hence an increase in sample size was thought to be needed to provide a better test of the theory. Nevertheless, it may be thought that if the concept of a hierarchical pattern of intersects has some merit, then too does the concept of an hierarchical transport network. Here is a subject for more empirical research.

Links with Other Theory

Empirical work tends to show that the formulation of central place theory free of the assumption of no excess profits and free of assumptions of the shape and character of trade areas is warranted. That is, the new formulation meets requirements of correspondence with reality. Another asset of the new formulation is its relation to alternate theories. Certain of these are explored below.

THEORY OF RETAILING / At first glance it appears that central place theory is compatible with the existing body of theory concerning the retail firm, as developed by such students as Aubert-Krier,[10] Smithies,[11] and Lewis,[12] since apparently central theory posits single types of business, or essentially single-product firms which read a competitive state of spatial equilibrium.

The lack of sophistication of such a single-product approach has been pointed out by Holton.[13] He has argued that a far more realistic theory of retailing can be developed within the framework of a multi-product firm, and has developed a model for this case. His conclusion is that the long-run equilibrium pattern of the multi-product firm is one which requires that all products in which marginal revenue exceeds marginal cost be added to the product line and sales of each expanded to the

[9] W. C. Wallace, "A Note on Transportation Network Models," unpublished manuscript, 1957.

[10] J. Aubert-Krier, "Monopolistic and Imperfect Competition in Retail Trade," in E. H. Chamberlain, ed., *Monopoly and Competition and Their Regulation*, London: Hutchinson's University Library, 1949.

[11] A. Smithies, "The Theory of Value Applied to Retail Selling," *Review of Economic Studies*, vol. 6, 1939, pp. 215-221.

[12] W. A. Lewis, "Competition in Retail Trade," *Economics*, vol. 12, 1945.

[13] R. H. Holton, "Price Discrimination at Retail: The Supermarket Case," *Journal of Industrial Economics*, vol. 6, 1957, pp. 13-32.

point where marginal profits are all zero. Empirical tests in the case of supermarkets have verified the conclusions of his model and the further finding that profit maximization will result in price discrimination, since products will face demand functions of different elasticities.

Central place theory is compatible with this formulation of the equilibrium of the retail firm. Consider each rank of the hierarchy of central functions as a firm. Many products will be supplied by this rank (the number of stores supplying them will, of course, be substantially less). All products will be sold for which marginal revenue exceeded marginal cost, and marginal cost is defined upon the threshold sales volume of the hierarchical marginal product. Sales are expanded to the point where marginal profits are all zero as determined by the upper limits of the range of each product.

Generally, stores will be located in a manner which minimizes consumer movement and hence will maximize profits. But for all products other than those of the marginal hierarchical goods it is possible to earn excess profits. Central place theory posits that these are allocated by spatial competition. It is obvious that notions concerning this competition should be broadened to include competition through the practice of price discrimination according to the elasticity of demand for different products. Ability to compete in these more general terms means that excess profits may be allocated in far from an equitable manner among existing firms.

NOTIONS OF CONSUMER BEHAVIOR / It is interesting to consider correspondence between central place theory and recent work regarding shopping behavior by consumers. Baumol and Ide [14] have produced a simple model displaying the choice variables in the determination of a shopping center by the consumer. A customer will shop at a center when his demand function is such that

$$f(N, D) = wp(N) - v(C_d D + C_n \sqrt{N} + C_i)$$

is positive. $f(N, D.)$ is a measure of the expected net benefit of the consumer from entering a store. It varies with D, his distance from the store, and N, the number of items offered for sale at the store. Assumed costs are C_d (a cost of transport assumed proportional to distance); $C_n \sqrt{N}$ is the assumed costs of actual shopping; and C_i represents the opportunity costs of other shopping opportunities foregone. $p(N)$ is the probabalistic satisfaction function. w and v are the subjective weights assigned by the consumer when he evaluates the size of each element in the equation.

The economic implications from this statement are many. For ex-

[14] W. J. Baumol and E. A. Ide, "Variety in Retailing," *Management Science*, vol. 3, 1956, pp. 93-101.

ample, the minimum number of items necessary to induce a customer to shop at a given store will increase with D. Maximum shopping distance is given by the equation of the indifference curve which offers the consumer net zero benefit from shopping at a store and is obtained by setting $f(N, D) = O$ and solving for D to yield:

$$D_n = \frac{w}{vC_d} p(N) - \frac{1}{C_d} (C_n \sqrt{N+C_i})$$

Given the hierarchical spatial system of central place theory:
  (1) $p(N)$ will be a step-function related to levels of goods available at each rank of the hierarchy.
  (2) $C_n \sqrt{N}$ will be a like step-function.
  (3) C_i will be dependent upon the spatial distribution of an hierarchical system.

Hence any solution D_n will be a step-function related to levels of the hierarchy. The Baumol and Ide system is entirely compatible with central place theory. This statement is also true for their development of total retail sales, since they base this model upon the previous one of maximum consumer distance, and of their notions of maximization of profits, since these are based upon N. Not only do consumers discriminate among centers hierarchically and spatially, but retail varieties and sales levels and the extent of potential profits are likewise determined.

Location of Strategic Research Problems

The preceding discussion has set forth in an expository manner several simple notions (especially, range of a good and threshold) and it has been argued that these notions satisfy the purposes of central place theory as well as do earlier formulations of the theory. One basis of argument was evidence from recent empirical research. Also, it was noted how notions of central place theory, when based on these simple notions, merge with other notions which bear on problems of retail business.

The discussion, thus, provides orientation and a useful way to end the discussion might be to elaborate needed research that may be identified at this time.

NATURE OF THE HIERARCHICAL SYSTEM / It has been argued that, whatever the areal circumstances, a hierarchical central place structure will exist. Put another way, it has been argued that a hierarchical structure will exist free of the assumptions of hexagonal tributary areas. Too, reference has been made to empirical studies which have tended to show the existence of hierarchies. These latter studies have been limited in scope and here is a place where much research is warranted. Namely, what is the nature of real world systems?

Several related problems are apparent. For example, city planners base actions on concepts of neighborhood and community shopping centers. How valid are these concepts on an empirical level? What is social gain and loss from planning other than "natural" locations? Another example question is, what relationship does a hierarchical structure bear to systems of urban rents? Here is yet another strategic and valid subject for both theoretical and empirical work. Indeed, both of these topics are the subject of studies at present being undertaken.[15]

Let us for the moment assume that there *is* an hierarchical structure of shopping centers. Other valid questions for research may be asked. One of these will now be explored at the theoretical level as an example. It relates to the relationships between the pre-equilibrium (*i.e.,* short-run) shopping habits of the consumer and the tendency for urban business to locate themselves in an hierarchical manner.

THE PROBLEM OF THE PRE-EQUILIBRIUM SPATIAL CONNECTION / Consider a hierarchical structure of urban shopping centers. This is a static pattern which masks a myriad of consumer movements to purchase goods and services. It is of such a nature that each individual movement is taken to be in equilibrium, with an optimal pattern of individual spatial connections existing. If a new consumer locates himself in the system the *ex post* view is taken that all his spatial connections must immediately be determinate.

But obviously this is not so. We know that a consumer newly locating himself in a city will tend to "shop around" and from personal experience will then develop his system of spatial connections. For goods which the consumer buys frequently the period of shopping around will be relatively short. A great number of contacts with stores will obviously lead to a rapid determination of some optimal shopping pattern. Accordingly we can think of stores which are visited quite frequently as being located within a framework of optimal spatial connections and therefore rationally within the hierarchical structure.

The same argument will apply to stores which are visited less frequently but which are few in number. They too will be positioned rationally within the hierarchical structure, for they will have relatively large proportions of their customers who have been in the city for long periods and hence stabilized their shopping habits.

However, there are certain types of business which are visited infre-

[15] Brian J. L. Berry, *The Spatial Structure of Intraurban Retail and Service Business,* in progress.

quently by the individual shopped and, because the purchase is large, visited by relatively few shoppers. For them the period of non-optimal spatial connection is long; indeed, the "shopping around" period may never cease. Many of the consumers will not have experienced sufficient shopping around to build up an optimal system of connections. For such types of business, advertising and product differentiation will be of particular significance. Since an optimal pattern of spatial connection is not present individual firms conceivably need not be located rationally relative to the hierarchical structure. Here is a force promoting the development of specialized shopping districts at one extreme, to facilitate the shopping around process, and apparently irrationally scattered business at the other, since no optimal patterns of spatial connections exist.

These ideas are extremely tentative, but they pose important problems for those concerned with spatial patterns of behavior.

26. Unified Field Theory

Stephen B. Jones

A major step forward in the theoretical development of political geography is Jones' unified field theory. Geopolitics, as well as political geography by implication, received a bad name as a result of its use by the Nazis in World War II to justify aggression. This negative association has now largely been eliminated and political geography is assuming its rightful place as a subdiscipline of the larger field. The political decision exerts a major impact upon earth space, and it is one of the important variables to be measured. The idea-area continuum of political idea-decision-movement-field-political area is the essence of the unified field theory.

The Idea-Area Chain

. . . [The] unified field theory of political geography . . . simply states that "idea" and "state" are two ends of a chain. The hyphen with which Hartshorne connects them represents the three other links of the chain.

Source: *Annals of the Association of American Geographers*, LX (June, 1954), 111-23. The author is professor of geography at Yale University.

One of the links is Gottmann's circulation, which I shall call movement.[1]

The chain is as follows: Political Idea—Decision—Movement—Field—Political Area. This "chain" should be visualized as a chain of lakes or basins, not an iron chain of separate links. The basins interconnect at one level, so that whatever enters one will spread to all the others.

Political idea, in this sequence, means more than just the state-idea. It means any political idea. It might be the idea of the state or it might be the idea of a speed limit on a country road. It might merely be a gregarious instinct, not consciously expressed. "War begins in the minds of men" and so does all other politics. But there are many political ideas that never reach the stage of action. They die aborning, remain in the realm of pure thought, or are rejected by the powers-that-be. A favorable decision is a necessary prerequisite to action. A formal, parliamentary decision is not necessarily meant. Much current research in political science is focussed on the informal or unconscious aspects of the idea-decision end of the chain, through studies of political behavior. Though most of the fishermen in the basins of idea and decision are political scientists, Gottmann and Hartshorne, both geographers, enter them when they speak of iconography and the idea of state.

Both political scientists and geographers have studied the phenomena at the other end of the chain—political areas. This term is used very inclusively to mean any politically organized area, whether a national state, a dependent area, a subdivision of a state, or an administrative region or district. It includes all three categories of areas listed by Fesler [2] : general governmental areas, special or limited-purpose governmental areas, and field service areas. The one common characteristic of all political areas is that they have recognized limits, though not necessarily linear or permanent. An administrative center within the area is common, but not universal.

Movement, I have said, is essentially Gottmann's circulation. What new twist it is given comes from placing it in a chain of concepts relating it to decisions. Every political decision involves movement in one way or another. There may be exceptions, but I have been unable to think of any. Some decisions create movement, some change it, some restrict it. Some create a new kind of movement to replace or to control the old. The movement may not involve great numbers of men or great quantities of matter—it may consist only of radio waves—but usually persons and things move as a result of political decisions. These politically-induced movements may be thought of as "circulation fields."

[1] Gottmann himself thinks "movement" an inadequate translation and suggests "movement factor" ("The Political Partitioning of Our World": 515). The present writer has adopted "movement" as more compact and commonplace than either "movement factor" or "circulation."

[2] James W. Fesler, *Area and Administration*. University, Alabama, 1949. p. 6.

The movements of state highway patrolmen produce a field, shipments of military-aid materials produce a field, the despatch and delivery of farm-subsidy checks produce a field.[3]

A concrete example may clarify the thought behind this chain of terms. National prohibition had a long history as an idea. The Eighteenth Amendment and the Volstead Act were the final decisions that took national prohibition from the realm of ideas to that of action, though, to be sure, many smaller decisions had preceded these or were necessary later to implement them. The prompt effect of the Volstead Act was to inaugurate sweeping changes in movement. Legal shipment of liquor ceased, raw materials no longer flowed to distilleries, illicit movements were organized along new lines, enforcement officers went patrolling and prowling. The fields of these movements were not of uniform density nor did they exactly coincide with the boundaries of the United States. City slums and Appalachian valleys became centers of activity. Zones near the international frontiers were heavily policed. Enforcement reached twelve miles to sea. The effect on movement was felt overseas. No change in national territory resulted, but new administrative areas were set up. Had the law remained and been rigidly enforced, it is conceivable that our concept of the marginal sea might have changed, as later it was changed by the expanding field of activity of oil exploration. An earlier and more successful attempt at compulsory reform—the suppression of the slave trade—produced a field of enforcement on the high seas and led to the establishment of colonial areas in West Africa. Similarly, the idea-to-area chain is beautifully illustrated by the founding of Liberia.

In the case of prohibition, the existence of the political area of the United States gave general shape to the major fields produced by the Volstead Act, for obvious reasons. A political area in being is a condition of political ideas, decisions, and movements. Our linked basins, I have said, lie at one level. Add something to one, and it spreads to others. There is a general distinction, however, between flow from idea towards area and in the reverse direction. The former is essentially a process of controlling or creating. The prohibition law controlled some movements and created others. The idea of colonizing free Negroes created a migration to Liberia. The reverse spread is more correctly described as conditioning. The existence of a political area, field, movement, or decision conditions what may take place in the basins lying idea-ward. Eric Fischer's paper, "On Boundaries," is full of good ex-

[3] The general outlines of this theory were presented to a small audience at the University of Toronto in the spring of 1952. At that time, Dr. Ali Tayyeb suggested that, since political science tends to focus on ideas and decisions and political geography on political areas, the links of movement and field might be called geopolitics. My feeling is one of regret that "geopolitics" has been used in so many ways that this interesting suggestion may be impractical.

amples of such conditioning.[4] Benjamin Thomas has shown how the political area of Idaho, created upon a flimsy and essentially negative idea in the first place, conditioned further political thoughts and decisions until the present Idaho-idea is as firm as any.[5]

The essential characteristic of a field, in physics, is not movement, but spatial variation in force. The gravitational field exists even when no apples fall. Since we are not bound to a physical analogy, this distinction need not greatly concern us. However, it may sometimes be important to keep in mind that movements and fields are not necessarily identical. A higher percentage of Democrats goes to the polls where the party is neck-and-neck with the Republicans than where the party is overwhelmingly strong. Movement to polls creates a field, but it is not identical with the field of party power.

In a recent publication,[6] Karl Deutsch has suggested a "field" approach to the study of political community. "According to this view, every individual is conceived as a point in a field consisting of his communications or other interactions with all other individuals." Deutsch suggests that this concept may be applied to both small and large "clusters," including families, villages, towns, counties, regions, peoples, nations, and federations. Some clusters are political areas, some are geographical but not political areas, others, like families and peoples, are not necessarily found in definable areas. Thus Deutsch's "interaction field" may be the general case of which the present writer's concept may be the politico-geographical sub-type. On later pages of the same publication,[7] Deutsch gives fourteen tests of integration and a check-list of thirty-two possible indicators of social or political community, which should prove of value to the geographer as well as the political scientist.

A field exists in time as well as in space. Applying the ideas of Whittlesey,[8] we may say it has a time dimension as well as space dimensions and that the time dimension has three derivatives: velocity, pace, and timing. Highway patrols produce a field, as was mentioned above, but obviously it is important for both law-breaker and law-enforcer to know when the patrolmen operate as well as where. The effective scheduling of their patrols is a problem in timing. The whole of traffic

[4] Eric Fischer, "On Boundaries," World Politics, I (Jan. 1949): 196-222. The final paragraph on page 197 is a good description of the conditioning process.
[5] Benjamin E. Thomas, "Boundaries and Internal Problems of Idaho," The Geographical Review, XXXIX (Jan. 1949): 99-109.
[6] Karl W. Deutsch, Political Community at the International Level: Problems of Definition and Measurement. Organizational Behavior Section, Foreign Policy Analysis Project, Foreign Policy Analysis Series No. 2, Princeton University, September 1953. 30-31.
[7] Deutsch, op. cit., 37-62 and 70-71.
[8] Derwent Whittlesey, "The Horizon of Geography," Annals of the Association of American Geographers, XXXV (March 1945): 1-36.

and of traffic regulation can be considered a space-time field. Warfare and traffic are alike in this respect as in some others.

Application to Political Areas

Application of this theory to a case of one new national state is fairly simple: zionism is the idea, the Balfour Declaration the conspicuous decision, permitting migration and other movements. A field of settlement, governmental activity, and war leads to the state of Israel. Such telegraphic brevity oversimplifies history, but the theory seems to fit. For a state with a longer and more complicated evolution, history could not be so readily compressed. The theory provides a path between geographical and political study, but not necessarily a short-cut. It does not reduce political geography to five easy steps. It does not permit world politics to be shown on a chart in five columns headed "idea," "decision," and so forth. It may, however, provide some intellectual clarification and it may prove a handy way of working back and forth among historical, political, and geographical ideas and data.

Karl Deutsch has recognized eight uniformities in the growth of nations from other political forms of organization.[9] Five of these are clearly "field" phenomena: the change from subsistence to exchange economy, the growth of core areas, towns, and communication grids, and the concentration of capital and its effect on other areas. The seventh and eighth are "iconographical," but have "field" connotations: the growth of ethnic awareness and its relation to national symbols and to political compulsion. The sixth item, the rise of individual self-awareness, is more difficult to relate directly to a field though decisions made in a framework of an increasingly individualistic philosophy would lead to changes in established fields. In short, the process of national integration, whether looked at by geographers, like Hartshorne or Gottmann, or by a political scientist, like Deutsch, can be interpreted as a process of changing fields. Conceivably the outlines of the political area may not change. The former colony of Burma is perhaps en route to becoming a true national state without change of boundaries or capital, but a study of the political fields would show changes.

One virtue of the field theory is that it is not confined to politically organized areas. It is applicable without difficulty to an unorganized area like the Mediterranean, which is undoubtedly a political field. As William Reitzel showed, decisions may affect the Mediterranean as a whole and may create or control movement over the entire sea.[10] The

[9] Karl W. Deutsch, "The Growth of Nations: Some Recurrent Patterns of Political and Social Integration," *World Politics*, V (Jan. 1953): 168-195.
[10] William Reitzel, *The Mediterranean: Its Role in America's Foreign Policy*. New York, 1948.

ideas may vary: Mussolini's dream of a new Roman empire, Britain's concern with sea command, the American strategy of the containment of communism. Reitzel showed how American policy in the Mediterranean evolved as the cumulative result of small decisions taken first with the idea of winning specific military campaigns. These decisions, and the successful military movements that resulted, involved the United States in political and economic administration. The Soviet Union replaced the Axis as the rival Mediterranean power, Britain slumped down the power scale, and the United States found itself deeply embedded in Mediterranean politics. The Truman Doctrine of support to Greece and Turkey was an outcome, indicating the unity of the Mediterranean sea-power field. The accumulation of decisions created a field, the sea conditioned it.

In the case of administrative areas, a political area may arise from a decision with little or possibly no intervening movement. A new governmental agency may lay out its field service areas before it actually engages in any actions. In some cases, analysis will show that these field service areas reflect pre-existing fields, such as the areas used by other branches of government or known fields of economic activity, and in many cases existing boundaries will be followed. It is possible, however, that an administrative area might spring directly from a decision and reflect no existing field. T.V.A. may be an example, unless we say a field had been created by river boatmen, hillside farmers, hydrographic surveyors, and so forth. This seems far-fetched; rather it seems that the Tennessee Valley was proclaimed a political area and that a field of activity resulted. It should be noted, however, that the field spread beyond the limits of the drainage basin, once electricity began to circulate.

There is nothing deterministic about the idea-area chain. A given idea might lead to a variety of areas, a given area might condition a variety of ideas. Pelzer's study of Micronesia under four rulers demonstrates this point.[11] Although the area ruled was not identical in all four eras, it was basically the same. The number of possible uses for these small islands was limited. Nevertheless, the four rulers—Spain, Germany, Japan, and the United States—made different choices. Their fields were different in kind and intensity. If one insists (which the dictionary does not) that a theory must be able to predict specific behavior, then the field theory may not deserve its name.[12] With no theory whatsoever, a well-informed person with some map-sense could have

[11] Karl J. Pelzer, "Micronesia—A Changing Frontier," World Politics, II (Jan. 1950): 251-266.
[12] The definition of "theory" most appropriate to the present paper is: "The analysis of a set of facts in their ideal relations to one another." Webster's Collegiate Dictionary, fifth edition, 1947.

predicted many American problems and decisions in Micronesia. As a guide to study, however, the field theory is applicable to such cases.

Studies of National Power

Studies of national power may also be fitted into the field theory. Lasswell and Kaplan define power as "participation in the making of decisions." [13] If power is participation in the making of decisions, if power is necessary before an idea can produce movement, then we can easily fit power into our theory. Hartshorne distinguished between political geography and the study of power. [14] He felt a geographer might sometimes tackle the question of "how strong is a state?" if no one else had done so, but that in so doing he was "migrating into a field whose core and purpose is not geography, but military and political strategy." That power is linked with decision supports Hartshorne, to the extent that geography has been more closely associated with the other end of the chain, but our aim is to pull political science and geography together, not to separate them. If power is more concentrated in the basin of decision, it is by no means absent in the others.

Boundaries, Capitals, Cities

The unified field theory fits boundary studies into the general pattern of political geography. A boundary is of course a line between two political areas, but it is also a line in a region, as was emphasized in Hartshorne's Upper Silesia study and in the present writer's book. [15] The boundary region is truly a field in which the line between the political areas conditions much of the circulation. [16] A boundary field may even be or become a political area as in the case of buffer states and frontier provinces.

Studies of capital cities also may be expressed in field-theory terms. Cornish listed the crossways, the stronghold, the storehouse, and the forward headquarters as characteristic situations for capital cities. [17] To

[13] Harold D. Lasswell and Abraham Kaplan, *Power and Society: A Framework for Political Inquiry.* New Haven, 1950, p. 75.
[14] "The Functional Approach . . .": 125-127.
[15] Richard Hartshorne, "Geographic and Political Boundaries in Upper Silesia," *Annals of the Association of American Geographers,* XXIII (1933): 195-228. Stephen B. Jones, *Boundary-Making: A Handbook for Statesmen, Treaty Editors and Boundary Commissioners.* Washington, 1945. Especially Part I.
[16] The pertinence of Eric Fischer's work on historical boundaries has already been mentioned.
[17] Vaughan Cornish, *The Great Capitals, an Historical Geogarphy.* London, 1923.

these Spate added the cultural head-link.[18] There are other possibilities, such as compromise sites and geometric centrality. All of these words have meaning in terms of movement and field either explicitly (as in the case of crossways, forward headquarters, and cultural head-link) or implicitly (as in the case of storehouse). The idea of, or need for, central administration leads to a decision on the site of the capital. The choice is conditioned by the field and in turn distorts or recreates the field. Once the capital is chosen and the field about it established, many further decisions and movements are conditioned, leading in most cases to the creation of a primate city much larger than any other in the country.[19]

Not only capitals, but other cities, may be brought into the scope of the theory. In Gottmann's terminology, many of the problems of a growing city arise from the fact that its circulation expands faster than its iconography. The metropolitan district outgrows the political limits, and vested local interests and loyalties make political expansion difficult. A sort of "metropolitan-idea" may develop, leading usually to functional authorities rather than to political integration. In a few words, the urban problem is to make the political area fit the field.[20] There are a number of choices possible such as annexation of suburbs, city-county consolidation, metropolitan districts, functional authorities, state assumption of local functions.

Kinetic and Dynamic Fields

Since politics consists of conflicts and the resolution of conflicts (though neither conflict nor resolution need be accompanied by violence), these fundamental activities must be expressible in field terms. There are conflicts of ideas, but they do not amount to much until they are embodied in decisions that create or obstruct movement. (It may be wise to re-emphasize that "movement" includes such things of little bulk as messages and money. A restriction on foreign exchange is a restriction on movement.) Fields may be in contact, but not in conflict, may indeed overlap but not conflict, if the movement is merely kinetic. But if there is a dynamic aspect, conflict often will arise. For example, New York City's growing need for water forces its activity in this respect to be dynamic, bringing conflict with other claimants to Delaware River supplies. The international oil industry is inherently dynamic, since new sources must be discovered. The result is potential

[18] O. H. K. Spate, "Factors in the Development of Capital Cities," *The Geographical Review,* XXXII (Oct. 1942): 622-631.
[19] Mark Jefferson, "The Law of Primate Cities," *The Geographical Review,* XXIX (April 1939): 226-232.
[20] A. E. Smailes, *The Geography of Towns.* London, 1953, pp. 153-156.

conflict, sometimes anticipated and resolved at least pro tempore. The relations of political dynamics to such fundamentals as resource needs and population pressures have of course been repeatedly studied,[21] and the present theory does little more than incorporate them into the concept of the field.

The general attitude of Americans toward world politics is that dynamic problems should if possible be reduced to kinetic situations by agreement, or in other words that dynamic fields should be converted to kinetic fields. The philosophy of communism, however, is in many respects the opposite, except for temporary tactical purposes. In its grand strategy, communism would like to convert kinetic fields to dynamic fields, with the pressure from the communist side, of course. (The Nazis held a similar philosophy.) The failure of the United States to understand this difference accounts for a number of American blunders in diplomacy. The notion of peaceful co-existence of capitalism and communism, sincerely held by millions outside the Iron Curtain and occasionally uttered, with what sincerity is not known, by major figures within the Curtain, expresses the belief that the fields of the two ideologies can be merely kinetic in their relations, a belief that so far has little to support it.

There are no upper or lower limits on the magnitude of an idea. Man thinks easily of world government and can dream of space-ships and planetary empires. There are upper limits on decisions, movements, fields, and political areas, though these limits change with events (often, but not necessarily, upwards). Such ideas as the great religions, nationalism, liberalism, and communism have, in so far as they could produce decisions and movements, created fields. Whittlesey has shown how man's ideas of space have changed through primal and regional to worldwide conceptions, and how the third and fourth dimensions of the human habitat have been explored and put to use.[22] Ideas, fields of exploration, in some cases political areas have expanded, reached above and below the earth's surface, and made better use of time. The idea of a Columbus, the decision of an Isabella, a voyage of discovery, a new field, a new empire—this progression might figuratively be compared to the idea of a chemist, the decision of an entrepreneur, an experiment, a new field of production, an economic domain.

Many of the most influential of ideas have been composite, or "culture-ideas." Western culture, for example, is more than just capitalism or democracy or Christianity—it is a composite of these and other factors. Toynbee holds that every culture tends to evolve its "universal state," a domain roughly co-extensive with the culture.[23] If this is true, then

[21] For examples, by Frederick S. Dunn, in his *Peaceful Change*. New York, 1937, and by Brooks Emeny, in *The Strategy of Raw Materials*. New York, 1934.
[22] "The Horizon of Geography."
[23] Arnold Toynbee, *A Study of History*. London, 1939. Vol. 4, pp. 2-3.

we have another example of the chain from idea through a vast number of decisions (not necessarily consciously derived from the general culture-idea) and movements, creating a field and tending towards a political area which would be the universal state of that culture.

Utility of the Theory

It is time to get back down to earth from the heights and ask that rude question, "So what?" Here is a theory; what can it *do*? Is it just word mongering? Of course, mere words have uses. A word of general meaning may replace phrases, sentences, even whole paragraphs. Whether "field" is such a word remains for time to tell. Or, as we said at the start, the word may die, but the clarification of thought that went into its coinage or adoption may be a useful accomplishment. Here, again, only time can tell whether thought has been clarified or made more murky by this paper.

On an earlier page it was said that a valid theory, however minor, is at least three things: a compact description, a clue to explanation, and a tool for better work. If this theory merely provides nomenclature it satisfies the first requirement. Perhaps it goes farther than merely supplying words. It may reduce the apparent diversity of aims and methods in political geography, found by Hartshorne and his students.[24] It may help to unify not only the theories of political geography, but political theories in general. It may help complete the tie between morphology and function, between region and process. It may show a relationship between "grand ideas" and the earth's surface.

This unified field theory can provide no more than a clue to explanation, if it even attains that success. It can hardly provide an ultimate answer to any question. But to relate several disciplines, to show connections, may give hints. The user of this theory is at least sure to be warned against single-factor explanations and be led to seek contributions from sister sciences.

It is as a tool for better work that I have the most hopes for this mental gadget. The chain of words in which the theory is expressed constitutes a sort of check-list ("check-system" might be better), by means of which one can orient oneself and tell where one should explore further. To return to the analogy of a chain of basins, one knows through which basin one has entered and where one can travel back and forth. If one begins with the study of a political area, ideas lie at the other end. If a study begins with movement, the scholar knows he should explore in both directions. For some of the basins one may need pilots from other disciplines, but at least one has a map of

[24] "The Functional Approach . . .": 96-97.

the chain. The theory tells students of geography and politics what (in very general terms) they need to learn from each other, what each has to add, but not how each fences himself off.

Another possible effect of this theory upon geographical work is that it may inspire the making of new types of studies and the compiling of new kinds of maps. Many maps either show or imply a field, but with the idea-area chain in mind, new sources of data suggest themselves: public-opinion polls, content analysis of publications, shipments of significant materials, movements of governmental officers, monetary transactions and so forth. The theory is "geographical" in that it makes mappable, through the concept of the field, the results of ideas and decisions that are themselves not mappable.

Conceivably the general plan of this theory can be extended to other than political studies. In fact, recent work in economic geography suggests a similar theory for that branch of our science. The idea-area chain may unite in one concept two main parts of geographical theory, the possibilist and regionalist views. Possibilism focusses on man's choices among environmental possibilities. Choices are decisions. They imply ideas and must lead to movements. The regional or chorological approach, beginning with the study of areas, can lead through movement to decisions and ideas.

Finally, the unified field theory may have utility outside academic circles. It seems possible that the concept can be used as an aid in evaluating diplomatic and strategic ideas and plans. This is an ambitious thought and may prove illusory. However, diplomacy and strategy begin with ideas, lead to decisions, result in movement, and therefore produce fields. In reverse, diplomacy and strategy are conditioned by the political areas and fields of the earth, which limit the possible decisions and practical ideas. No doubt such thinking goes on in high places unaided by our theory, but perhaps this bit of intellectual guidance will clarify some cases.

27. Cultural Geography
Edward Ackerman et al.

Cultural geography, as defined in the following article, is one of the rapidly growing segments of the field. Man's cultures, in modifying the face of the earth, have become a major factor in the study of the nature of the earth's surface. Research is placing increasing emphasis on the impact of the

cultural process both historically and functionally. The
study of that process provides an important key to
understanding the world.

Cultural geographers, through application of the concept of culture, seek understanding of the spatial distribution and space relations of man and those features on the earth's surface which have been produced or modified by human action. To this end they have focused their attention upon study of the differences from place to place in the ways of life of human communities and their creation of man-made or modified features. In such research the holistic concept of *culture* is implicit, and the partitive concept of *cultures* [1] becomes much more significant for cultural geography. The idea of cultures has a lower level of abstraction that recognizes the pluralism of particular ways of life and distinguishes one human group from another. The partitive concept concerns the thousands of more or less cohesive segments or subsystems, (e.g., Japanese culture, Navaho culture) that comprise the whole. The concept of cultures as subsystems offers a means for systematic classification of human beings into well-defined groups according to verifiable common characteristics. It also offers a means of classifying the phenomena or processes associated with people who habitually share communication and inhabit a common territory.

Cultural geographers are not concerned with analysis and explanatory description of the totality of cultures in all their forms and functions. They study the material and nonmaterial phenomena and processes relevant for an understanding of the spatial distribution and spatial relations of cultures. Emphasis thus far has been upon the past achievements, present capacities, and future capabilities of human communities to produce and to consume resources and, in so doing, to create and to change their habitats on the earth's surface. Cultural geography is thus "earth-bound"; the earth is the home of man who, by means of culture, has become the ecological dominant.

Sub-groups Engaged in Active Research

American cultural geographers are composed of two subgroups of research workers: (1) those who study their own culture, and (2) those who engage in foreign-field research and use foreign languages as tools

SOURCE: *The Science of Geography*, Report of the Ad Hoc Committee on Geography, Earth Sciences Division, National Academy of Sciences–National Research Council, Publication 1277 (Washington, D. C.), pp. 23-31.
[1] Cultures—functional parts of the abstract whole—total human culture; important for study because men with different cultures react differently to similar physical-biotic environments.

for research and analysis of cultures other than their own. This sub-grouping is not simply the result of training, but reflects the complexity of problems chosen for study. For example, in studying and reporting on his own culture a geographer knows that the people being observed and the audience for the report are of the same culture. To study and interpret a foreign culture the geographer must successfully carry through "cross-cultural" communication. In such a situation the cultural geographer has to cope with his audience's American predilection for economic explanation of all phenomena. When presenting the results of foreign-field research a cultural geographer must give much descriptive detail to compensate for readers' ignorance of the other culture's postulates and beliefs.

Problem Areas in Cultural Geography

The foundations of cultural geography were laid in Europe, with the work of Ratzel, Hahn, Brunhes, Fleure, Meitzen, Hettner, Vidal de la Blache. In the United States cultural geography has had a gradual but productive growth over the past 50 years. Much effort has been spent in disentangling it from the relics of post-Renaissance European thought that viewed nature in a mechanical analogue devoid of intelligence or of life, with the parts designed, arranged, and set going for a definite purpose by an intelligent mind outside of nature. Such a view (nature ordered by the intelligence of a Divine Creator) supported scientific study focused upon unchanging matter or substance and upon the "laws" or unchanging rules which explained change. From such thought was derived the idea of nature as non-man, that which lies all about but outside of man; hence, there developed the concepts of "man *and* nature" or "man *versus* nature." This conceptual separation of man from nature did much to postpone cultural geography's fullest contributions to fundamental research. The establishment of scientific geography in central Europe during the early nineteenth century insured the inclusion of such dichotomous thought in geography's concern with the earth created as the home of man. Geography often was defined as the study of man *and* the earth. In a sense it was concerned with the study of two supposedly distinct systems.

Modern science focuses upon change itself, recognizing that through time things begin to exist, then later cease to exist. On the earth new material and non-material phenomena are constantly emerging. From the physical earth emerged the organic which in turn evolved man who developed culture as a new mechanism for adaptation and change supplementing natural selection. Man, viewed thus, is a part of nature.

Science now concentrates on the study of processes, often described

as development, evolution, improvement, and progress. All are movements occupying space and taking time. Cultural geography, as a part
of science, now also concentrates on the study of processes. The differences in methods among cultural geographers depend upon the
process or processes of change selected for study. How the external
world appears depends upon the length of time of observation—one
minute, one hour, one day, one year, one century, one millennium.
Different processes take time periods of different lengths. What problems man can observe are determined by space limits and time limits.
Our limits for observation are human-bounded, because man is a
creature of a definite size range and living at a definite rate over
an average time span of about 70 years. The processes upon which the
geographer concentrates are those whose time phase and space range
are within human limits of observation.

Ackerman suggested that the significant processes for geographic
study are short range (from the point of view of earth history). Assuming that cultural processes now are the major forces altering the continually changing earth-space content, he outlined at least three
processes fundamental to cultural geography:

(1) Demographic Movement
      Natural increase and net migration of people (numbers of
        people)
      Traditions of material consumption (social qualities of
        people)
(2) Evolution of Organization and Administration
      Political territories; economic corporations
      Systems of communication (including education)
(3) Development of Technology
      Resource-converting techniques [2]
      Space-adjusting techniques [3]

A Hierarchy of Problems

As his usual approach to a problem, the cultural geographer studies
the spatial distribution of elements or traits of a culture. One appropriate technique is to record observations by plotting distributions on a
map. The analysis of the content of a culture into elements or traits

[2] Resource-converting techniques—Those arts which turn the materials of the physical world and the life-products of the biotic world to satisfaction of the needs of
man. Land-use technology is an example.
[3] Space-adjusting techniques—Those arts which either shorten the effective distance
of travel and transportation or permit intensification of space employment beyond
that possible on the natural land surface. Civil engineering and architecture are
examples.

(religious beliefs, languages, voting behavior, prehistoric artifacts, barns, fences, house types) is the important beginning to problem recognition but does not in itself constitute a problem. A thorough knowledge of culture content and form must precede an understanding of the functioning of a culture or of the process of cultural change. Such thorough knowledge may require decades of painstaking descriptions of relatively small areas. Much important research in cultural geography has been of an inventory character in order to create "building-blocks" so that further research may be cumulative rather than repetitive.

Two different integrative methods have been used widely in cultural geographic research. These are: (1) developmental, which emphasizes the time depth of such relatively long-term processes as cultural evolution, origin and diffusion, cultural growth and retrogression; and (2) functional, which focuses upon the short-term processes of cultural interaction, spatial organization, and flow or movement.

In American geography the developmental or genetic orientation was established by Carl O. Sauer in the late 1920's with a concern, as in geomorphology, for explaining both the present scene and the dynamics of landscape change through historical reconstruction of the successive agents (cultures) active in an area, beginning with the earliest and proceeding to the present. From a quarter-century association with anthropology at the University of California, Berkeley, the label "culture-historical" often shortened to become simply "historical geography," was derived from this approach. Its method rests largely upon direct field observations, combined with the use of available historical data. By piecing together evidence from culture-trait and trait-complex distributions, linguistics, place names, the characteristics of domesticated plants and animals, archaeological artifacts, documents, oral traditions, and other sources, this developmental approach seeks to determine: (1) the origin in place and time of specific cultural features; (2) the routes, times, and manner of their diffusion; (3) the distribution of former and present cultural areas [4]; and (4) explanatory descriptions of the character of former and present cultural landscapes.[5]

---

[4] Culture area—A region in which the culture is relatively uniform, as empirically determined from the mapping of trait and trait-complexes.

[5] Cultural landscape—The composite of man-made features in an area (e.g., dwellings and other structures, cultivated plants and man-induced wild vegetation, and altered landforms such as gully and sheet erosion and silt deposits in stream valleys and coastal margins). Broadly conceived, such a view of landscape includes all man-induced alterations of and additions to the earth's physical-biotic surface, some utilitarian and some non-utilitarian, many purposeful, and some the indirect, even unintended, results of human activity. This concept stems from the 1920's when geographers were seeking to delimit the subject matter of geography and increase objectivity in observations by focusing upon visible elements of material culture that give character to area.

Implicit is a concern for culture changes which occur slowly, often taking more than single lifetimes in which to be readily apparent.

The second integrative method in American cultural geography had its principal center in middle western United States. Attention has been directed to the works of man as functional problems in the local environment (for example, types of buildings and farm crops distinguished by utility and setting), or to data on human interaction in the endeavor to define regularities in spatial arrangement and flow phenomena (for example, studies of central-place hierarchy that indicate conformal distributions of settlements in many parts of Anglo-America and other major culture areas of the world). The functional approach emphasizes the observation of the present-day scene to determine how things are organized and operated. The key word is "process": what are the cultural processes that create landscapes and human attitudes? Studies are usually direct: to discover, to analyze, and to describe step by step the actual activities creating a given cultural feature. Cultural changes of primary interest are those occurring with some suddenness, often clearly recognized by the persons involved.

Recent cultural geographers recognize the value of both the cultural-historical approach and the functional-pattern approach.

The relation of research in cultural geography to the overriding problem of geography, the need for understanding the world-wide man-environment system, has been direct and significant. As soon as the dominant thought in cultural geography had shifted from the view of "man *and* nature" to that of "man as the new emergent *in* nature," the way was open for significant contributions. Modern cultural geography has taken the lead among the branches of science in recognizing that man, as a result of culture, has spread over the world, has learned to adapt to the most diverse climates and habitats, and in so doing has drastically altered the landscape of large parts of the earth. Cultural geographers record and analyze the effects of man's changing cultures in modifying the face of the earth; the emphasis is upon what has happened, is happening, and the determinants of what is likely to happen to the earth's surface.

Relation to Other Branches of Science

The closest past relation of cultural geography to other disciplines has been with anthropology. The concept of culture has been given greatest exploration and conceptual development during this century by anthropologists. Since 1950 there has been a high degree of unanimity concerning the value of the concept. It has become common for anthropologists to discuss their subject in terms of their key concept, "culture."

Anthropological interest, by and large, is now shifting away from past treatment of material phenomena. Two major growing edges in contemporary cultural anthropology have had a profound effect in this change: the emphases on (1) behavioral studies and (2) value systems.

Behavioral studies seek means of deeper penetration into analyses of the functioning of a culture and to validate (through refinement of predictions about behavior) the cultural constructs depicted by anthropologists.

More important for geography is the anthropological growing edge focused upon value systems. Values are those configuring principles of a culture (the values of a way of life) that lace together the cultural whole and determine the particular patterns (rules or understandings) that motivate and guide its behavior. Values are the essence of cultural study, for without them one cannot comprehend the "slant" of the culture or its organizing principles. Of prime importance for cultural geography is that part of value systems expressed in the phrase "man's *attitudes* toward his physical-biotic environment." Much can be predicted about the probable directions of change in a given part of the earth's surface (e.g., rates of consumption of resources) if one knows the attitudes of the occupying cultures, i.e., passively submissive to natural forces, or slowly adjusting to physical-biotic changes, or seeking a balance or harmony (long-term equilibrium), or actively modifying the physical-biotic surroundings and creating an increasingly artificial habitat, or determined to gain power over and to control natural processes. Influenced by anthropological thought, many cultural geographers are coming to realize that ideas, attitudes, and other non-visible entities of a culture are of importance in understanding spatial distributions and space relations of phenomena.

Another joint interest, representing a growing edge, is with sociology, especially in research on spatial processes that lend themselves to computer analysis and the application of simulation techniques. Emphasis has been upon the study of diffusion (such problems as the spread of new ideas, the extent and direction of local migration, and marriage contacts). The geographer Hägerstrand of Lund, Sweden, used the Monte Carlo simulation technique to replicate within a computer a diffusion process, person-to-person contacts over space. In cultural geography techniques of simulation also are being applied in such studies as the diffusion of a farm subsidy in Sweden, the spread of hand tractors in Japan, the process of frontier settlement, and the acceptance of innovation in Latin America.

There are long-established intellectual joint interests between cultural geographers and economic historians, agricultural historians, human ecologists, and economic botanists. One of the most active research interests in American geography has been in the function of settlements; this has been a growing edge between cultural geography, economics, and other social sciences. An emerging frontier is with medical ecology (public health) on the contacts that man makes with his environment, as revealed in differences in food habits, diets, the deficiency diseases, and disease resistance.

Some Unfulfilled Opportunities for Research

The greatest opportunities for cultural geographers lie in contributing their insights, in cooperation with other geographers and other branches of science, to understanding of the world-wide man-environment system. An essential question for cultural geography is whether its findings return to the system via human society to regulate and control further release of energy or information by the system. To translate this into geographic research problems we need first to consider some of the fundamental questions about the existing cultural pattern of the world and cultural dynamics.

Man as a culture-bearing creature is capable of affecting the course of his own evolution; but what can geographic research contribute toward man's understanding of the effects of his actions upon his own longevity on the earth? We know that biological (organic) evolution produced phenotypes by natural selection, suppressing those genetic traits that were not adapted to conditions of their particular time and place. A biotic process operated over vast periods of time with prodigal elimination, resulting in a rich variety of plants and animals, including man. Culture, involving tools, speech, and cumulative transmittible knowledge, combined with the rapid evolution of man's remarkable cerebral cortex to add a new dimension to evolution. Cultural evolution, a process combining invention and diffusion, is thousands of times faster in effecting changes than is biological evolution.

In the modern period, with the spread over the world of the urban-industrial pattern marked by large per-capita consumption of materials and energy, man's cultural development has reversed the whole trend of evolutionary diversification by reducing (eliminating or absorbing) human diversity in cultures (traditional systems or ways of life) with a trend toward one, great, increasingly complex, interconnecting, specialized system.

A fundamental question is: What does the modern evolutionary trend toward cultural convergence portend for the future of *Homo sapiens?* Does the "putting of many eggs in a single basket" enhance or

impair the outlook? Scholars are well aware that the modern near-ex-
ponential population growth and the world-wide "revolution of rising
expectations" are tending to produce a world of uniform economic
orientation. Where, and for what reasons, are the cultural groups which
remain less committed to developing and/or maintaining such a uniform world? How successful will they be in maintaining their own
identity and existence? What are the relevant spatial elements in their
cultures?

Comparative studies are needed of sequences of cultural development in similar natural environments. Is there any evidence that a
particular combination of physical and cultural environmental features
leads to a given institutional organization in a society? Has the recent
establishment of many new nation states in Africa and Asia contributed
toward human diversity or been the means of hastening cultural uniformity through dominance of minorities by the political elite (admin-
istratively sophisticated, better educated, more numerous)?

Demographers are successfully coping with the problems of counting and locating the increasing numbers of people (natural increase and
net migration) as the methods and results of census enumerations have
improved, but much more work is needed on determining the amounts
and rates of material consumption. Answers are needed not only to
"who? and where?" but also to "how much?" and "why?" before reliable
comparisons of human qualities of living and of the impact of man
upon the world's material resources can be made. For example, much
research is needed on food-consumption habits, tolerances, and limits.
A common assumption of students of resource-converting techniques
has been that if only more food were produced the world could feed
itself. But it already is evident that huge surpluses exist in some places
that people in other places would not eat (a problem in human values)
even if they could be transported elsewhere. What is the nature of these
consumption incompatibilities, where are they, and what are their spatial extent and dynamics?

If we are to assume that planned beneficial cultural changes are
possible in the world, perhaps the most important research question of
all is the study of cultural diffusion processes so as to determine optimal
ways of obtaining the spread of beneficial material and non-material
innovations.

These broader problems suggest some specific research areas of high
social and scholarly significance for cultural geography. Building on
the interests, competences, and communications of the recent past,
this cluster in geography is in an advantageous position to develop
needed knowledge about the space relations of the several major cultures in the world and their values. The focus of its interest could well
be on the interaction between culture and the physical-biotic environ-

ment. Cultural geography study should be so conducted as to capitalize on its bridge position between physical geography and social
anthropology.

Specifically it offers promise for:

(1) Applying modern techniques to studying the nature and rate
of diffusion of key culture elements and establishing the evolving spatial pattern of culture complexes.

(2) Measuring cultural effects, and the processes of diffusion that
lead to cultural divergences or convergences.

(3) Delineating the critical geographical zones of contact for culture complexes and identifying incipient "hybrids," or conversely
discovering "sensitized" areas.

(4) Identifying regions of culture traits (e.g., consumption) incompatible with the traits of the major "aggressive" cultures of today.

(5) Identifying type regions and specific regions where certain cultural values and practices are causing unstable relations between
a society and its natural environment.

These opportunities suggest that the subgroup devoted to study of
foreign cultures has a key position in the problem area of cultural
geography, as does the student of diffusion techniques. Furthermore,
the contribution of students in this problem area is likely to have positive value in proportion to their familiarity with social anthropology on
the one hand and physical geography on the other. The student committed to research in cultural geography has indeed an exacting study
if he seeks the full measure of its potentiality. But thus practiced it
has an importance that no perceptive scholar can deny.

·   ·   ·   ·   ·

28. Theoretical Geography

William Bunge

*As statistical and mathematical techniques have increased
the ability of scientists to test various hypotheses and
enable them to replicate the work of others, a growing group
of theoretical geographers, employing these new methods,
is attempting to increase man's ability to predict spatial*

SOURCE: William Bunge, *Theoretical Geography* (Lund, Sweden: C. W. K. Gleerup, 1962), pp. 5-37, 195-97. The author is assistant professor of geography at Wayne State University.

changes in a region or the effect on the earth's surface of
physical and cultural "movements" or activities.
Consequently, a controversy has developed over whether
it is possible to make valid predictions based upon
investigations of unique phenomena or individual cases.
Bunge is a vigorous proponent of a more theoretical
geography, and the following excerpts highlight some of
his major arguments.

Two Problems Involved in Considering Geography as a Science

Methodological analysis is centered on the question of the relationship between geography and science. There is no dispute here with what appears to be the concensus of American geographers over confining the subject matter of geography to the earth's surface [1] and to phenomena of human significance. This agreement immediately lends vast unity to geography. The arguments presented deal with how the subject is to be treated.

There are two particularly bothersome problems in treating geography as a science. The first problem is concerned with the role of description in geography and the second with the predictability of geographic phenomena.

The Role of Description in Geography

A methodological issue frequently raised in geography concerns the function of description. The issue takes two forms. First, is description scientific? And second, is description peculiarly geographic?

Some take the position that description is non-scientific.[2] This position cannot stand. There is an infinitude of facts around us and any description of them is highly selective. This selection can be made at random, but geographers are always seeking facts they judge to be significant. Significance can be judged only in relation to some other phenomenon. The establishment of this relationship means that theory has been formulated. The so-called "mere describers" in geography do not go out into the world with empty heads. They have the *feel* of an area and a well-developed spatial intuition. This means that they possess theory, though it might be vaguely formed, implicit, and per-

[1] It might be pedantically neat to refer to the earth's surface as "the planet earth minus its interior." To allow for the space age and the possible penetration of the earth's crust by explorers the statement might be modified to read, "that portion of the universe directly available to man."

[2] F. Lukermann, "Toward a More Geographic Economic Geography," *The Professional Geographer,* Vol. 10, No. 4 (1958), pp. 2-10.

haps subconscious. Out of this process of describing has come increasingly explicit and rigorous theory. There is no escape. Description, by its very nature, is scientific.

Still there are real operational differences between those interested in description and those interested in "science." While the former, thinking through classificatory schemes, spend some effort on implicit theory, they spend more of their effort on inventory, completing their classification. Their work becomes repetitious. They will, of course, discover as many categories and classes in their classification as they seek. Their expectation is that some day, some way, someone will find these results invaluable. In contrast, the "scientists" concentrate their efforts more on ideas and imagination. Ironically, they are much less interested in statistics, in the sense of the *World Almanac*, than the "describers." The "scientists" are, however, heavily involved with mathematics—often highly abstract mathematics—which they use as framework for their theories. They imagine more and repeat less.

Lukermann and others feel that geography is peculiarly descriptive and description deserves a favored place in geographic research. He writes:

A more geographic economic geography would start from observations with the recording of data on maps. Research in geography would begin with the description of the geographic phenomena and associations so arranged and ordered. . . . Description so stated has as its culminating study the investigation of process, and geographic research thus defined would prescribe a synoptic as well as an analystic [sic] approach. The formulation of theory and model building in geography would serve only heuristic ends; furthering investigation of empirical observations.[3]

There is in geography, as in any other science, a continuous interplay of logic, theory and fact (description). One cannot be separated from the others. Due to their inseparability, it is absurd to claim that one, in this case description, is "more geographic" than the others. All are geographic. The problem in geography, as in any other science, lies in trying to find more and more economical ways of ordering our perception of facts. In this constant search for efficiency, it must be asked, "Where is the bottleneck?" Without hestitation it can be answered that it lies in the construction of theory. In this connection Berry says:

. . . Is it valid to argue that "Research in geography would begin with the description of geographic phenomena and associations so arranged and ordered?" This is a common view expressed frequently in methodological notes in geography. It is apposite to ask whether continued emphasis upon description is efficient. As Zetterberg remarks, "The quest for explanation is the quest

[3] *Ibid.*, pp. 9-10.

for theory." . . . observation is necessarily proceeded [sic] by the hunch or hypothesis which needs to be tested against reality by problem-orientation rather than by inventory.[4]

The Predictability of Geographic Phenomena

The question of predictability is crucial since it is the basic assumption of all theory. The predictability of geographic phenomena depends in turn on the answer to a question: Are geographic phenomena unique or general? If they are unique, they are not predictable and theory cannot be constructed. If they are general, they are predictable and theory can be constructed. The clarification of this issue may be drawn from the philosophy of science. Science assumes phenomena to be general, not unique. Whether a phenomenon is unique or general can be considered to be a matter of point of view or of the inherent property of the phenomenon itself.

UNIQUENESS AS A POINT OF VIEW / Imagine that we are extremely acute observers; then, if we look closely at any two objects we will find them to be totally different because *every* property investigated will be found to be different. Suppose we are considering two white rocks. Are they identical in color? Of course not. Then calling them both white is an error. Certainly, if we look closely at all rocks we will find that no two have exactly the same color. So in order to be accurate, the color of each rock needs a special identifying name. But rather than invent a name for the color of every rock in the universe, we can save much work by indicating the rock to which we are referring and pronouncing "Its color is thus." The same reasoning applies to the concept of rock. No two rocks are identical. Then, for accuracy, we should not use the word "rock" but have an individual name for each object. By admitting that no two objects are exactly alike we end up abandoning our language and pronouncing, "Things are thus." Therefore, according to the doctrine of uniqueness, nothing can be described, much less explained or predicted.

This chain of reasoning leads to a conclusion probably so unpalatable to most readers that they might look for some error in it. But this reasoning is one of man's great intellectual achievements.

Bergson writes:

. . . Were all the photographs of a town, taken from all possible points of view, to go on indefinitely completing one another, they would never be equivalent to the solid town in which we walk about. Were all the translations

[4] Brian J. L. Berry, "Further Comments Concerning 'Geographic' and 'Economic' Economic Geography," *The Professional Geographer*, Vol. 11, No. 1, Part 1 (1959), p. 12.

of a poem into all possible languages to add together their various shades of meaning and, correcting each other by a kind of mutual retouching, to give more and more faithful image of the poem they translate, they would yet never succeed in rendering the inner meaning of the original. A representation taken from a certain point of view, a translation made with certain symbols, will always remain imperfect in comparison with the object of which a view has been taken, or which the symbols seek to express. But the absolute, which is the object and not its representation, the original and not its translation, is perfect, by being perfectly what it is.[5]

This is the doctrine of *uniqueness*. It is consistent, logical, and unscientific.

Science is diametrically opposed to the doctrine of uniqueness. It is willing to sacrifice the extreme accuracy obtainable under the uniqueness point of view in order to gain the efficiencies of generalization. Therefore, science will accept the class "white rocks." Science is cheerful in that it assumes it can become constantly more general and more nearly accurate through its inventive efforts, though it realizes it can never become completely accurate. Since inaccuracies can always be reduced, science does not ascribe the ever-present existence of these inaccuracies to uniqueness, but to the state of the art.

UNIQUENESS AS AN INHERENT PROPERTY OF OBJECTS / Hartshorne has written recently on the subject of uniqueness as an inherent property of objects. His statement is so clear and typically thorough that it is necessary to draw mainly on his arguments knowing full well they are not peculiar to him.

Hartshorne confuses *unique* with *individual* case. Individual case implies generality, not uniqueness. For example, assume there is a theory that explains the existence of islands. There is only one Manhattan Island. Yet, if Manhattan Island conforms to the theory of islands, it is different from other islands only in that the variables are in peculiar quantitative combination. Manhattan Island is an individual case, as are all other islands, and the theory is still applicable. Thus individual case, properly defined, cannot be opposed to generality; yet Hartshorne writes, "It may facilitate understanding if we speak more simply of generic studies in contrast to studies of individual cases." [6]

Hartshorne explicitly takes the position that "every case is unique." This appears to contradict his statements regarding generality. Perhaps he means every case is partly unique and partly general in the sense

[5] Henri Bergson, *An Introduction to Metaphysics* (New York: The Liberal Arts Press, 1950), pp. 22-23.
[6] Richard Hartshorne, *Perspective on the Nature of Geography* (Chicago: Rand McNally & Co., 1959), p. 149.

that no events can be exactly predicted. If this is what he intends, there is no disagreement, but this is not what he writes. He comments:

Literally, the term "nomothetic" refers to the search for general laws, as opposed to "idiographic," the intensive study of an individual case, but I agree with Ackerman that any generic concepts, whether or not leading to scientific laws, should be considered as contrasted with "idographic" as the intensive study of the individual case. In translating the latter term (which is not to be confused with "ideaographic"), I have found that to speak of the study of "unique cases," though correct in the sense that every case is unique, may be misleading in suggesting the sense of "rare" or "unusual." [7]

Hartshorne's difficulty over this point is fundamental. Also, unique is so rare and unusual as to be singular.

He also feels that the qualities of uniqueness and generality are inherent qualities that reside in objects and that they help account for the success or failure of geography to establish theories. Hartshorne writes:

The fact that geography is one of the fields of knowledge in which a comparatively large amount of effort is spent in studying individual cases rather than constructing scientific laws has been a matter of concern to critics within our midst for more than half a century. Before concluding that drastic changes are in order, it will be well to consider to what degree this may be a necessary consequence of the nature of our subject.[8]

This attitude is crippling because it leads us to distinguish between the unique and the general by the following process. If we have been able to construct theory involving phenomena, the phenomena are general. But if we have not been able to construct theory, it is because the phenomena are unique. Since unique phenomena cannot be explained, there is no sense in attempting to develop generalities. Thus, we are defeated before we try.

Schaefer has a strong grip on the problem of uniqueness.

He writes:

The systematic geographer, studying the spatial relations among a limited number of classes of phenomena, arrives by a process of abstraction at laws representing ideal or model situations; that is, situations which are artificial in that only a relatively small number of factors are causally operative in each of them. Practically, no single such law or even body of laws will fit any concrete situation completely. In this noncontroversial sense every region is, indeed, unique. Only this is nothing peculiar to geography.[9]

And,

[7] *Ibid.*
[8] Hartshorne, *op. cit.*, p. 149.
[9] Schaefer, *op. cit.*, p. 230.

The main difficulty of the uniqueness argument is that, as Max Weber has pointed out, it proves too much. Are there really two stones completely alike in all minute details of shape, color, and chemical composition? Yet, Galileo's law of falling bodies holds equally for both. Similarly, limited as our present psychological knowledge is, it seems safe to say that no two people would register identical scores on all tests as yet devised. Does it follow that our psychologists have so far discovered not a single law? What it all comes down to is a matter of degree.[10]

And Schaefer explicitly notes what is enervating in the uniqueness argument. Assuming the uniqueness position he draws the necessary conclusion when he writes:

But there are no laws for the unique; little use, then, in looking for historical or geographical laws or prediction.[11]

Hartshorne introduces several pieces of evidence in support of the uniqueness position that must be answered. First, he states that geography is at a disadvantage because it is often faced with a limited number of cases.[12] The solution to this problem, though not easy, is to produce more general theory, hence more cases. Before Newton, no one realized that the falling of an apple and the movement of the moon were similar cases.

Hartshorne also argues:

In studying the integration of phenomena in geography, even if limited to those of natural phenomena, we are concerned with highly complex situations which we must observe without means of control.[13]

As for complexity, occurrences always appear complex until order is discovered. Newton demonstrated this when he discovered order in celestial chaos. The lack of laboratory control, on the other hand, is a problem of experimental design. No laboratory experiment is completely controlled. The effect of uncontrolled factors is eliminated by randomization.[14] The greater the variance the larger the sample drawn, is a rule that applies in the laboratory and out. In the laboratory it is possible to lower the variance, thus decreasing the sample size. This, in turn, decreases the expense of experimentation. Therefore, the difference between laboratory and non-laboratory experimentation reduces to one of difference in expense.

[10] *Ibid.*, p. 238.
[11] *Ibid.*, p. 236.
[12] Hartshorne, *op. cit.*, pp. 149-50.
[13] *Ibid.*, p. 151.
[14] Sir Ronald A. Fisher, "Mathematics of a Lady Tasting Tea," James R. Newman, ed., *The World of Mathematics* (New York: Simon & Schuster, 1956), Vol. 3, pp. 1512-21.

Hartshorne goes on to tell, *a priori,* just where it is that prediction of human actions will fail, when he writes:

The explanation of any problem in human geography by use of scientific principles will fall short of completion at the point where it is necessary to interpret the motivations and resultant decisions of particular persons.[15]

Many geographers bet their lives regularly that they can predict the decisions of particular persons when they step across a street in front of motorists held back by a red light. Powerful advances in individual and small group behavior by psychologists and sociologists refute Hartshorne's assertion.

Perhaps his most revealing statement reads:

Thus, in order to explain fully by scientific laws of cause and effect a single decision of any single human being, we would need to know all the factors of his biological inheritance and all the influences which molded his character from infancy on—far more data than we could ever hope to secure.[16]

But science has long since stopped pretending that it can "explain fully". As stated before, it does not strive for complete accuracy but compromises its accuracy for generality. Any effort dedicated to *full explanations* must conclude with consideration of *unique events* since absolute accuracy would require a "generalization" of infinite, and therefore, impossible, detail.

Thus, Hartshorne's objections to generality in geography can be answered.

Symptomatically, throughout Schaefer's work runs the generic term *spatial* while Hartshorne uses the idiographic word *place*. The *space* versus *place* dispute is a direct consequence of their positions on general versus unique. Hartshorne is pessimistic as to our ability to produce geographic laws, especially regarding human behavior. Schaefer has done us a great service in sweeping away our excuses and thereby freeing us from self-defeat.

THE IMPOSSIBILITY OF COMPROMISE ON THE ISSUE OF UNIQUENESS / A single methodology cannot embrace both the unique and the general. In this regard it is instructive to consider Ackerman's attempt to reconcile the two positions. Ackerman endorses generality when he endorses theoretical geography. He writes:

. . . analysis of the nature of two-dimensional distributions *in the abstract* should be able to furnish a theoretical framework with capacity to illuminate actually observed distributional patterns and space relations. Such a theoretical

15 Hartshorne, *op. cit.,* p. 156.
16 Hartshorne, *op. cit.,* p. 155.

framework is probably as important at this time as definition of the earth's physical matrix for observation was at an earlier stage in the science. Geography thus far has been notably weak in its attention to this possible building block.[17]

But concomitantly, Ackerman clings to the notion of regionalism as the contemplation of the unique, and this leads him to a serious difficulty which he himself admits:

It has been observed that geographers are not yet satisfied with the generalizations which they have produced. They have been beset with difficulties as they attempted to extend and refine their framework of concepts. These difficulties are greatest as the science reaches the culmination of its work, the analysis and description of the element-complexes which characterize areas on the real earth . . .

. . . The methodological maze which confronts the student attempting to determine the nature of fundamental research in geography is all too evident. The development of generic concepts in the field has aided the comprehension of geographic reality, but the end product of geographic research still has been contemplation of the unique. Small wonder that the subject was open to characterization as an "art." The only ready way of integrating unlike entities has appeared to be through an intuitive process, and geography appears to be concerned with unlikes at a critical step.[18]

The solution to this difficulty of the incompatibility of the unique in regional geography and the general in theoretical geography is provided by Schaefer:

. . . regional geography is like the laboratory in which the theoretical physicist's generalizations must stand the test of use and truth. It seems fair to say, then, in conclusion, that regional and systematic geography are codign, inseparable, and equally indispensable aspects of the field.[19]

In other words, if regional geography is associated with generic facts instead of unique facts and if systematic geography is associated with theoretical, Ackerman's difficulty evaporates, for the highly theoretical is not expected to approach the factual though they are inseparable and complementary. Only by the complete rejection of uniqueness can geography resolve its contradictions.

· · · · ·

In order to emphasize the isomorphism between uniform regional

---

[17] Edward A. Ackerman, *Geography as a Fundamental Research Discipline*, University of Chicago, Department of Geography Research Paper No. 53 (1958), p. 28.
[18] *Ibid.*, pp. 15-16.
[19] Schaefer, *op. cit.*, p. 230.

geography and classification systems, the following tabulation presents the corresponding terms.

Regional Terms	*Classificatory Terms*
Uniform region	Areal class
Regional system	Classificatory system
Single-feature region	Classification using a single category (besides location)
Multiple-feature region	Classification using more than one category
Compage	Classification using many categories
Place	Individual
Earth's surface	Population of areal classifications
Map	Representation of population
Element of geography	Differentiating characteristic
Purpose (for creating regional system)	Objective (of classification system)
Systematic geography	Attention focused on particular categories
Regional geography	Attention focused on areal class
Core of region	Modal individual(s) and individuals extremely similar to it
Regional boundary	Class interval
Scale	Number of areal classes
Continents and oceans	Examples of kingdoms
Homogeneous	Low areal variance
Heterogeneous	High areal variance
Areal differentiation	Areal classification
Regional hierarchy	Scale where sudden shift in areal accuracy occurs

Does equating uniform regions with areal classes depreciate uniform regional geography? Is the work worthy of serious minds? Perhaps these questions can best be answered by considering the problems confronting the areal classifier. First, there are the technical statistical problems alluded to and to be treated more fully in the chapter entitled "Descriptive Mathematics." Geographers cannot seriously hope that others will solve these problems for them since others are not so constantly concerned with the problem of areal classification. Second, there is the problem of continued exploration. The areal classification of the earth's surface requires additional data. The exploration of the earth's terrain and the distribution of land and water is much more complete than that of its soils, to mention nothing of its housing conditions, incomes, age structure, etc. Many "dark continents" remain. Also, features that change rapidly, such as river deltas or human population statistics, require constant re-exploration. Third, knowledge of significant areally correlated phenomena (accessory characteristics) can be improved. Recent study by McCarty and Salisbury[20] indicates that formal statistical correlations are much more accurate than visually ascertained correlations. The elements (differentiating characteristics) of physical geography should be re-examined using the new statistical techniques. Cultural elements still await more than crude identification, and studies of areal correlation are badly needed to establish these elements by the determination of accessory characteristics.

In addition it should be pointed out that many sciences have started as purely classificatory. To disparage uniform regional geography as "merely" classificatory would be to disparage most other sciences at some period in their development and such individual scientific geniuses as Linneaus.

The equating of classification systems with systems of regional geography produces results which show startling resemblance to Hartshorne's classic *Nature of Geography*,[21] a study based on the scholarly examination of the content of geography over many years. The only area of disagreement appears to be the concept of uniqueness. The resemblance might be explained by assuming that geography, like other sciences, has started as a classificatory science and geographers have independently rediscovered the entire logic of classification systems, no mean intellectual feat.

A substantive work using the concept of uniform regions will not be given in this book since the book is primarily concerned with theoretical geography. This lack of illustration is not serious since every geographer is highly familiar with many examples.

· · · · ·

Conclusion

It might prove advantageous to regard uniform regional geography as classificatory and to make methodological room for a theoretical geography. The history of science is replete with developments of precisely this sort and it would be quite natural to attribute the current methodological gropings to the confusions of growth as geography moves rapidly from an overwhelmingly classificatory science to a classificatory-theoretical science.

The methodology endorsed here is one which leaves geography no excuse for not reaching full maturity as a science. While nothing in present-day geography is discarded, the overall importance of theory

[20] Harold H. McCarty and Neil E. Salisbury, "Visual Comparison of Isopleth Maps as a Means of Determining Correlations between Spatially Distributed Phenomena," Department of Geography, State University of Iowa, Series No. 3 (1961).
[21] Hartshorne, *"The Nature of Geography . . . ," op. cit.*

and the inevitability of mathematization is insisted upon. By identifying regional geography with facts (description), systematic geography with theoretical geography, and cartography with mathematics, and their interactions with arrows, the following arrangement of the discipline appears:

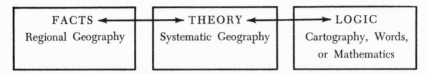

FACTS ◄——————► THEORY ◄——————► LOGIC
Regional Geography | Systematic Geography | Cartography, Words, or Mathematics

FIGURE 1: The interaction of fact, theory, and logic in geography.

Is this a successful arrangement? It has some qualities that recommend it. It is a simple arrangement that gives all elements of geography a natural home. It is conservative in that it discards nothing in geography and it is the classical arrangement which other sciences have found useful. Still we are faced with the question of its success in producing substantive work. The rest of this book produces partial evidence. If the discipline ultimately judges work based on such a methodology a failure, then the search for an effective methodology will have to continue.

. . . . .

The Central Problem of Geography and Other Conclusions

Geography is the science of locations. Regional geography classifies locations and theoretical geography predicts them. The discussion in this section concentrates on theoretical geography.

In the chapter on central place, optimal solutions take the form of placing interacting objects as near to each other as possible. That is, the solutions were those which minimized movement between objects. The necessity to minimize movements determines which definition of distance is appropriate in a given situation. In the chapter on movement theory, all the optimal theories minimize movement. Thus, it is suggested that the central problem of geography is to place interacting objects as near to each other as possible when the definition of distance is chosen which minimizes total movement. The central problem applies with equal strength to such diverse subject matters as climatology and human migration though in the second case some inefficiencies of movement must be introduced to blur the optimal pattern into its somewhat irrational human form.

In a recently discovered unpublished manuscript Schaefer wrote,

. . . geography . . . seems to be a field inclined and compelled to produce morphological laws rather than process laws. A typical theoretical situation in geography is described usually by way of patterns. Patterns are morphological laws. Köeppen's Hypothetical Continent is such a law. The theoretical nature of patterns has been somewhat neglected by geographers and it looks as if here a real scientific contribution could be made to scientific method by geography.[22]

It is interesting to notice that the solution of nearness problems typically leads to a pattern of optimal locations.

Every explanation we have of how geographic phenomena obtained their location involves the notion of movement, most often of the optimal sort of the nearness problem but with the important exception of diffusion theories. Whatever the type of movement, it leaves its mark on the face of the earth. That is, it produces the geometry. In turn the geometry produces the movements. Thus geometry and movement are the inseparable duals of geographic theory. Davis's streams move the earth material to the sea and leave the earth etched with valleys; Thünen's agricultural products are moved to the market and leave their mark on the earth with rings of agriculture; the circulations in the nation-states are created by and creator of the national boundaries; air masses move cross the continents to dampen and warm the land into the patterns of Koeppen's Hypothetical Continent; farmers scattered on plains move to their hamlets and form Christaller's hexagonal network on their landscape; species evolve on continents and in oceans and diffuse their way into their present distributions; agricultural innovations creep across Europe, as do glacial fronts, to yield Hägerstrand's regions of agricultural progress and terminal moraines.

Schaefer, writing about location theory, predicted:

The pioneer work in this area has, in fact, been done by economists, if we except Christaller who is a geographer. But, as the theory is being refined, the geographer's skill will increasingly come into its own. For, he is more expert than others in the treatment of spatial factors and he knows from his rich store of experience with which others they typically interact.[23]

His foresight has been confirmed by events. With few exceptions, some of which have been cited in this volume, the works of nongeographers leave an impression of spatial aridity. As Schaefer points out, our ability to deal with spatial problems *per se* gives us great advantages

[22] Fred K. Schaefer, "Political Geography," from an unpublished and incomplete book on the subject of political geography, chapter 3, p. 8. This manuscript available along with other important papers, articles and speeches of Schaefer's at the American Geographical Society in New York where they have been generously placed by his wife, Mary Schaefer.
[23] Schaefer, "Exceptionalism in Geography: A Methodological Examination," *Annals of the Association of American Geographers*, Vol. 43 (1953), p. 248.

over other systematic sciences whose interest in the spatial aspects of their subject matter is only casual and usually inexpert. Geography, which for some time has been nibbled away by other disciplines, should begin to recapture and more firmly hold lost ground for the only legitimate reason for such an expansion, the natural strength of the geographic point of view.

Another prediction is that geography faces a period of continued mathematization. The heavy use of the various geometries seems assured. Also, the distinctions between various systematic branches of geography might diminish at the theoretical level as common spatial skills are mastered. As was especially clear in the chapter on movement theory, certain spatial solutions cut across traditional geographic subject matter and the profession might, as a matter of efficiency, start dividing itself into various theoretical spatial fields, such as point problems, area problems, description of mathematical surfaces, and central place problems rather than the current arrangement of climatology, population geography, landforms, etc. Further, the strategic position of cartography should become even clearer while concomitantly the distinction between cartography and spatial mathematics should decrease. Now that the science of space is maturing so rapidly, the mathematics of space—geometry—should be utilized with an efficiency never achieved by other sciences. Because of the lushness of the spatial logic of geometry and its increasing utilization as a tool to discover spatial facts, I am of the opinion that the originality and power of geography as a basic science will soon establish a first rank position for geography among the developed sciences.

29. A Spatial Behavior Analysis of Decision Making in Middle Sweden's Farming

Julian Wolpert

Emphasis on theory and mathematics has led to the development of the technique Wolpert employs here— model building. His work is evidence of the trend among

SOURCE: This paper, reprinted with the author's permission, was presented at the 1963 meeting of the Association of American Geographers. Dr. Wolpert is associate professor of geography at University of Pennsylvania.

spatial analysts toward evaluation of the decision process.
As Bunge notes in the previous article, decisions by man,
whether economic, political, or social, create movements that
change the nature of the earth's surface. Thus, human
behavior as a variable is of increasing concern in geographic
research.

The individual farmer, just as the industrial manager, must periodically make decisions with respect to the allocation of available resources among alternative uses. The farmer, functioning as a manager, must decide how his land, labor and capital will be used—the crop livestock combination, the investments in machinery and the other operating necessities. His family income and the survival of his farm are dependent upon his decisions. The consequences of these resource-use decisions are partly reflected in the distribution of income. The yearly labor income for a sample of Middle Sweden's farmers is illustrated in Figures 1 and 2. The variations in income are partly attributable to differences in farming resources, but to an extent which must be determined. If we were to assume that the income distribution reflects merely the variations in resources, then we would be assuming tacitly that the farmers had perfect knowledge about alternative opportunities and their consequences, and had the single desire of maximizing profits, i.e., they are economically rational. These assumptions are not valid, however, as is evident from the distribution of potential income for the same farmers (Figure 3).

The potential income values were determined by means of a linear programming analysis and reflect the optimum or limiting income which can be achieved with the present distribution of resources. This is the income that would be achieved if farm organization and technology were optimum, if the decision behavior of Middle Sweden's farmers conformed to that of Economic Man. The shortage of capital and the underemployment of labor largely account for the spatial variations. This limit or ceiling appears especially awesome when one considers that nowhere in Middle Sweden do even these potential values approach parity with the general income level in Sweden. The variations in the distribution are an indication of the varying degree of resource maladjustment.

Imposed upon this structural maladjustment is the additional gap between the income that is realized and the potential income. In Figure 4, we have combined the two distributions and labor input into a single ratio of actual to potential productivity to illustrate the extent and the variations in the gap from place to place. The surface, to which we shall refer as the Productivity Index or *PI* surface, represents essentially the human element in farming, the consequences of

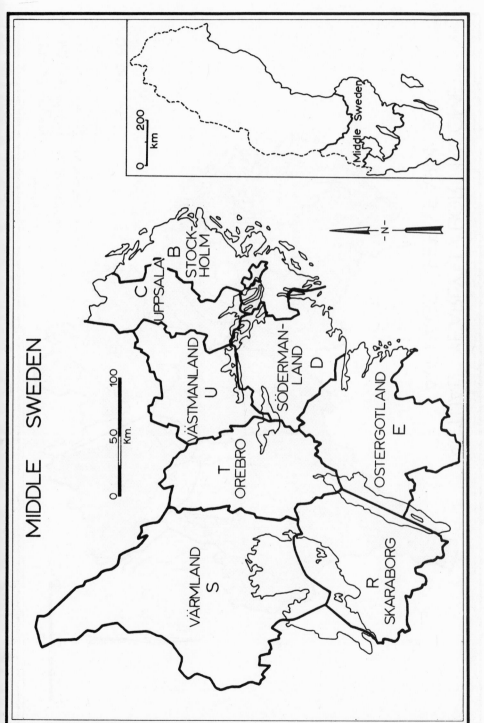

FIGURE 1: The sample area, Middle Sweden, and its counties.

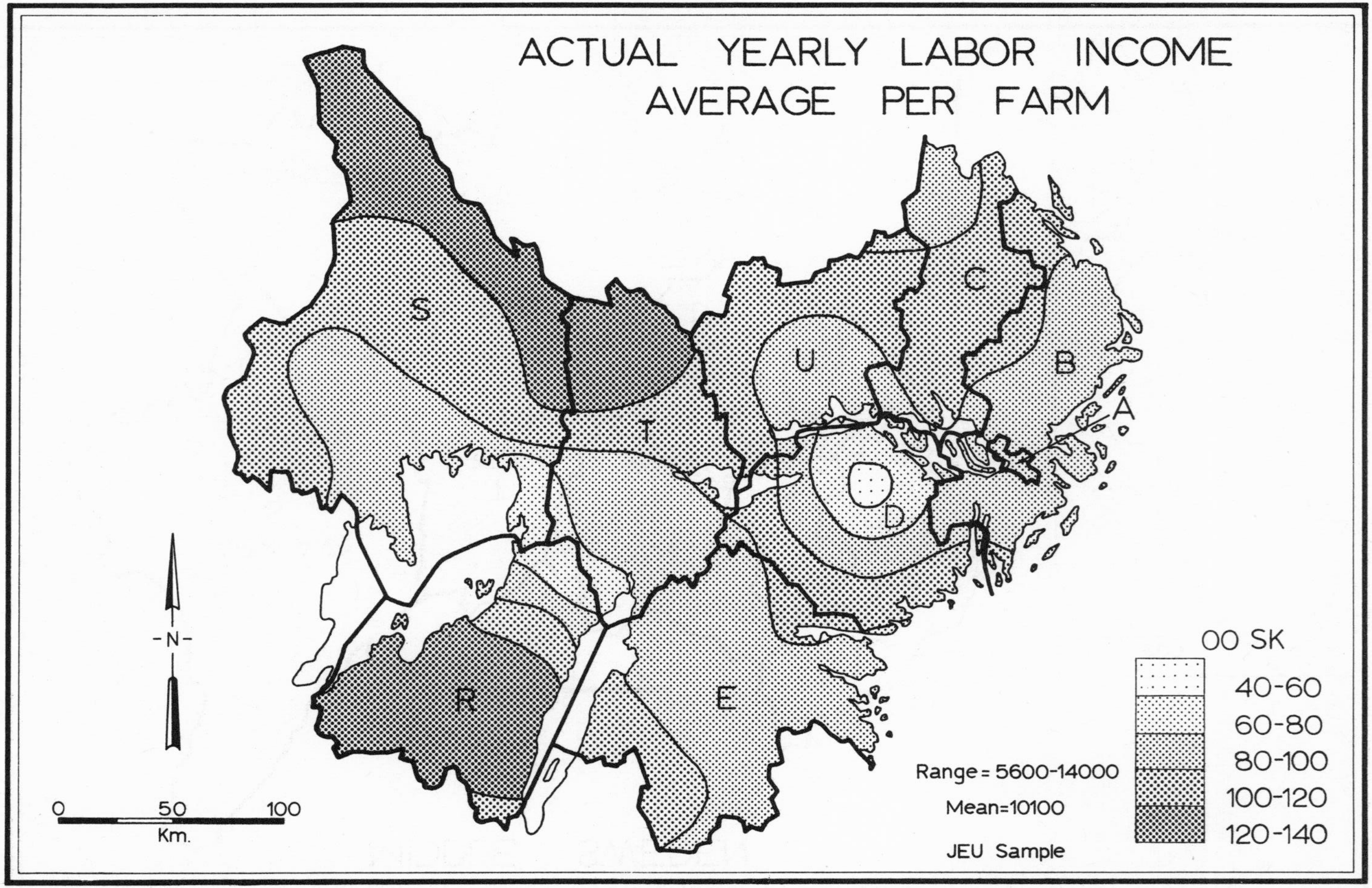

ACTUAL YEARLY LABOR INCOME
AVERAGE PER FARM

OO SK

40-60
60-80
80-100
100-120
120-140

Range = 5600-14000

Mean = 10100

JEU Sample

FIGURE 2.

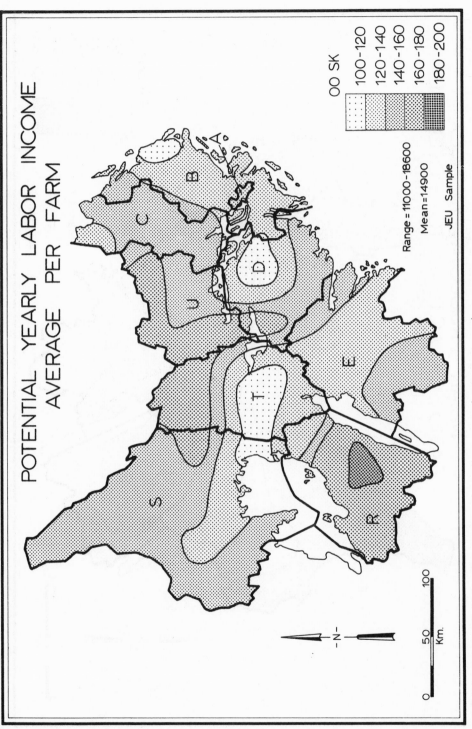

POTENTIAL YEARLY LABOR INCOME
AVERAGE PER FARM

OO SK

100-120
120-140
140-160
160-180
180-200

Range = 11000-18600

Mean = 14900

JEU Sample

-N-

0   50   100
        Km.

FIGURE 3.

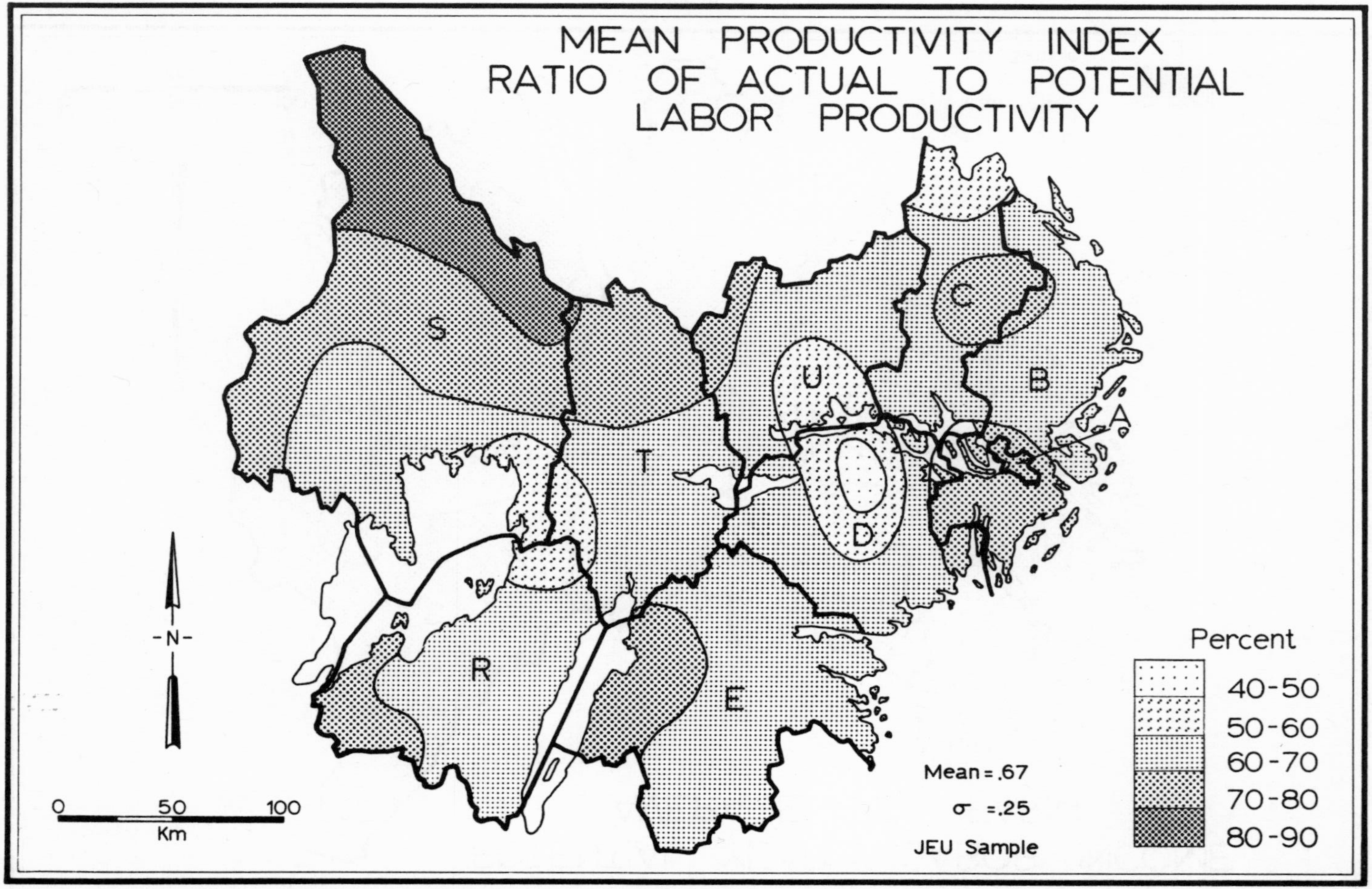
MEAN PRODUCTIVITY INDEX
RATIO OF ACTUAL TO POTENTIAL
LABOR PRODUCTIVITY
S
T
U
D
C
B
A
R
E
-N-
0
50
100
Km
Mean = .67
σ = .25
JEU Sample
Percent
40-50
50-60
60-70
70-80
80-90

FIGURE 4.

the decision behavior of Middle Sweden's farmers with the resource differences removed. The gap as it varies spatially reflects the departure of the decision behavior of our sample population from that of Economic Man.

The *PI* surface represents not only the ratio of actual to potential income but the explanation for its variation. The average is two-thirds, which is an indication that with their organization of resources and level of technology, only two-thirds of the potential level of income is achieved. In the counties of R, central E and northern S, not only are the average *PI* values relatively higher, but because they are higher, then, of necessity, one would expect to find that resources are more knowledgeably combined and integrated so as to achieve higher profits. On the other hand, the lower average *PI* values in the central core areas would be an indication that decision behavior was less directed toward maximum profit, that farm organization and technology were hampered to a relatively greater extent by imperfect knowledge.

The framework of matched comparison between Middle Sweden's farmers and Economic Man was introduced with several purposes in mind. The initial objective was to demonstrate the inappropriateness of the rational model in accounting for spatial variations in decision behavior or in the consequences of that behavior. A secondary purpose was to locate regions of maladjustment or "disequilibrium" where resource restrictions or the level of farm organizations and technology limit the attainment of income parity. The primary objective, however, is to be able to substitute for economic rationality and its assumptions of optimizing behavior and omniscience, a more descriptive behavioral theory which allows for a range of decision behavior and spatial variations in decision environments.

Within Middle Sweden, farmers do not achieve maximization of income considering their supply of resources. They do not combine or integrate their resources so as to achieve optimum returns. Their knowledge is *imperfect* with respect to available alternatives and the outcome of following alternative courses of action. In short, their decision behavior is unlike that of Economic Man. To explain the existence of the gap between actual and potential income and its variations among Middle Sweden's farmers, we must relax the assumptions of optimizing behavior and omniscience.

We may substitute for the assumption of optimizing behavior the behavioral concept of the "satisficer," where allowance is made for the entire continuum of human responses from optimization to that minimum of adaptation essential for survival. In selecting from among alternatives, Middle Sweden's farmers seek a course of action which is *satisfactory or good enough* rather than the *best* course of action."

They maintain a normal production program and adjust in the direction of alternatives which they perceive as better or more likely to enable them to realize their aspiration levels. A partial explanation for the gap between actual and potential income, therefore, may be found in the value system of the decision-makers. They are satisficers and not optimizers.

We may substitute for the assumption of omniscience or perfect knowledge a descriptive view of the actual knowledge situation of our sample population. There are spatial lags in the diffusion of information and imperfect knowledge or uncertainty about the future course of events which will affect the outcome of their decisions. "They simplify decision problems by considering not all possible alternatives but only some subset which is commensurate with their capabilities of solution." They are exposed to, perceive and utilize only a small portion of the information necessary for an optimal solution.

The variations in the *PI* surface, therefore, may be explained only through the variations in the aspiration levels and the knowledge situation of the individual decision-makers, which must vary in the spatial dimension also. We do not mean to imply that distance and relative

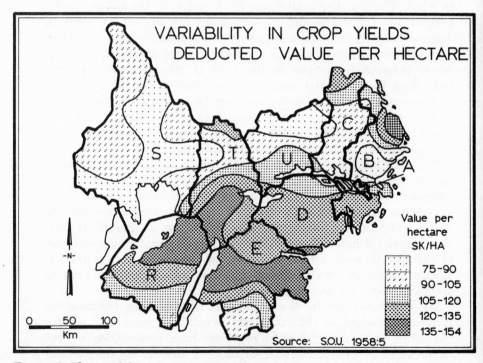

FIGURE 5: The variability of crop yields—deducted value per hectare. (Data drawn from *Permanent skördeskadeskydd* [Permanent Protection against Crop Damage], Statens offentliga utredningar 1958:5, Ministry of Agriculture, Stockholm.)

position, in themselves, determine how decisions are made. Instead, we are merely recognizing that the elements upon which decisions are based, information, expectations and values, are not randomly distributed among our population.

The degree of uncertainty to which Middle Sweden's farmers are subject, for example, varies in the spatial dimension. Through price stabilization and the development of credit institutions, a good deal of market uncertainty has been eliminated. Now, yield variability arising from unpredictable weather changes remains as the leading cause of income fluctuations. In Figure 5, we have indicated the normal variability in crop revenue will normally depart by $12 an acre from the average. For the farm with 75 acres, a normal yearly variation of $900 will occur. Weather instability is not greater here than in central S where the revenue fluctuation is only half, but attitudes toward the avoidance of risk differ. Crops such as wheat and oil seeds, which are subject to a higher degree of risk are emphasized in E, while the farmers in S concentrate more on low risk crops such as oats and hay. This point must be stressed that not only does the inherent instability of planning environments differ spatially but also the degree of precaution taken by the decision-maker to avoid the full impact of uncertainty. The farmers attempt "to arrange a *negotiated environment* to avoid uncertainty"—individually through diversification of enterprises, flexibility and shifting, and collectively through price stabilization and crop insurance. To an extent, they create their own environment of uncertainty to balance their desire for profit with a measure of stability and security. Factors such as age, education, indebtedness and family responsibility affect attitudes toward the avoidance of risk, and these characteristics are clustered spatially among our population and reflected in the variations in the decision behavior.

Superimposed upon the environment of uncertainty or imperfect knowledge about the future course of events is a spatial lag in the communication of information. The communication networks through which information is diffused discriminate between individuals in the spatial dimension. At any given time, therefore, there are variations in the amount of information about technology and prices that is available to the individual decisionmakers. While none of Middle Sweden's farmers are aware of all alternative opportunities and their comparative advantages, there are special variations in the extent of their information which partly accounts for the variations in the *PI* surface. By incorporating some of the observed dimensions of the communication process into a diffusion model, we have attempted to rank sample zones in Middle Sweden according to the relative speed with which information is disseminated from the "experts." (Figure 6). Thus the lag may be expected to be least in the zone from central R eastward into E and greatest in northern S. The ranks give an indication only of the supply of information which is diffused through the channels of mass communication. We must take account, however, of the other side of the relationship, the demand for information which evidence indicates is related to the attainment levels of the individual farmers. Thus, while the lag in the supply of information to the farmers in northern S is relatively high, they are well informed about prices and technology and their organization is relatively close to optimality. It is necessary to recognize the variations which may occur in the dissemination and distribution of information in order to understand the decision environment of Middle Sweden's farmers.

Imposed upon the satisficing decision behavior of our sample population is the stress to rationalize their farm enterprises. Middle Sweden's farmers are being encouraged to imitate Economic Man in their decision behavior and to narrow the gap between their actual income and the potential. Under their own impetus as well, adaptations are being made in the direction of greater profitability. The gap appears, therefore, to assume significance beyond that of a purely theoretical nature—it reflects a transitional stage in a process of adjustment. The

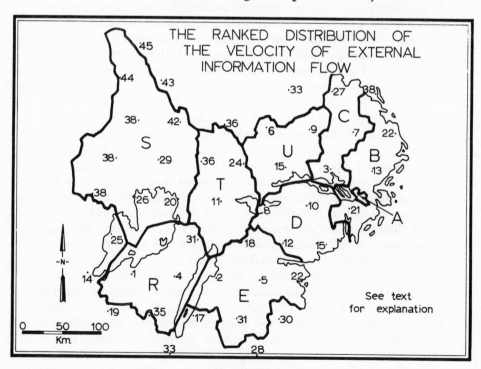

FIGURE 6.

process of adjustment is dependent upon the variations in the lag of information, the impact of uncertainty and the aspirations of Middle Sweden's farmers. These are the elements which explain the variations in the decision behavior of Middle Sweden's farmers and in the consequences of that behavior.

Only the barest essentials of a spatial theory of decision behavior have been outlined. In this investigation, we have concentrated more on indicating factors, such as information flow and uncertainty, which must be considered in analyzing spatial variations in economic activities. Our empirical analysis has been confined purely to the decision behavior of Middle Sweden's farmers. A series of follow-up studies involved with decision-makers in other economic activities and in other cultural situations would be necessary before a general formulation may be proposed or forecasts made about decision behavior as a spatial process. With a change in variables—aspiration levels tending closer to optimization, a shorter lag in communication and a more controlled environment of risk, as among large-scale industrial firms, spatial processes may be less important in decision behavior and the rational model may provide a satisfactory explanation. With a change in the other direction—a society of isolated, subsistence farmers, for example, investigation of value systems and interactance patterns becomes an essential prerequisite for understanding the distribution of economic activities. Clearly, much further investigation is in order before conclusive results may be expected.

30. Where Is a Research Frontier?

Edward A. Ackerman

Ackerman's article depicts the new face geography is assuming to solve the age-old problem of understanding areas and finding spatial correlations. The new face brings new terminology like "earth-wide man-environment system," and new tools like systems analysis. The cogent suggestions made by Ackerman are indeed pertinent for consideration by students of geography. "The way lies open" to establish new "research frontiers" or to attach old ones with more rigorous methods.

SOURCE: *Annals of the Association of American Geographers*, LIII (December, 1963), 429-39. The author is a geographer with the Carnegie Foundation, Washington, D. C.

Science in the Last Fifty Years

I was born in the year 1911. The half century since that time has contained some of the most tremendous events in the history of the human race. Among them have been two world wars of unprecedented extent and violence, the near doubling of the total population of the world,[1] the rise of the great Communist states, and other events profoundly changing the course of human history. But preeminent among all are the growth of science and the growth of man's capacity to apply his mind to the problems of learning and discovery.

Many striking examples might be offered by the changes within science, and the changes wrought by science, in these 50 years. To me, a most striking illustration is a comparison of our knowledge of the universe in 1911 and now. In 1911 what men knew of space was confined to our own galaxy. Our solar system was thought to be near the center of that galaxy, whose shape was only dimly conjectured. Now we know that the sun and its secondary satellite, the earth, are far out on one arm of our vast, beautiful, spiral galaxy. We know also that there are at least a billion such galaxies within the space our telescopes have penetrated. Furthermore, we have seen the photographic record of objects five billion light-years away, moving away from us at half the speed of light. These 50 years have brought a more profound change in our knowledge of the cosmos than was achieved in all man's previous existence.

Although astronomy may stretch our minds most of all, there are other examples of advances in our learning and knowledge, of the deepest meaning and most comprehensive impact. Among them we might mention the general theory of relativity, the dismembering of the atom by nuclear physics, the discovery of the biochemical basis of heredity, the developments in engineering that made possible the Manhattan Project and the orbiting of men in space, and the chemical discoveries and developments in social organization that have promoted the world population explosion. It has been a truly epochal period, without any equal in history. Not least has been the final world acceptance of science as a tremendous social force.

As one views this panorama of glorious scientific achievement in the last 50 years, he cannot fail to be impressed by two things: the unity of scientific effort as it progresses; and great differences in the rates of progress among the subdivisions of science.

The first observation was skillfully described by the biologist Frank

[1] Estimated mid-1963 world population, 3.25 billion; 1910 population, 1.7 billion (1963, extrapolated from United Nations data; 1910 extrapolations from estimates by W. F. Willcox and A. M. Carr-Saunders).

R. Lillie in 1915. "Scientific discovery is a truly epigenetic process in which the germs of thought develop in the total environment of knowledge. Investigation of particular problems cannot be accelerated beyond well-defined limits; progress in each depends on the movement of the whole of science."[2]

Lillie's observation must be considered in the light of the second point, the differentials of progress among separate subfields of the scientific community. The progress of "science as a whole" at any given time in large measure is the progress of a relatively few subjects with growing points. As growing-point salients move, they furnish ground for practitioners in other disciplines to stand on and in turn push into new territory. This is what makes intercommunication among the sciences so important, and even more the proper choice of those with whom we communicate. To paraphrase an ancient observation, every scientist stands on the shoulders of giants. But one might add that it is important to stand on the shoulders of the right giant. The selection is as important as the standing. In the period between 1910 and the mid-1940's, physics and the mathematical disciplines stood out as examples of the giants.[3] Chemistry was of shorter stature in this comparison, biology considerably shorter, and geology less visible. Comparisons among the social sciences were more difficult, but perhaps anthropology, psychology, and economics deserve some distinction for their accomplishments in the pre-World War II period. However, the differences among sub-groups within a field were in most cases as pronounced as differences between major fields.

The Place of Geography in the Advancing Front

We are, naturally, especially interested in the place that geography occupied in this advancing front of science. There is no reason to avoid frankness. I am sure that all but a few here would agree that our contributions have been modest thus far. We have not been on the forward salients in science, nor, until recently, have we been associated closely with those who have. The reasons are not difficult to find. During the early part of this 50-year period, in the 'teens and early twenties, our closest associations were with history and geology. Geological study of that period, and of the thirties, was not among the inspiring growing points in science. The history and the geology con-

[2] Frank R. Lillie, "The History of the Fertilization Problem," *Science*, Vol. 43 (1916), pp. 39-53.
[3] The above comparison is not intended to reflect popular, or even professional, evaluations of the time. General appreciation of events in mathematics and physics during the late thirties, for example, did not come until the mid-forties. Yet they were sources of basic thought on methods that have affected all sciences.

nections did not correct the predisposition of our scholars of the 'teens and early twenties to the deceptive simplicity of geographic determinism. This was perhaps one of the last appearances of the Newtonian view of the world.

As determininism began to fade and independent geography departments sporadically appeared in this country, geography turned to association with the social sciences of the period. "Possibilism" in man's relation to the earth took the place of determinism. Because of the limitations of the social sciences and history at the time, these associations were only slightly more productive sources of inspiration than geology. It was only much later, indeed in the early fifties, when association with the social sciences bore its soundest fruits for geography. This was in the methods descended from mathematical statistics, first applied in biometrics, anthropometry, and econometrics. Their full application has not yet run its course.

Independence and Separation of Geography

I began my professional interest in geography at a time when the old moorings to geology were almost severed. The groping for solid footing among the social sciences was well under way.[4] The geographers who turned in the direction of the social sciences made a prescient choice of direction, but the difficulties confronting us were enormous, considering the methods then at our disposal. In the face of those difficulties, it was only natural that we became somewhat introspective. We tried to build a platform, as it were, from our own materials and to anchor it ourselves.[5] This search for a professional identity was, of course, found during other periods in the history of geography. It goes back at least to the 19th century German geographers. Alfred Hettner and others in Germany undertook influential studies from the early 1900's onward. But the succession of methodological appraisals in the United States that commenced with Harlan Barrows' "Geography as Human Ecology"[6] in 1923 and continued for nearly forty years must certainly rank as one of the most intensive efforts toward this end.

Our search for a professional identity led to an intellectual independence and eventually to a degree of isolation against which a

[4] Cf. J. M. Blaut, "Objective and Relationship," *The Professional Geographer*, Vol. 14 (1962), pp. 1-7. "In this respect we behaved like the social sciences: our philosophical weakness, like theirs, had its roots in chronically unsolved problems. Their problems concerned values, causes, and social wholes. Our problem, then as now, concerned the nature of our subject matter."

[5] The work of Carl Sauer and the "California School" in collaboration with cultural anthropology was an exception.

[6] Harlan H. Barrows, "Geography as Human Ecology," *Annals of the Association of American Geographers*, Vol. 13 (1923), pp. 1-14.

number of the rising younger generation of geographers have now reacted. In our search for a solid footing, a meaningful image of ourselves, many of us tended to separate ourselves from other sciences. Our principal interdisciplinary communications were with other sciences which also had problems of isolation, like cultural anthropology and geomorphology. In effect, some of us saw geography as an end in itself rather than in the broader context as a contributor to a larger scientific goal. Perhaps this is the fate of many specializations.

Insistence on the independence and separation in the 1930's and 1940's may seem a shockingly incorrect statement to some of you. Did not geography alone recognize its relations to both the physical sciences and the social sciences? Did not geography deal constantly with the data accumulated through the efforts of other disciplines? Indeed, was not geography even alert to analogous methods of inquiry from other disciplines? One can cite such major statements in the field as Barrows' "Geography as Human Ecology," and Sauer's "The Morphology of Landscape"[7] as proof of this alertness. But I must note that both these statements came in the mid-twenties, and thereafter for at least 25 years an atmosphere of separatism and independence characterized the profession.[8] Furthermore, morphology was not a particularly happy choice as an analogue method, and the hint given by Barrows on ecology was never seriously followed up by his colleagues. For science at large, morphology already was becoming a somewhat sterile concept when we took to it, and the analytical methods of the twenties and thirties were not yet equal to the multivariate problems of ecology.[9] The concept that became dominant among us was that of "areal differentiation," derived from Hettner and introduced in the United States by Sauer.[10] This concept favored (although did not demand logically) a goal of investigation independent of the goals of other sciences. The same might be said of another important concept in the field, that of areal functional organization, introduced by Platt.[11] On the other hand, the work of Sauer and his disciples did find common ground with

[7] Carl O. Sauer, "The Morphology of Landscape," *University of California Publications in Geography*, Vol. 2 (1925), pp. 19-53.

[8] The drive for the independent department typified this atmosphere at the time. Again the interest of the California group in cultural anthropology may be cited as an exception.

[9] Barrows had true insight in stressing "place relations," but his concept of geography as human ecology set forth too ambitious a field. Neither qualitative nor quantitative methods of the time offered much solid ground for exploiting the ecological concept. At least in retrospect we can see the ecological concept of Barrows' time as incompletely formed (i.e., the adjustment of an organism to environment). It has now been replaced by the much more powerful monistic concept of an ecosystem, in which organism and environment are one interacting entity.

[10] Sauer, *op. cit.*, p. 20.

[11] See R. S. Platt, *Field Study in American Geography*, University of Chicago Department of Geography Research Paper 61 (Chicago: 1959), especially pp. 302-51.

cultural anthropology, but it also was a somewhat isolated science until the 1940's.

In our desire to make our declaration of independence viable, we neglected to maintain a view of the advancing front of science as a whole. We acted as though we did not believe in anything more than the broadest generalities about the universality of scientific method. In effect we neglected to appraise continuously the most profound current of change in our time. We neglected an axiom: The course of science as a whole determines the progress of its parts, in their greater or lesser degrees.

Influence of Mathematical Statistics

What did we miss in the course we took? For one thing, we missed early contact with developments in mathematical statistics, and early touch with the antecedents of systems analysis. The scholars whose thought influenced life (and social) systems concepts greatly, like R. A. Fisher and Karl Pearson in biology and anthropology, Alfred Lotka in biology. Sewall Wright in genetics, and L. L. Thurstone in psychology, were all active in the 1920's and 1930's. The flowering of the application of their techniques and concepts awaited the availability of electronic computers and mathematical progress in the late 1940's and early 1950's, but they provided forceful organizing advances in genetics and other biological fields, in physical anthropology, demography, psychology, and economics from 15 to 25 years earlier than in geography. We thus missed for a period the new thought their techniques generated, because the techniques were essential keys to communication of that thought.[12]

Within the last decade we have made good our initial failure to respond to these modern techniques. We have even felt the influence of physics, as a few have experimented with the application of physical analogues to the phenomena of distribution. Although not a few among us have been uneasy about their meaning, these techniques already

[12] An interesting demonstration of these techniques falling on sterile ground in geography occurred in 1938, when the mathematical statistician M. G. Kendall presented his paper "The Geographical Distribution of Crop Productivity in England" before the Royal Statistical Society (*Journal Royal Statistical Society*, Vol. 102 [1939], pp. 21-62). This study was an analysis of covariance among ten crops in the 48 English counties. Besides the interesting direct conclusions he drew, Kendall made some provocative observations about the similarity of statistical techniques for studying a psychological problem and for studying a geographical problem. However, the two geographers present, L. Dudley Stamp and E. C. Willats, devoted their comments on Kendall's paper mainly to its shortcomings in interpreting the observable landscape. So far as I know, there was no sequel in geographical study to Kendall's interesting exploration. I am indebted to Brian J. L. Berry for calling my attention to Kendall's paper.

have proved their power. Mathematical analysis is a recognized part of instruction in alert departments of geography. We can only welcome the growth of these methods, because they have been a notable and needed stimulus to the rigor of our thinking. Even more important, they increase our capacity to communicate precisely with workers in other fields of science.

Is the mathematicization of our discipline the way of our future? In a sense, yes. The year is not far off when a geographer will be unable to keep abreast of his field without training in mathematics. Furthermore, he will find it increasingly difficult to conduct meaningful research without such training. But here we must enter more than a word of caution. There is a great deal more to science than the application of mathematics, or of rigorous logic. We must take care to examine carefully the paths of research down which our computerized mathematical colleagues lead us, or perhaps push us. The danger of a dead end and nonsense is not removed by "hardware" and symbolic logic. Before we go too far we should see what else there is about science at large that produces its "growing points." What determines how productive the use of statistics and hardware will be? In a few other fields scientists are facing problems of this kind that are somewhat out of control today. Recent attention to the scientific part of space exploration is an illustration.[13]

Nonquantifying Attributes of Science

Can we make any observation about the methods of science at large that will enable us to keep needed mathematicization under control? There are a great many definitions of science. I am sure that many of you are familiar with most of them. One definition I like is: "Science is a quest for regularity underlying diverse events." This quest proceeds through careful, verifiable observation and description; through the construction of hypotheses, to project reality into the unknown; testing of the hypotheses through the conduct of experiment or further observation;[14] replication of experiment and observation; and the building of a body of theory from verified hypotheses which in turn becomes the basis for new hypotheses, and new observations and experiments. Mathematical and statistical analyses have found their important place in this procedure because they aid in obtaining exact observation, and

[13] Some scientists fear that space "hardware" is causing an inefficient, even dangerous, misallocation of high-quality scientific talent in the United States. (See P. H. Abelson, Testimony before the United States Senate Committee on Aeronautical and Space Sciences hearings on National Goals in Space, June 10, 1963.)
[14] The geographer may observe through field investigation; he may experiment with the use of statistical models (or idealized reality).

because they aid enormously in designing hypotheses that lead into the unknown.

I might stop here, and you would recognize this as a portrait of science. However, it is a portrait only of its skeleton. Three important additions provide the all-important life and direction that have figured wherever great strides in science have been made. I have already mentioned one: cross-disciplinary communication.

The second is what some men have described as the intuitive side of science. Warren Weaver has said, ". . . science is, at its core, a creative activity of the human mind which depends upon luck, hunch, insight, intuition, imagination, taste, and faith, just as do all the pursuits of the poet, musician, painter, essayist, or philosopher." [15]

But there is more to it than this. The mind of the scientist, no less than that of the poet or musician, must be structured by thought and experience before it reaches the creative stage. Some persons are able so to structure their minds more easily than others. It has been said, for example, that Irving Langmuir always saw matter, of whatever form, wherever he was, in terms of its molecular structure, thus opening the way automatically for his many remarkable insights. Every scientist does this in some degree. There is no doubt that there is such a thing as "thinking geographically." To structure his mind in terms of spatial distributions [16] and their correlations is a most important tool for anyone following our discipline. The more the better. If there is any really meaningful distinction among scientists, it is in this mental structuring. It is one reason why we should approach the imposition of analogues from other fields, as from physics, with the utmost care. The mental substrate for inspiration does differ from field to field.

A third important ingredient of science is a highly developed sense of problem. In my pleasant and valued association with Professor Charles Colby at the University of Chicago, I can remember his frequent reference to the cultivation of such a sense. I now realize how wise and perceptive his advice was. In my duties of the past five years at the Carnegie Institution of Washington, I have had to maintain current knowledge about research in several biological and physical sciences. In all of them this sense of problem is very keen where outstanding progress is being made. Herbert Simon has observed that science is essentially problem solving.[17] This observation is so important that it deserves a few words of elaboration. A sense of problem, at its

[15] Warren Weaver, "Science, Learning and the Whole of Life," Address at 70th Anniversary Convocation, Drexel Institute of Technology, December, 1961.
[16] By "spatial distributions," "earth-spatial distributions" is, of course, understood here. They are the parallel of distributional associations in other sciences.
[17] Herbert Simon, *The New Science of Management Decision* (New York: 1960), p. 34. There are other similar statements, like that of T. S. Kuhn, who calls it "puzzle-solving" (*The Structure of Scientific Revolutions* [Chicago: 1962], pp. 35 ff.).

most meaningful, is really a sense of the hierarchy of problems in a broad field, and possibly in all science.

Every major field with which I am familiar has an easily recognized overriding problem. The overriding problems always lie behind the frontiers of investigation. They are remarkably few, and all fade into infinity in their ultimate forms. Indeed, the overriding problems of all science may be reduced to four: (1) the problem of the particulate structure of energy and matter, which physics treats; (2) the structure and content of the cosmos, which astronomy, astrophysics, and geophysics treat; (3) the problem of the origin and physiological unity of life forms; and (4) the functioning of systems that include multiple numbers of variables, especially life systems and social systems. Others might express these problems differently, but I believe that each of them is a beacon orienting research on the frontiers of the rapidly advancing fields.

Beneath each overriding problem are major second-level problems, and finally the problems translatable directly into experiment or observational investigation. For example, a major secondary problem related to the overriding one of the origin of life is the description of life in pre-Cambrian times. It is translated directly into a search in pre-Cambrian rocks for stable chemical compounds known to be indicators of life. In this way Philip Abelson and his collaborators at the Carnegie Institution have produced firm evidence of the existence of life at least 2.6 billion years ago.

The same relation among the hierarchy of problems can be seen in growing-point research in astronomy, geophysics, biology, and elsewhere. I do not mean that all research is so organized, or is distinguished by the sense of problem. Most commonly an appreciation of the hierarchy of problems is shared by relatively few in each field. It is indeed one of the most troublesome questions facing the administrator of public research funds in the nation at the present time.

Geography in the Mirror of All Sciences

By now my theme should be obvious: The geographer should seek his personal identity in the mirror provided by all sciences. How is this translated into future geographic progress? The development of a professional identity in geography has two aspects: the future development of the theoretical study of spatial distributions; and a reappraisal of the overriding problem recognized by our discipline.

The first, further development of the theoretical, is our true inner refuge as specialists. It is what helps to structure the mind "geographically." The more rigorously the structuring is done, the more likely the discipline will have a cutting edge that places it on a research frontier.

However unrelated and esoteric it may seem, the cultivation of theoretical study of spatial distributions is basic.

If we have had any generally accepted overriding problem in the past, it is areal differentiation, a concept widely accepted and usefully employed, particularly by American and German geographers. Its rationale has been ably presented and skillfully defended by Richard Hartshorne. His most recent definition of areal differentiation as the "accurate, orderly, and rational description and interpretation of the variable character of the earth surface" [18] still stands as a useful general guide to geographic method. A second preoccupation, but less widely held, was with the geographical expression of culture processes. I shall refer mainly to areal differentiation in the remarks of the next few paragraphs.

A New Look at Geography's Overriding Problem

At a time when the social sciences provided us with very little firm assistance, and we were stressing our independence, areal differentiation of the earth's surface did serve as an overriding problem. It is time that we recognize the limitations of this concept. Do we need something more for a purposeful selection of research problems leading us to significant research frontiers? If we look at the concept of areal differentiation carefully, we see that it did not often lead us to common ground with the other sciences. We see it also as ending in a somewhat static goal. In effect, it stressed a hierarchy of regions as our hierarchy of problems.

I suggest that we take a fresh look at the hierarchy of problems, ignoring for the moment some of our traditional points of view. I noted earlier that science is problem solving. The problems that can be examined meaningfully depend on the methods which are available for their solution. As the centuries have gone on, men have steadily increased their capacity for problem solving, but the truly important changes in methods of problem solving have been remarkably few. They might read somewhat as follows: writing; Arabic numerals; analytical geometry and calculus; and the combination of techniques that comprise systems analysis. There was a time, perhaps just after the Second World War, when the inclusion of systems analysis in such a list might have been considered controversial. That is no longer true. Systems, as you know, are among the most pervasive and characteristic phenomena in nature. Each human being, man or woman, is a system,

[18] Richard Hartshorne, *Perspective on the Nature of Geography* (Chicago: 1959), p. 21. The concept of areal differentiation as Hartshorne explains, "stems from Richthofen's synthesis of the views of Humboldt and Ritter, and has been most fully expounded in Hettner's writings" (*ibid.*, p. 12).

that is, a dynamic structure of interacting, interdependent parts.[19] Perhaps that is less appealing than a poet's definition of a pretty girl, but it has meaning in that it relates the girl as a system to all other systems, such as a colony of ants, or a city, or a business corporation.

Systems analysis provides methods of problem solving which might be said to have been created for geography, if there were not also many other uses for them. Geography is concerned with systems. Indeed, we may now state its overriding problem. It is nothing less than an understanding of the vast, interacting system comprising all humanity and its natural environment on the surface of the earth. This might be compared with Humboldt's statement of a century ago, "Even though the complete goal is unobtainable, . . . the striving toward a comprehension of world phenomena remains the highest and eternal purpose of all research." [20] It may also be compared with Hartshorne's definition of the purpose of geography as "the study that seeks to provide scientific description of the earth as the world of man." [21] Compare also Barrows' "geographers . . . define their subject as dealing solely with the mutual relations between man and his natural environment. By 'natural environment' they of course mean the combined physical and biological environments. . . . Thus defined, geography is the science of human ecology." [22] All these statements have some similarity. However, the concept of the world of man as a vast interacting, interdependent entity permits us an effective orientation to a set of problems *at different levels* in a way that we have never had before.[23] Furthermore, it puts us in a context of sharp new problem-solving methods.[24] If we are willing, it also places us in association and in close communication with other sciences whose overriding problems are similar.

Viewed in this way one can see a host of beneficial results. We no longer are concerned about whether what we are doing is geography

[19] A useful short categorization of systems is given by Kenneth E. Boulding in his "General Systems Theory—The Skeleton of Science," *Management Science,* Vol. 2 (1956), pp. 197-208. He distinguishes nine "levels" of systems in increasing order of complexity. A social system is of the eighth order among his levels.

[20] Alexander von Humboldt, *Kosmos: Entwurf einer physischen Weltbeschreibung,* Vol. 1 (Stuttgart: 1845), p. 68. Quoted from Richard Hartshorne, *Perspective on the Nature of Geography,* p. 162.

[21] Hartshorne, *Perspective on the Nature of Geography,* p. 172.

[22] Barrows, *op. cit.,* p. 3.

[23] The closest approach to this in the geography of the '30's and '40's was in Robert S. Platt's view of geography "as the science of regional process patterns of dynamic space relations." Platt, "A Review of Regional Geography," *Annals of the Association of American Geographers,* Vol. 47 (1957), p. 190. However, the appropriateness of formal systems concepts to geographic research is not mentioned by Platt.

[24] A very gracefully stated description of the indivisible attribute (and others) of systems is given by Sir Stafford Beer in "Below the Twilight Arch—A Mythology of Systems," in *Systems: Research and Design* (Donald P. Eckman, ed.) (Wiley, New York: 1961), pp. 1-25.

or not; we are concerned instead with what we contribute toward a larger goal, however infinite it may seem. As in other sciences, an overriding problem of infinite extent should be a challenge, not cause for resignation or despair. We no longer debate about whether geography can construct "laws." At the same time we do retain an identity by structuring our minds to handle spatial distribution patterns in all their complexity. But as we go about our task of analyzing spatial distributions and space relations on the earth we should keep in mind the question, "What, if anything, do geographic observations and analyses tell us about systems generally, and the man–environment system particularly?"

Summary Statement of Concept and Method

We might elaborate this position in summary manner: (1) The basic organizing concept of geography has three dimensions. They are: extent, density, and succession.[25] "Spatial distribution and space relations" are a verbal shorthand for discribing the dimensions of the concept. A theoretical framework for investigation may be developed from this basic concept, as observations confirm hypotheses.[26] (2) The universe treated by geographers is the worldwide man–natural environment system. Geographers share their overriding problem, an understanding of this system, with other sciences. (3) The worldwide system is composed of a number of subsystems. The subsystems assist in identifying a hierarchy of problems for research. (4) The techniques of systems analysis are of particular value to geographers in applying their organizing (space) concept to the analysis of subsystems of the worldwide man–environment system. These techniques, because of their rigor, permit replications of analysis and comparability of results among different research investigations. They also state the results of geographic research in terms comparable to those of other sciences using systems techniques, and therefore make such results of greater potential use in treating the overriding problem, or any subproblem.

[25] Extent is measurable as size, shape, and orientation. Density is shown by the amount of "betweenness." Simultaneity is a special case of succession.

[26] Cf. Blaut (op. cit., pp. 5-6), who interprets Hartshorne (op. cit., pp. 74-80, 133, 144-45) and states the organizing concept as "areal integration." I do not find Blaut's statement inconsistent with the statement given in this paragraph, but his does leave the epistemological problem of what space is. (Discussed by Blaut in his "Space and Process," Professional Geographer, Vol. XIII [July, 1961], pp. 1-6.) In addition, the word "integration" has a connotation of study technique that (to me) detracts from clarity.

By extension I also do not find the statements of this paragraph inconsistent with Hartshorne's latest careful analysis of geographic concept and method (Hartshorne, op. cit.). It may be noted that Hartshorne, always precise in his definitions, has described the components of geographic study in a manner that allows them to fit the view of geography suggested here, and probably other views also.

Systems Methods Are Changing Society

Events in the world of today make it absolutely essential that geographers adopt such a view if they have aspirations to the frontier of research. Not only do much sharper probes exist for examining man's activities, but society itself is responding to scientific change. It is being organized in ways that are more easily evaluated. The scientific revolution we have been going through is being accompanied by a revolution of rationalism in our economic structure. Indeed, it has been called a "second Industrial Revolution," with effects already very profound for all humankind. Industrial engineering years ago removed the individual decision making of the artisan. "Cybernation," or systems design and systems engineering,[27] are now rapidly moving individuality from "middle management" decision. This development is part of the social problem of automation. Not least, systems design and engineering, through the nation's defense program, is having a dominant role in domestic political affairs and international relations. Research approaches have even been made toward understanding the process of human thought itself. Herbert Simon has said, "We shall be able to specify exactly what it is that a man has to learn about a particular subject— . . . how he has to proceed—in order to solve effectively problems that relate to that subject." [28] And, as you know, already a great deal is known about manipulating some aspects of society, like consumer demands, in a more or less controlled fashion. What we in the United States are experiencing is also going on in Europe and in Japan. Quite a different form is found in the Soviet Union, but it still is certainly an aspect of rationalization. We may expect similar developments in other parts of the world. And we may expect systems engineering to play an increasingly large role in coping with the social and economic crises that technological change has brought.[29]

These events and trends have the profoundest significance for the

[27] See Donald N. Michael, *Cybernation: The Silent Conquest,* for a summary account of the social changes caused by systems engineering. Simon, *op. cit.,* also describes them.

[28] Simon, *op. cit.,* p. 34.

[29] E. A. Johnson has stated one aspect of this problem, from a national point of view: ". . . the increase in physical knowledge has made the future . . . uncertain, . . . we must plan much further ahead in a way that will provide much greater flexibility, whether this be in peaceful or military affairs, whether it be for the individual or for the country. . . . Our primary problem is to find a way to manage our very big systems affairs in this new situation. . . . We will have to examine our individual, group, and national values to see what it is we want to do in a rapidly changing world, and to see what we can do consciously to manipulate in our favor the real and perhaps hostile physical and world environment so that it will serve us better. This is a problem of big systems." E. A. Johnson, "The Use of Operations Research in the Study of Very Large Systems," *Systems: Research and Design* (Donald P. Eckman, ed.), pp. 52-93.

future spatial distribution of human activities, and we could not hope to anticipate or understand that distribution without being fully abreast of what is taking place. On the other hand, there must be something that the study of spatial distributions can tell us about these phenomena. To say this in brief, the methods that have created important salients on the frontier of the physical sciences are changing society itself, both directly and through their impact on the behavioral sciences.

Systems and Geography's Frontiers

We are, then, concerned not only with a vast interacting system, but with one that is being altered by knowledge of systems. We now come to the most difficult part of our determination. Recognition of the overriding problem is of little significance unless we relate it to the direction of everyday research, and, by extension, to the fields with which we seek common ground in the definition of problems. What does this tell us about our own frontiers?

The one thing that most distinguishes a system is the flow of information within it. "Information" is not to be confused with the ordinary meaning of the word, for it refers here to any mechanism that holds together the interdependent, interacting parts of a system. This is an interesting and critical point as far as geography is concerned, because the *connectivity* within a system is its most important characteristic. Many geographers, on the other hand, have stressed *differences*, as exemplified in the term "areal differentiation." If you accept my proposal of the overriding problem for our science, it then follows that to choose a research problem without reference to the connectivity of the system is to risk triviality. What space relations tell us of connectivity in the system is significant to science as a whole. Areal differences are significant *only* insofar as they help to describe and define the connectivity or "information" flow. We now see that the geographers who have been concerned with cultural and other processes have had an insight of significant direction in research. Eight such processes were suggested in the past—four physical and four cultural. Among the cultural you may remember demographic movement, organizational evolution, the resource-converting techniques, and the space-adjusting techniques. Among the physical dynamics of the soil mantle, movement of water, climate, and biotic processes were suggested.[30]

A second important characteristic of a system is the existence of subsystems within it. The pretty girl, if you like, can be broken down into an astonishing number of subsystems, like any complex being. The

[30] Ackerman, *Geography as a Fundamental Research Discipline* (Chicago: 1958), p. 28.

same is true of other complex systems. This is another important and critical point, for we must make the proper selection of subsystems for study if we are to maintain significance. We already have a clue in the past suggestions made about the importance of processes. It is the functional subsystems that are generally the significant ones. Thus the systematic aspects of geography, insofar as they treat functions, are disposed to a high level of significance. Those geographers who have thought in terms of areal functional organization again have had a significant insight as to research direction.

However, not all types of region have equal significance for research. Political regions are territorial units with a high level of significance because they are functional. A watershed is an example of a physically determined region that is significant. On the other hand, the old concept of a "geographic" region may have very little significance. We may need to review critically the significance of other types of regions within the context we are considering. The concept of a region is potentially valuable in systems study, but we should take care that the regional concepts we actually use are significant to the overriding system.

Selection of Significant Collaborating Sciences

This brings us through the second level in the hierarchy of problems, down to a level where one must seek specific examples of significance. As geographers have long appreciated, the flow of "information" within the man–natural environment system is indeed vast. Selection of a research problem at random again risks triviality, even though it may be entirely "geographic" in conception. At this point one commences to be most actively concerned about clues from other sciences as to significant working problems.

Here we may go back to one of the first observations made in this discussion: The sciences differ enormously in their rates of progress. For example, not all divisions of the behavioral sciences or the earth sciences offer channels for productive communication. Without doubt we can benefit greatly from some collaborative definition of research problems with other sciences, but the cooperation must be selectively chosen. A good rule of thumb would be: Where systems analysis techniques are understood and incorporated at the working face of the discipline, a collaborative definition of problem may profitably be sought. In other words, cooperation is likely to be rewarding where methods made familiar in the physical sciences are now reaching into the neighboring earth sciences and the behavioral sciences. Where the concepts and approaches using systems analysis methods are making inroads, a possible place of interest is suggested for geography. Relations with other sciences which at times have been loose, vague, and hard to define may thus become more meaningful.

The profession is becoming equipped gradually to take such a view in its fundamental research. The wind of change which we have felt for the last decade includes the application of some methods of systems analysis. Thus far they generally have been the application of more rigorous techniques to old geographic problems. Except for collaboration with economists and others of the "regional science" group, and the older collaboration between cultural geographers and cultural anthropologists, we thus far have done relatively little to explore common ground with other sciences on the definition of significant problems. In almost any direction we turn, interesting possibilities appear. Indeed, there are so many opportunities that the number of people undertaking geographic research seems remarkably few.

The relation of geography and the neighboring natural sciences is particularly interesting. By the neighboring natural sciences I mean studies that focus on the surface features of the earth, like soils, biotic features, and water movement. The logical point of contact of these sciences with the human part of the great man–land system is geography. In all of them there is increasing appreciation of the role of man. For example, it is realized that pollution has become a major feature in world hydrology; biological ecologists now admit that even the most "inviolate" natural preserves will be affected by man, no matter what protection is given; and a few geomorphologists now recognize the significance of man as a part of geomorphic processes. We should be particularly alert to overtures from these neighboring sciences, like that of Geoffrey Robinson in geomorphology, who suggests that at least some geomorphologists are interested in a collaborative definition of problems.[31] We should continue to capitalize on a point of view that geography alone, until recently, has maintained among the sciences concerned with man: land is half of the man–land system.

There are signs that geography's position as a "gateway" between the behavioral sciences and the earth sciences is being challenged somewhat by the behavioral sciences themselves. Economists, for example, in the last ten years have become increasingly concerned with natural resource development problems. To be sure, geographers helped to start them along these lines, but there is now a direct working relation between economics and hydrology. It is significant that the aspects of economics emphasizing a systems approach provided the important recent contributions to study of resources.

[31] Geoffrey Robinson, "A Consideration of the Relations of Geomorphology and Geography," *The Professional Geographer*, Vol. XV (1963), pp. 13-17.

Relations with the Behavioral Sciences

These events suggest that we need to maintain a comprehensive view of the frontiers in the behavioral sciences, and that we have a good clue to common interest in looking for those investigators who pursue a systems approach. It has been said, "The behavioral sciences are diverse in subject matter and state of development, yet ideas and concepts circulate quite freely among them. . . ." [32] The quotation may be a slight overstatement, but it does represent an agreed-upon ideal in these sciences which we might well contemplate. How far do we join them in the shaping of goals and in the exchange of methods which we have commenced to use?

An illustration or two may direct our attention to possibilities. We have mentioned that a most important characteristic of a system is the flow of "information," broadly defined. "Information" may be in the form of goods, people, messages containing data or ideas, or other dynamic phenomena. The geographer, by definition, looks at what spatial distributions tell concerning this information flow, or vice versa. Geographers already have attacked some of these problems of information flow successfully. [33] Probably the most important general question of this kind familiar to geographers is: "What can we say about how people distribute themselves and their culture on the earth, given free choice?" Much of the work geographers have done thus far is within the context of economic constraints, but they also respond to their concepts of amenities, to neighborhood and other group attachments, to the diffusion of information, and perhaps to other factors. There is a wealth of significant problems here to examine. Attention to them can bring us into a common area with students of motivation in the behavioral sciences. This is a key area in behavioral science research. We may find eventually some interesting common ground with psychology, thus finally connecting with the inferences of M. G. Kendall twenty-five years ago.[34] Indeed, study of the brain is considered one of the most useful approaches to the study of systems generally.[35]

Geographers recently have been alert to noneconomic "information"

---

[32] Behavioral Sciences Subpanel, President's Science Advisory Committee, Strengthening the Behavioral Sciences (Washington: April 20, 1962), p. 13.

[33] A number of reports on such research have appeared in the *Annals;* e.g., articles by W. L. Garrison and others. Publications of the "regional science" group also are illustrative.

[34] See footnote 12 above.

[35] Beer, *op. cit.*, p. 19. "The brain is itself the most resplendent system of them all. . . ." We may well reflect to what degree social reality reflects the structure of the brain.

flow studies. For example, a much respected pattern for geographical research with mathematical methods has been the diffusion of innovation studies by Torsten Hägerstrand in Sweden.[36] These studies, well known to American geographers, have stimulated diffusion research in this country. Such research is also a natural outgrowth of long-continued American interest in diffusion phenomena, followed particularly by cultural geographers.[37]

At the same time the interest in diffusion studies illustrates our past relations with other scientific subjects. American sociologists have been carrying on very similar work since the early 1940's, including some elaborately designed experiments.[38] As far as I can discover there was little cross-disciplinary communication on this remarkably similar path of research until about a year and a half ago. It is obvious that collaboration here between geography and sociology can be of value. This is of more than academic interest, for as Ullman has noted, "the relative 'stickiness' of society, the resistance of certain areas to spread of innovations and improvements," has strong implications for public policy both nationally and internationally.[39]

Allow me another and more unusual example. An interesting offshoot in the behavioral sciences at the present time is the study of conflict theory, to which Kenneth Boulding of the University of Michigan and others have contributed. Looked at from the point of view of systems and their information flow, conflict theory is essentially a search for "redundancy," or the capacity to handle in channels multiple movements with the same destination. Boulding has suggested that the theory may be of interest in studying land use.[40] Here is an opportunity to help in exploring the overriding system through a fresh idea.

A common front with the behavioral sciences is important not only in framing significant research questions but also because of geography's long association with historical study. Increasingly, it looks as though history would acquire scientific meaning through the dimensions given it by behavioral science.

[36] Torsten Hägerstrand, "The Propagation of Innovation Waves," *Lund Studies in Geography* (Sweden: Lund, 1952) and succeeding publications.
[37] See, for example, Fred Kniffen, "The American Covered Bridge," *Geographic Review* (1951), p. 114.
[38] See, for example, James S. Coleman, "The Diffusion of an Innovation among Physicians," *Sociometry*, Vol. 20 (1957); Melvin DeFleur and Otto Larsen, *Flow of Information* (New York: Harper, 1958); Anatol Rapoport, "Spread of Information through a Population with a Social Structure Bias," *Bulletin of Mathematical Biophysics*, Vol. 15 (1953).
[39] Edward L. Ullman, "Geography Theory in Underdeveloped Areas," *Essays on Geography and Economic Development* (Norton S. Ginsburg, ed.), University of Chicago, Department of Geography Research Paper 62 (Chicago: 1960), pp. 26-32.
[40] Kenneth Boulding, *Conflict and Defense* (New York: Harper, 1962), p. 1.

Conclusion

We emerge with four general points that could help to place our science on a research frontier. (1) Continue to strengthen quantifying methods. Attempt to add to them rigorous analytical approaches in our theory and habits of constructing hypotheses. (2) Recognize an earth-wide man–environment system as our overriding problem. We can seek significant research questions in the study of subsystems at different levels, amenable to our spatial distribution analyses. (3) Choose our research problems in the light of the advancing frontier of the behavioral sciences, and with attention to systems-oriented study in the neighboring earth sciences. Finally, (4) supplement our present heavy commitments to studies within economic constraints and to morphology studies by other approaches. The rising interest in cultural geography is healthy, but we could diversify still more. I particularly commend to your attention political geography within the systems framework. It is concerned with regions that have true functional significance in the great man–land system.

Seeking and staying on a research frontier is a most exacting task. It is now very clear that, in this age of specialization, special knowledge and specialized concepts are not sufficient to hold a science on the frontier. The sense of overriding problem is essential, and so is a view of at least a part of the spectrum of all science. This does not mean that future accomplishment will be entirely by those who are mathematically sophisticated. For those of us not so endowed it is comforting to remember that A. A. Michelson, the first American to win the Nobel Prize, was, by his own admission, poorly prepared in mathematics. But he did have an extremely keen sense of the overriding problem in his field, a passion for exactness, and an alertness to the contributions of neighboring disciplines. There is an important place for a comprehensive view, but it must be a view based on something more than undergraduate and graduate courses. I believe the time is near when postgraduate training and a second doctoral degree may be the price for reaching a research frontier. In our plans for future professional action and in our advice to those in professional training, we must think about these matters before it is much later. It we do not, others will cultivate our frontier, for that is the way of science. If we do, perhaps we may come closer to justifying Charles Darwin's words, ". . . that grand subject, that almost keystone of the laws of creation, Geographical Distribution." [41]

[41] Charles Darwin, letter to Joseph Dalton Hooker, 1845.

Correlation of This Book with Representative Texts

	DICKEN AND PITTS *Introduction to Human Geography* Blaisdell, 1963	FINCH, TREWARTHA, ROBINSON, AND HAMMOND *Elements of Geography: Physical and Cultural* McGraw-Hill, 1957	JAMES *A Geography of Man*, 3d ed. Blaisdell, 1966	KENDALL, GLENDINNING, AND MAC FADDEN *Introduction to Geography*, 3d ed. Harcourt, Brace, & World, 1962
Text chs.	Related Selections in *Introduction to Geography*			
1	1, 7	14, 16, 17, 18, 21	2, 3, 4, 7	1, 2, 6, 7, 30
2	5, 6, 19, 30		2, 7, 26, 27	
3			12	14, 15, 16, 17, 18, 19, 21
4	2		13	12
5	25		13	
6	19, 28	13	5	
7	7	12	11	11, 12, 13
8	8, 9	11	12, 13	
9	12	12	29	12
10				12
11			2, 26	11
12		23		
13	12	7, 23		12, 13
14	25, 27	12		11, 12, 13
15	29	11, 12		19, 25
16		11, 12		25, 29
17	2			15, 29
18	25			13
19				
20	11, 13	7		
21				
22				
23	24	24		2, 4, 13, 24, 26
24	24, 25	24		2
25	26	2, 13		
26	2, 27	2, 12, 13, 14, 25, 27		
27	15, 16, 17, 19, 20, 29	15, 29		
28		2, 4, 24		
29		24, 25		
30				
31				
32				
33				
34				
35				
36				

	MEYER AND STRIETELMEIER *Geography in World Society* Lippincott, 1963	MURPHEY *An Introduction to Geography* 2d ed. Rand McNally, 1966	PHILBRICK *This Human World* Wiley, 1963	WHEELER, KOSTABADE, AND THOMAN *Regional Geography of the World* Holt, Rinehart, & Winston, 1961
Text chs.	Related Selections in *Introduction to Geography*			
1	3, 5, 6, 7, 8, 9	1, 6, 7, 8, 27, 30	1, 6, 7, 16, 22, 28, 30	1, 2, 6, 7, 23, 30
2	1, 22, 28, 30	4, 10, 16, 17, 25, 28	1, 2, 3, 26	2
3	14, 15, 16, 17, 18, 21	6, 7, 8, 9		11
4	2, 12, 26	1, 3, 4, 19	7, 23	
5	2, 19	7, 8, 9, 12	2, 7, 27	
6	7, 8		11	
7	12	12	2, 11	
8				29
9				5
10				
11	2, 13	7, 24		
12	24	2	12	
13	15	11		
14	2, 24		13	
15	24	29		
16	12			
17	8			
18				
19	12			
20	12		2, 4, 26	
21		5		
22	13			
23	5			
24				13
25	11, 29			13
26				12
27				12
28				
29				
30				
31				
32				
33	11			
34	2, 26			
35	7, 15	13		
36	19, 29, 30	4, 12		